AIRCRAFT CONSTRUCTION
REPAIR & INSPECTION

Other TAB books by the Author

AIRCRAFT CONSTRUCTION REPAIR & INSPECTION

BY JOE CHRISTY

TAB BOOKS Inc.
BLUE RIDGE SUMMIT, PA. 17214

FIRST EDITION

FIRST PRINTING

Copyright © 1984 by TAB BOOKS Inc.

Printed in the United States of America

Library of Congress Cataloging in Publication Data

Christy, Joe.
Aircraft construction, repair, and inspection.

Includes index.
1. Airplanes—Design and construction. 2. Airplanes,

Home-built. I. Title.
TL671.2.C527   1984   629.134′2   83-18163
ISBN 0-8306-2377-9(pbk.)

Contents

Introduction

Professional aircraft mechanics and constructors of homebuilt airplanes, as well as those who refurbish older airplanes, must reference the FAA's manual AC 43.13-1A & 2A, *Aircraft Inspection and Repair* (formerly, *Manual 18*), when building, repairing, or altering any airframe. This old standby establishes the standards one must honor if the structure is to be approved as airworthy by FAA inspectors.

This large volume, however, contains much that is not applicable to light aircraft and homebuilts, and while "Forty-Three-Thirteen" (as it is usually called) is the final authority on how things must be, it sometimes offers too little on how to do it. Therefore, we reproduce here, verbatim, only those parts of 43.13 that directly apply to lightplanes and homebuilts and omit the sections that pertain to heavy multi-engine aircraft, helicopters, and turbine-powered airplanes. Then, where appropriate, we provide additional "how-to" data to aid the aircraftsman—both professional and amateur—in achieving those standards in the most efficient way.

Aircraft Wood Structures

(Reprinted from FAA 43.13 Chapter 1)

Section 1. MATERIALS AND PRACTICES

1. MATERIALS. Three forms of wood are commonly used in aircraft: solid wood, plywood, and laminated wood. Although several kinds of modified wood are sometimes used for special purposes, these three forms constitute the bulk of all wood aircraft construction materials.

a. Quality of Wood. All wood and plywood used in the repair of aircraft structures should be of aircraft quality. Figure 1.2 lists the permissible variations in characteristics and properties of aircraft wood.

b. Species Substitution. The species used to repair a part should be the same as that of the original whenever possible; however, permissible substitutes are given in figure 1.2.

c. Effects of Shrinkage. When the moisture content of wood is lowered, its dimensions decrease. The dimensional change is greatest in a tangential direction (across the fibers and parallel to the growth rings), somewhat less in a radial direction (across the fibers and perpendicular to the growth rings), and is negligible in a longitudinal direction (parallel to the fibers). These dimensional changes can have several detrimental effects upon a wood structure, such as loosening of fittings and wire bracing and checking or splitting of wood members.

A few suggestions for minimizing these shrinkage effects are:

(1) Use bushings that are slightly short so that when the wood member shrinks the bushings do not protrude and the fittings may be tightened firmly against the member.

(2) Gradually drop off plywood face plates either by feathering or by shaping as shown in figure 1.1.

2. REPLACEMENT OF DRAINHOLES AND SKIN STIFFENERS. Whenever repairs are made that require replacing a portion that includes drainholes, skin stiffeners, or any other items, the repaired portion must be provided with similar

1

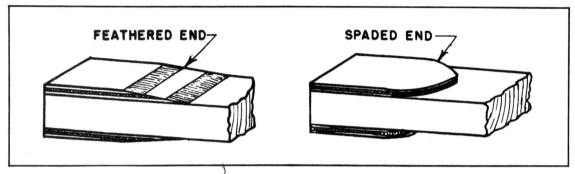

FIGURE 1.1.—Tapering of face plates.

drainholes, skin stiffeners, or items of the same dimensions in the same location. Reinforcing, under skin repairs, that interferes with the flow of water from some source, such as inspection holes, is to be provided with drainholes at the lowest points.

3. CONTROL SURFACE FLUTTER PRECAUTIONS. When repairing control surfaces, especially on high-performance airplanes, care must be exercised that the repairs do not involve the addition of weight aft of the hinge line. Such a procedure may adversely disturb the dynamic and static balance of the surface to a degree which would induce flutter. As a general rule, it will be necessary to repair control surfaces in such a manner that the structure is identical to the original so that the weight distribution and resulting mass balance are not affected in any way.

4. GLUING PRECAUTIONS. Satisfactory glue joints in aircraft will develop the full strength of wood under all conditions of stress. To produce this result, the gluing operation must be carefully controlled so as to obtain a continuous, thin, uniform film of solid glue in the joint with adequate adhesion to both surfaces of the wood. Some of the more important conditions involve:

   a. Properly prepared wood surfaces.

   b. Glue of good quality, properly prepared.

   c. Good gluing technique.

5. PREPARATION OF WOOD SURFACES FOR GLUING. It is recommended that no more than 8 hours be permitted to elapse between final surfacing and gluing. The gluing surfaces should be machined smooth and true with planers, jointers, or special miter saws. Planer marks, chipped or loosened grain, and other surface irregularities will not be permitted. Sandpaper must never be used to smooth softwood surfaces that are to be glued. Sawed surfaces must approach well-planed surfaces in uniformity, smoothness, and freedom from crushed fibers.

   a. Tooth-planing, or other means of roughening smooth well-planed surfaces of normal wood before gluing is not recommended. Such treatment of well-planed wood surfaces may result in local irregularities and objectionable rounding of edges. While sanding of planed surfaces is not recommended for softwoods, sanding is a valuable aid in improving the gluing characteristics of some hard plywood surfaces, wood that has been compressed through exposure to high pressure and temperatures, resin-impregnated wood (impreg and compreg), and laminated paper plastic (papreg).

   b. Wood surfaces for gluing should be free from oil, wax, varnish, shellac, lacquer, enamel, dope, sealers, paint, dust, dirt, oil, glue, crayon marks, and other extraneous materials.

   c. Wetting tests are useful as a means of detecting the presence of wax. Drops of water placed on the surface of wax-coated wood do not spread or wet the wood. At present, pre-

2

liminary gluing tests appear to be the only positive means of actually determining the gluing characteristics of plywood surfaces.

6. GLUES. Glues used in aircraft repair fall into two general groups: casein glues and resin glues. Any glue that meets the performance requirements of applicable United States military specifications or has previously been accepted by the FAA is satisfactory for use in certificated civil aircraft. In all cases, glues are to be used strictly in accordance with the glue manufacturer's recommendations.

a. *Casein Glues.* Casein glues have been widely used in wood aircraft repair work. The forms, characteristics, and properties of water-resistant casein glues have remained substantially the same for many years, except for the addition of preservatives. Casein glues for use in aircraft should contain suitable preservatives such as the chlorinated phenols and their sodium salts to increase their resistance to organic deterioration under high-humidity exposures. Most casein glues are sold in powder form ready to be mixed with water at ordinary room temperatures.

b. *Synthetic Resin Glues.* Synthetic resin glues for wood are outstanding in that they retain their strength and durability under moist conditions and after exposure to water. The best known and most commonly used synthetic resin glues are the phenol-formaldehyde, resorcinol-formaldehyde, and urea-formaldehyde types. The resorcinol-formaldehyde type glue is recommended for wood aircraft applications. Materials, such as walnut-shell flour, are often added by the glue manufacturer to the resin glues to give better working characteristics and joint-forming properties. The suitable curing temperatures for both urea-formaldehyde and resorcinol glues are from 70° F. up. At the 70° F. minimum temperature it may take as long as 1 week for the glueline in a spar splice to cure to full strength. Thinner pieces of wood and/or higher curing temperatures shorten curing time considerably. The strength of a joint cannot be depended upon if assembled and cured at temperatures below 70° F.

7. MIXING OF RESIN GLUES. Liquid resin glues may come ready for use or in a form which requires only the addition of a hardener. In all cases, the mixing, glue consistency, assembly time, etc., should comply with the glue manufacturers' recommendations and instructions. Cold-setting synthetic-resin glue, when prepared for use, is limited in working life, and care should be taken to discard the glue and clean the equipment before the end of the working life period. In very warm weather it may be found advisable to keep the gluepot in a bath of cool water, approximately 70° F., to prolong the working life of the mixture.

8. SPREADING OF GLUE. To make a satisfactory glue joint, spread the glue evenly on both surfaces to be joined. It is recommended that a clean brush be used and care taken to see that all surfaces are covered. The spreading of glue on but one of the two surfaces is not recommended.

9. ASSEMBLY TIME IN GLUING. Where pieces of wood are coated and exposed freely to the air, a much more rapid change in consistency of the glue occurs than where the pieces are laid together as soon as the spreading has been done. The condition of free exposure is conveniently referred to as "open assembly" and the other as "closed assembly."

When cold-setting glues are coated on wood parts and left exposed to the atmosphere (open assembly), the time for complete assembly is appreciably reduced compared with closed assembly periods. Use assembly time and gluing pressures recommended by the glue manufacturer.

The pressing time for casein and resin glue joints should, in general, be 7 hours or more. Other types of glue require various times and temperatures for curing. Glue joints increase in strength mainly as a result of drying; hence, where it is convenient to do so, it is better to maintain pressure from one day to the next. The longer pressing periods are desirable, as this enables the joints to reach a higher proportion of their final strength before being disturbed.

FIGURE 1.2.—Selection and properties of aircraft wood.

Species of wood	Strength properties as compared to spruce	Maximum permissible grain deviation (slope of grain)	Remarks
1	2	3	4
Spruce (Picea) Sitka (P. Sitchensis) Red (P. Rubra) White (P. Glauca).	100%	1:15	Excellent for all uses. Considered as standard for this table.
Douglas Fir (Pseudotsuga Taxifolia).	Exceeds spruce _____	1:15	May be used as substitute for spruce in same sizes or in slightly reduced sizes providing reductions are substantiated. Difficult to work with hand tools. Some tendency to split and splinter during fabrication and considerable more care in manufacture is necessary. Large solid pieces should be avoided due to inspection difficulties. Gluing satisfactory.
Noble Fir (Abies Nobiles) _____	Slightly exceeds spruce except 8 percent deficient in shear.	1:15	Satisfactory characteristics with respect to workability, warping, and splitting. May be used as direct substitute for spruce in same sizes providing shear does not become critical. Hardness somewhat less than spruce. Gluing satisfactory.
Western Hemlock (Tsuga Heterophylla).	Slightly exceeds spruce	1:15	Less uniform in texture than spruce. May be used as direct substitute for spruce. Upland growth superior to lowland growth. Gluing satisfactory.
Pine, Northern White (Pinus Strobus).	Properties between 85 percent and 96 percent those of spruce.	1:15	Excellent working qualities and uniform in properties but somewhat low in hardness and shock-resisting capacity. Cannot be used as substitute for spruce without increase in sizes to compensate for lesser strength. Gluing satisfactory.
White Cedar, Port Oxford (Charaecyparis Lawsoniana).	Exceeds spruce _____	1:15	May be used as substitute for spruce in same sizes or in slightly reduced sizes providing reductions are substantiated. Easy to work with hand tools. Gluing difficult but satisfactory joints can be obtained if suitable precautions are taken.
Poplar, Yellow (Liriodendrow Tulipifera).	Slightly less than spruce except in compression (crushing) and shear.	1:15	Excellent working qualities. Should not be used as a direct substitute for spruce without carefully accounting for slightly reduced strength properties. Somewhat low in shock-resisting capacity. Gluing satisfactory.

(*See notes following table.*)

4

Notes for figure 1.2.

1. *Defects Permitted.*

a. *Cross grain.* Spiral grain, diagonal grain, or a combination of the two is acceptable providing the grain does not diverge from the longitudinal axis of the material more than specified in column 3. A check of all four faces of the board is necessary to determine the amount of divergence. The direction of free-flowing ink will frequently assist in determining grain direction.

b. *Wavy, curly, and interlocked grain.* Acceptable, if local irregularities do not exceed limitations specified for spiral and diagonal grain.

c. *Hard knots.* Sound hard knots up to ⅜-inch in maximum diameter are acceptable providing: (1) they are not in projecting portions of I-beams, along the edges of rectangular or beveled unrouted beams, or along the edges of flanges of box beams (except in lowly stressed portions); (2) they do not cause grain divergence at the edges of the board or in the flanges of a beam more than specified in column 3; and (3) they are in the center third of the beam and are not closer than 20 inches to another knot or other defect (pertains to ⅜-inch knots—smaller knots may be proportionately closer). Knots greater than ¼-inch must be used with caution.

d. *Pin knot clusters.* Small clusters are acceptable providing they produce only a small effect on grain direction.

e. *Pitch pockets.* Acceptable, in center portion of a beam providing they are at least 14 inches apart when they lie in the same growth ring and do not exceed 1½ inch length by ⅛-inch width by ⅛-inch depth and providing they are not along the projecting portions of I-beams, along the edges of rectangular or beveled unrouted beams, or along the edges of the flanges of box beams.

f. *Mineral streaks.* Acceptable, providing careful inspection fails to reveal any decay.

2. *Defects Not Permitted.*

a. *Cross grain.* Not acceptable, unless within limitations noted in 1a.

b. *Wavy, curly, and interlocked grain.* Not acceptable, unless within limitations noted in 1b.

c. *Hard knots.* Not acceptable, unless within limitations noted in 1c.

d. *Pin knot clusters.* Not acceptable, if they produce large effect on grain direction.

e. *Spike knots.* These are knots running completely through the depth of a beam perpendicular to the annual rings and appear most frequently in quartersawed lumber. Reject wood containing this defect.

f. *Pitch pockets.* Not acceptable, unless within limitations noted in 1e.

g. *Mineral streaks.* Not acceptable, if accompanied by decay (see 1f).

h. *Checks, shakes, and splits.* Checks are longitudinal cracks extending, in general, across the annual rings. Shakes are longitudinal cracks usually between two annual rings. Splits are longitudinal cracks induced by artificially induced stress. Reject wood containing these defects.

i. *Compression wood.* This defect is very detrimental to strength and is difficult to recognize readily. It is characterized by high specific gravity; has the appearance of an excessive growth of summer wood; and in most species shows but little contrast in color between spring wood and summer wood. In doubtful cases reject the material, or subject samples to a toughness machine test to establish the quality of the wood. Reject all material containing compression wood.

j. *Compression failures.* This defect is caused from the wood being overstressed in compression due to natural forces during the growth of the tree, felling trees on rough or irregular ground, or rough handling of logs or lumber. Compression failures are characterized by a buckling of the fibers that appear as streaks on the surface of the piece substantially at right angles to the grain, and vary from pronounced failures to very fine hairlines that require close inspection to detect. Reject wood containing obvious failures. In doubtful cases reject the wood, or make a further inspection in the form of microscopic examination or toughness test, the latter means being the more reliable.

k. *Decay.* Examine all stains and discolorations carefully to determine whether or not they are harmless, or in a stage of preliminary or advanced decay. All pieces must be free from rot, dote, red heart, purple heart, and all other forms of decay.

10. GLUING PRESSURE. Pressure is used to squeeze the glue out into a thin continuous film between the wood layers, to force air from the joint, to bring the wood surfaces into intimate contact with the glue, and to hold them in this position during the setting of the glue.

Pressure should be applied to the joint before the glue becomes too thick to flow and is accomplished by means of clamps, presses, or other mechanical devices.

Nonuniform gluing pressure commonly results in weak and strong areas in the same joint. The amount of pressure required to produce strong joints in aircraft assembly operations may vary from 125 to 150 pounds per square inch for softwoods and 150 to 200 pounds per square inch for hardwoods. Insufficient pressure or poorly machined wood surfaces usually result in thick gluelines which indicate a weak joint, and should be carefully guarded against.

a. Method of Applying Pressure. The methods employed in applying pressure to joints in aircraft gluing operations range from the use of brads, nails, screws, and clamps to the use of hydraulic and electrical power presses. Handnailing is used rather extensively in the gluing of ribs and in the application of plywood skins to the wing, control surfaces, and fuselage frames.

On small joints, such as found in wood ribs, the pressure is usually applied only by nailing the joint gussets in place after spreading the glue. Since small nails must be used to avoid splitting, the gussets should be comparatively large in area to compensate for the relative lack of pressure. At least 4 nails per square inch are to be used, and in no event must nails be more than 3/4-inch apart. Small brass screws may also be used advantageously when the particular parts to be glued are relatively small, and do not allow application of pressure by means of clamps.

Clamp spar splices by means of cabinet makers, parallel clamps or similar types. Use handspring clamps in conjunction with softwood only. Due to their limited pressure area, they should be applied with a pressure distributing strip or block at least twice as thick as the member to be pressed.

11. SCARF JOINTS. The scarf joint is the most satisfactory method of making a joint in the grain direction between two solid wood members. Cut both parts accurately because the strength of the joints depend upon maximum contact between the surfaces being glued.

a. Grain Direction. Make the scarfcut in the general direction of the grain slope as shown in figure 1.3. (See figure 1.3 for note concerning allowable deviation from grain direction.)

12. SPLICING OF SPARS. A spar may be spliced at any point except under wing attachment fit-

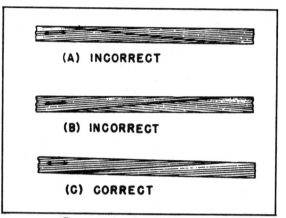

FIGURE 1.3.—Consideration of grain direction when making scarf joints.

No grain deviation steeper than 1 in 15 should be present in an outer eighth of the depth of the spar. In adjacent eighths, deviations involving steeper slopes, such as a wave in a few growth layers, are unlikely to be harmful. Local grain slope deviations in excess of those specified may be permitted in spar flanges only in the inner one-fourth of the flange depth.

tings, landing-gear fittings, engine-mount fittings, or lift-and-interplane strut fittings. Do not permit these fittings to overlap any part of the splice. Splicing under minor fittings such as drag wire, antidrag wire, or compression strut fittings is acceptable under the following conditions:

a. The reinforcement plates of the splice should not interfere with the proper attachment or alinement of the fittings. Do not alter the locations of pulley support brackets, bellcrank support brackets, or control surface support brackets.

b. The reinforcement plate may overlap drag or antidrag wire or compression strut fittings, if the reinforcement plates are on the front-face of the front spar or on the rear-face of the rear spar. In such cases it will be necessary to install slightly longer bolts. The inside reinforcement plate should not overlap drag strut fittings, unless such overlapping does not require sufficient shortening of compression struts, or changes in drag-truss geometry to prevent adjustment for proper rigging. Even though takeup is sufficient, it may be necessary to change the angles on the fittings. Space splices so that they do not overlap. (Acceptable methods of splicing the various types of spars are shown in figures 1.4 through 1.7.) Reinforcement plates must be used as indicated on all scarf repairs to spars and the slopes of scarfs shown are minimum slopes.

13. SPLICING OF BOX SPAR WEBS. Always splice and reinforce plywood webs with the same type of plywood. Do not use solid wood to replace plywood webs, as plywood is stronger in shear than solid wood of the same thickness due to the variation in grain direction of the individual plies. The face-grain of plywood replacement webs and reinforcement plates must be in the same direction as the original member to insure that the new web will have the required strength. (The method of splicing plywood webs is shown in figure 1.8.)

14. REPLACING SOLID-TYPE SPARS WITH LAMINATED TYPE. Solid spruce spars may be replaced with laminated ones or vice versa, provided the material is of the same high quality. External plywood reinforcement must always be replaced with plywood as in the original structure.

15. SPAR LONGITUDINAL CRACKS AND LOCAL DAMAGE. Cracked spars (except box spars) may be repaired by gluing plates of spruce or plywood of sufficient thickness to develop the longitudinal shear strength to both sides of the spar. Extend the plates well beyond the termination of the cracks as shown in figure 1.9. A method of repairing small local damage to either the top or bottom side of a spar is also shown in this figure.

a. Longitudinal Cracking of Wood Wing Spars in Airplanes Operating in Arid Regions. Airplanes having wood spars and being operated in arid

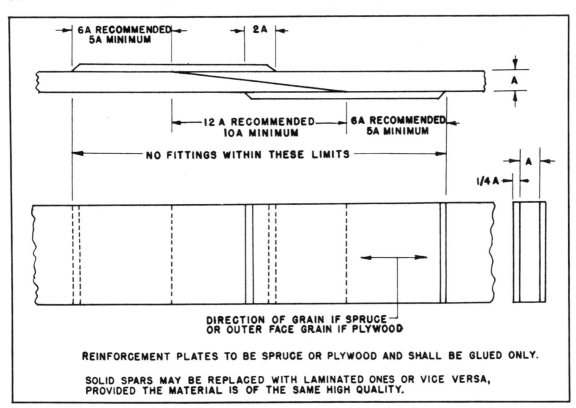

FIGURE 1.4.—Method of splicing solid or laminated rectangular spars.

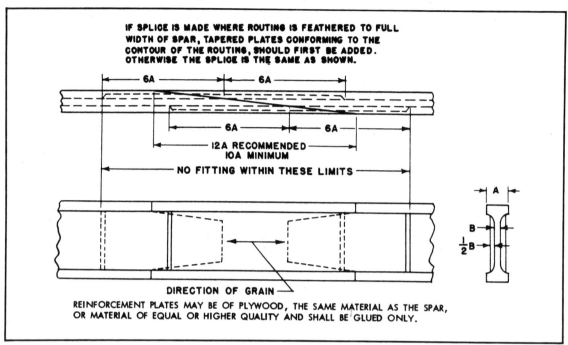

IF SPLICE IS MADE WHERE ROUTING IS FEATHERED TO FULL WIDTH OF SPAR, TAPERED PLATES CONFORMING TO THE CONTOUR OF THE ROUTING, SHOULD FIRST BE ADDED. OTHERWISE THE SPLICE IS THE SAME AS SHOWN.

12A RECOMMENDED
10A MINIMUM

NO FITTING WITHIN THESE LIMITS

DIRECTION OF GRAIN

REINFORCEMENT PLATES MAY BE OF PLYWOOD, THE SAME MATERIAL AS THE SPAR, OR MATERIAL OF EQUAL OR HIGHER QUALITY AND SHALL BE GLUED ONLY.

FIGURE 1.5.—Method of splicing solid "I" spars.

regions may develop longitudinal spar cracks in the vicinity of the plywood reinforcement plates. These cracks result from the tendency of the spar to shrink when drying takes place. Plywood resists this tendency and causes a cross-grain tensile failure in the basic spar. Cracks start under the plywood plates, usually, but not necessarily, at a bolthole or cutout and spread in each direction until, in most cases, they extend a short distance beyond the ends of the plates where the resistance to spar shrinkage disappears. Other factors which have been found conducive to the formation of cracks, due to spar shrinkage in the region of plywood plates, are poor protective finishes, large cutouts, and metal fittings which utilize two lines of large diameter bolts.

The presence of cracks does not necessarily mean that the spar must be discarded. If the crack is not too long or too close to either edge and can be reinforced properly, it will probably be more economical and satisfactory to effect a repair than to install a new spar or section. However, a generally acceptable procedure suitable for all airplane models cannot be

described here. It is recommended the manufacturer or the Federal Aviation Administration be contacted for specific instructions before making repairs not in accordance with the manufacturer's approved instructions or the recommendations of this advisory circular, because of the possibility of strength deficiencies.

16. ELONGATED HOLES IN SPARS. In cases of elongated boltholes in a spar or cracks in the vicinity of boltholes, splice in a new section of spar, or replace the spar entirely, unless the method of repair is specifically approved by a representative of the FAA. In many cases, it has been found advantageous to laminate the new section of the spar (using aircraft plywood for the outer faces), particularly if the spar roots are being replaced.

17. RIB REPAIRS. Make replacement ribs from a manufacturer's approved drawing, or from a drawing made by the repair agency, and certified by the manufacturer as correct. The original rib may be used as a pattern in making the new rib if it is not too seriously damaged to permit comparison. Wood ribs should not be attached to wood spars by nails driven through the rib capstrips, as this weakens the rib materially. The attachment should be by means of glue with cement-coated, barbed, or spiraled nails driven through the vertical rib members on each side of the spar. The drawing or pattern should be retained by the repair agency for use by the FAA inspector when making his inspection. (Acceptable methods of repairing damaged ribs are shown in figure 1.10.)

a. Compression Ribs. Acceptable methods of repairing damaged compression ribs are shown in figure 1.11. (A) illustrates the repair of a compression rib of the "I" section type; i.e., wide, shallow capstrips, a center plywood web with a rectangular compression member on each side of the web. The rib is assumed to be cracked through capstrips, web member, and compression member. Cut the compression

member as shown in (D), remove and replace the shortest section, adding the reinforcement blocks as also shown in figure 1.11(D). Cut and replace the aft portion of the capstrips, and reinforce as shown in figure 1.10 except that the reinforcement blocks are split in the vertical direction to straddle the center web. The plywood sideplates, as indicated in figure 1.11(A), are glued on. These plates are added to reinforce the damaged web. (B) illustrates a compression rib of the type that is basically a standard rib with rectangular compression members added to one side and plywood web to the other side. The method used in this repair is essentially the same as in (A) except that the plywood reinforcement plate shown in solid black in section B–B is continued the full distance between spars. (C) illustrates a compression rib of the "I" type with a rectangular vertical member each side of the web. The

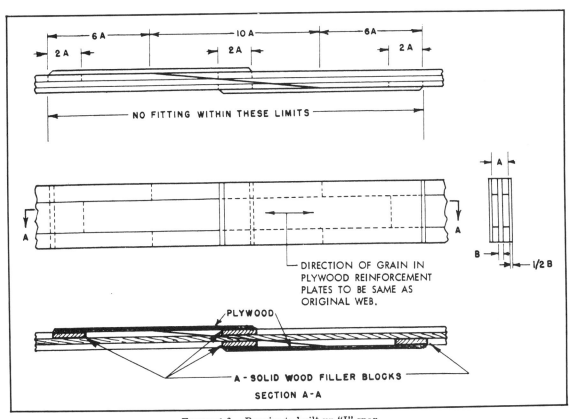

FIGURE 1.6.—Repairs to built-up "I" spar.

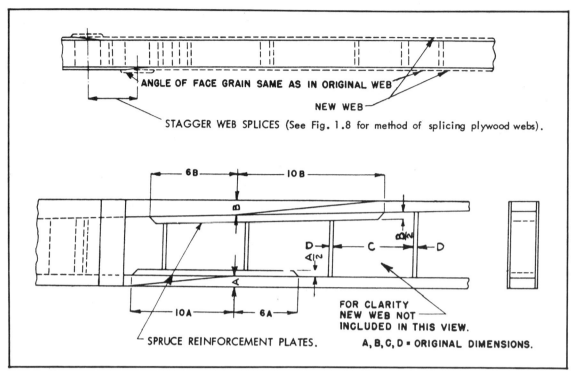

FIGURE 1.7.—Method of splicing box-spar flanges (plate method).

method of repair is essentially the same as in (A) except the plywood reinforcement plates on each side shown in solid black in section C–C are continued, as in (C), the full distance between spars.

18. PLYWOOD SKIN REPAIR. Make extensive repairs to damaged stressed skin plywood structures in accordance with specific recommendations from the manufacturer. It is recommended that repairs be made by replacing the entire panel from one structural member to the next, if damage is very extensive. When damaged plywood skin is repaired, carefully inspect the adjacent internal structure for possible hidden damage. Repair any defective frame members prior to making skin repairs.

a. Types of Patches. Four types of patches—the surface or overlay patch, the splayed patch, the plug patch, and the scarf patch—are acceptable for repairing plywood skins. Surface patches should not be used on skins over 1/8 inch thick. Splayed patches should not be used on skins over 1/10 inch thick. There are no skin thickness limitations for the use of scarf patches and plug patches.

b. Determination of Single or Double Curvature. Much of the outside surface of plywood aircraft is curved. On such areas, plywood used for repairs to the skin must be similarly curved. Curved skins are either of single curvature or of double (compound) curvature. A simple test to determine which type of curvature exists may be made by laying a sheet of heavy paper on the surface in question. If the sheet can be made to fit the surface without wrinkling, the surface is either flat or has single curvature. If, however, the sheet cannot be made to fit the surface without wrinkling, the surface is of double curvature.

19. REPAIRS TO SINGLE CURVATURE PLYWOOD SKIN. Repairs to skins of single curvature may usually be formed from flat plywood, either by

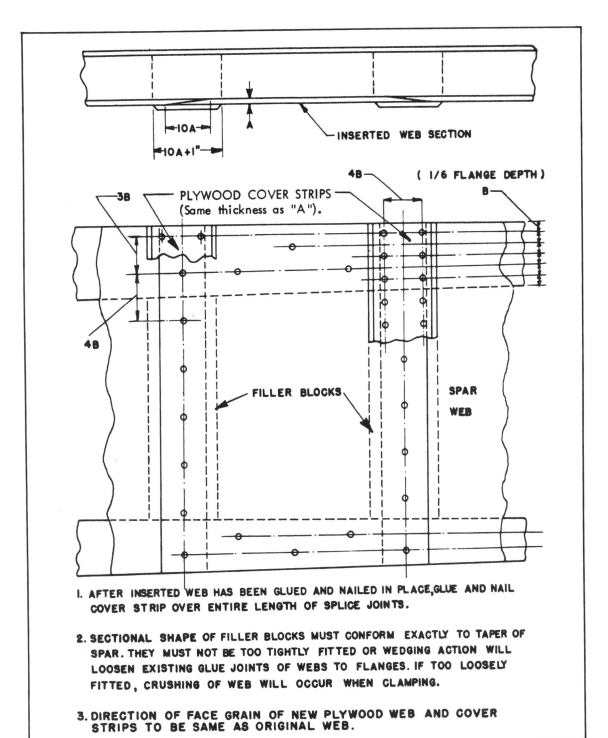

INSERTED WEB SECTION

—|0A—|

—10A+1"—|

4B (1/6 FLANGE DEPTH)

3B

PLYWOOD COVER STRIPS
(Same thickness as "A").

4B

B

FILLER BLOCKS

SPAR
WEB

1. AFTER INSERTED WEB HAS BEEN GLUED AND NAILED IN PLACE, GLUE AND NAIL COVER STRIP OVER ENTIRE LENGTH OF SPLICE JOINTS.

2. SECTIONAL SHAPE OF FILLER BLOCKS MUST CONFORM EXACTLY TO TAPER OF SPAR. THEY MUST NOT BE TOO TIGHTLY FITTED OR WEDGING ACTION WILL LOOSEN EXISTING GLUE JOINTS OF WEBS TO FLANGES. IF TOO LOOSELY FITTED, CRUSHING OF WEB WILL OCCUR WHEN CLAMPING.

3. DIRECTION OF FACE GRAIN OF NEW PLYWOOD WEB AND COVER STRIPS TO BE SAME AS ORIGINAL WEB.

FIGURE 1.8.—Method of splicing box-spar webs.

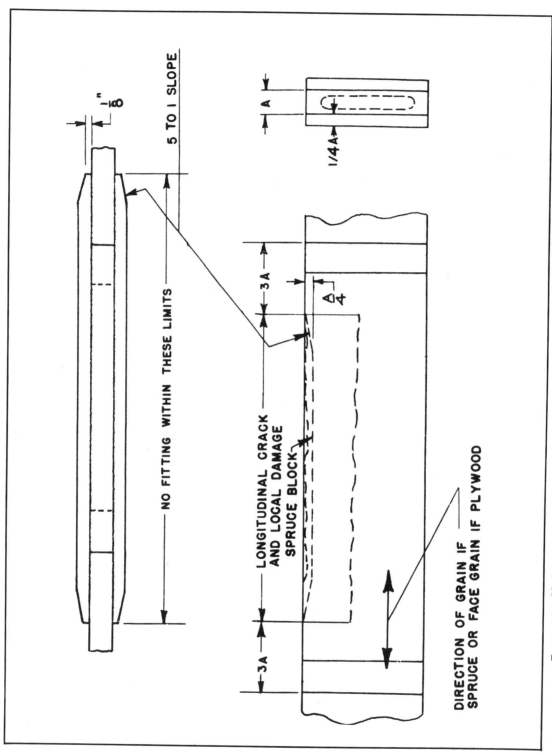

Figure labels:

1/8"

5 TO 1 SLOPE

A

1/4A

3A

A/4

3A

NO FITTING WITHIN THESE LIMITS

LONGITUDINAL CRACK AND LOCAL DAMAGE

SPRUCE BLOCK

DIRECTION OF GRAIN IF SPRUCE OR FACE GRAIN IF PLYWOOD

FIGURE 1.9.—Method of reinforcing a longitudinal crack and/or local damage in a solid or internally routed spar.

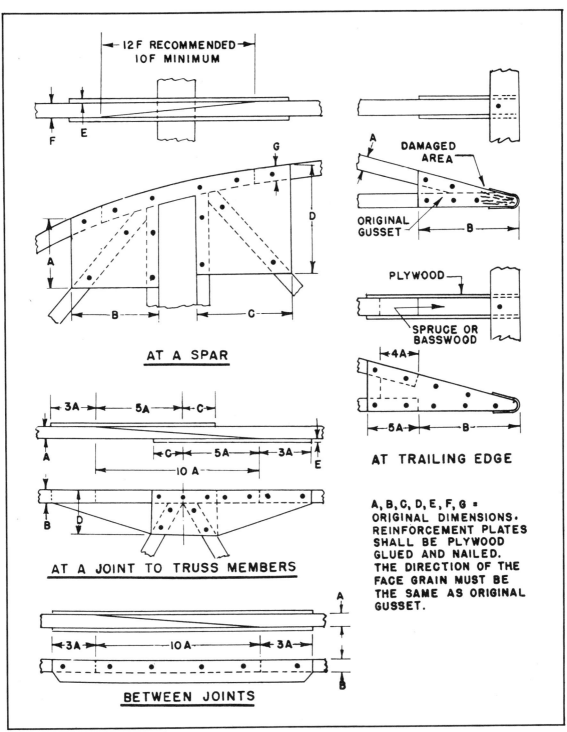

FIGURE 1.10.—Repair of wood ribs.

13

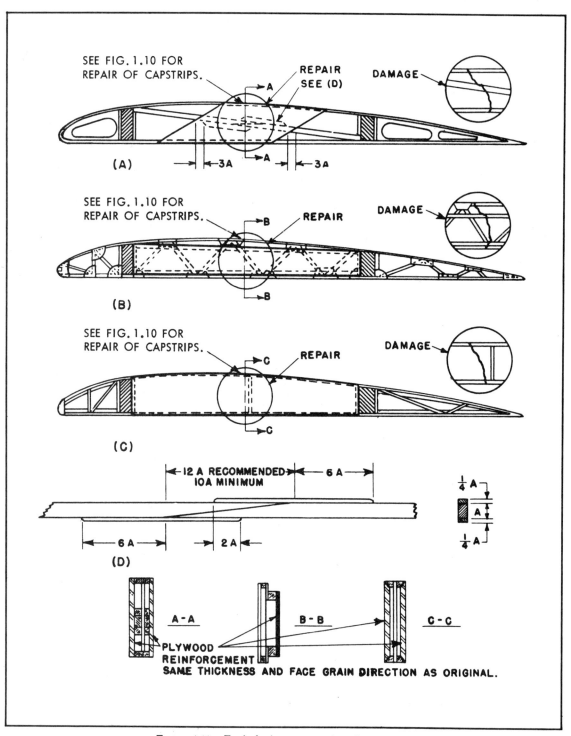

FIGURE 1.11.—Typical wing compression rib repairs.

Plywood thickness	No. plies	10 Percent moisture content, bent on cold mandrels		Thoroughly soaked in hot water and bent on cold mandrels	
		At 90° to face grain 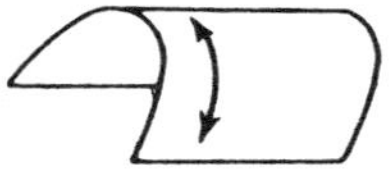	At 0° or 45° to face grain 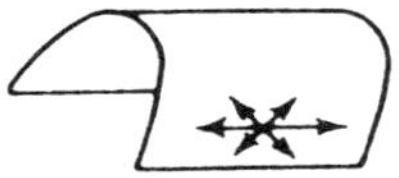	At 90° to face grain 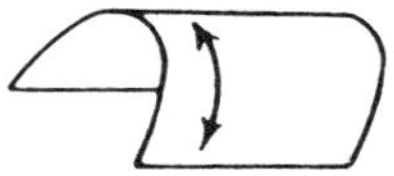	At 0° or 45° to face grain 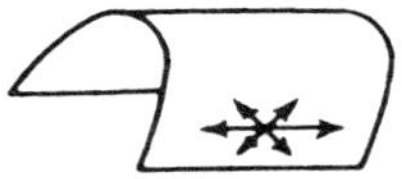
(1)	(2)	(3)	(4)	(5)	(6)
Inch	No. plies	Inches	Inches	Inches	Inches
0.035	3	2.0	1.1	0.5	0.1
.070	3	5.2	3.2	1.5	.4
.100	3	8.6	5.2	2.6	.8
.125	3	12	7.1	3.8	1.2
.155	3	16	10	5.3	1.8
.185	3	20	13	7.1	2.6
.160	5	17	11	6	2
.190	5	21	14	7	3
.225	5	27	17	10	4
.250	5	31	20	12	5
.315	5	43	28	16	7
.375	5	54	36	21	10

Columns (1) and (3) may also be used for determining the maximum thickness of single laminations for curved members.

FIGURE 1.12.—Minimum recommended bend radii for aircraft plywood.

bending it dry or after soaking it in hot water. The degree of curvature to which a piece of plywood can be bent will depend upon the direction of the grain and the thickness. Figure 1.12 is presented as a guide in determining which process of bending should be used for the curvature being considered. Plywood, after softening, may be bent on a cold ventilated form, or it may be bent over the leading edge near the part being patched if space permits. In either method it should be allowed to dry completely on the form. When bending plywood over a leading edge, drying may be hastened by laying a piece of coarse burlap over the leading edge before using it as a bending form.

A fan to circulate the air over the bent piece will speed the drying. In bending pieces of small radii, or to speed up the bending of a large number of parts of the same curvature, it may be necessary to use a heated bending form. The surface temperature of this form may be as high as 149° C. (300° F.), if necessary, without danger of damage to the plywood. The plywood should be left on the form, however, only long enough to dry to room conditions.

20. REPAIRS TO DOUBLE CURVATURE PLYWOOD SKIN. The molded plywood necessary for a repair to a damaged plywood skin of double curvature cannot be made from flat plywood unless the area to be repaired is very small, or is of exceedingly slight double curvature; therefore, molded plywood of the proper curvature must be on hand before the repair can be made. If molded plywood of the proper curvature is available, the repair may be made following the recommended procedures.

21. SPLAYED PATCH. Small holes with largest dimensions not over 15 times the skin thickness, in skins not more than 1/10 inch in thickness, may be repaired by using a circular splayed patch as illustrated in figure 1.13. The term "splayed" is used to denote that the edges of the patch are tapered, but the slope is steeper than is allowed in scarfing operations. The steps shown in figure 1.13 should be taken in making a splayed patch.

a. Lay out the patch according to figure 1.13. Tack a small piece of plywood over the hole for a center point, and draw two circles, the inner one to be the size of the hole, and the outer one marking the limits of the taper. The difference between the radii is 5T (5 times the thickness of the skin). If one leg of the dividers has been sharpened to a chisel edge, the dividers may be used to cut the inner circle completely through.

b. Taper the hole evenly to the outer mark with a chisel, knife, or rasp.

c. Prepare a circular tapered patch to fit the prepared hole and glue the patch into place with face-grain direction matching that of the original surface.

d. Use waxed paper between the patch and a plywood pressure plate cut to the exact size of the patch. This prevents extruded glue from binding patch and plate together. Center the plate carefully over the patch.

e. Apply pressure. As there is no reinforcement behind this patch, care must be used so that pressure is not great enough to crack the skin. On horizontal surfaces, weights or sandbags will be sufficient. On patches too far in for the use of standard hand clamps, jaws of greater length may be improvised.

f. Fill, sand, and refinish the patch.

22. SURFACE PATCH. Plywood skins that are damaged between or along framing members may be repaired by surface or overlay patches as shown in figure 1.14. Trim the damaged skin to a rectangular or triangular shape and round the corners. The radius of rounded corners should be at least 5 times the skin thickness. Cover surface patches with fabric before finishing. Fabric should overlap the original skin at least 2 inches. Surface patches located entirely aft of the 10 percent chordline, or which wrap around the leading edge and terminate aft of the 10 percent chordline are permissible. Bevel forward edges of patches located entirely aft of the 10 percent chordline to 4 times the skin thickness. Surface patches may have as much as a 50-inch perimeter and may cover as much as 1 frame (or rib) space.

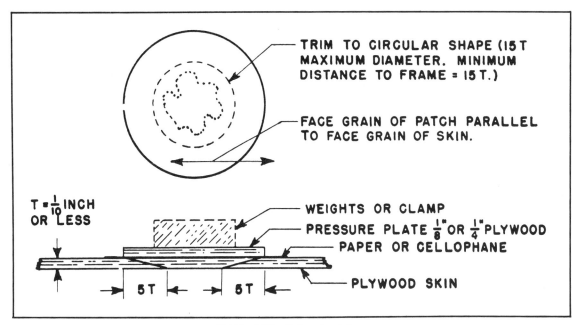

TRIM TO CIRCULAR SHAPE (15 T MAXIMUM DIAMETER. MINIMUM DISTANCE TO FRAME = 15 T.)

FACE GRAIN OF PATCH PARALLEL TO FACE GRAIN OF SKIN.

$T = \frac{1}{10}$ INCH OR LESS

WEIGHTS OR CLAMP
PRESSURE PLATE $\frac{1}{8}"$ OR $\frac{1}{4}"$ PLYWOOD
PAPER OR CELLOPHANE
PLYWOOD SKIN

5 T   5 T

FIGURE 1.13.—Splayed patch.

The face-grain direction must be the same as the original skin.

23. SCARF PATCH. A properly prepared and inserted scarf patch is the best repair for damaged plywood skins and is preferred for most skin repairs. Figure 1.15 shows the details and dimensions to be used when installing typical scarf skin patches when the back of the skin is accessible. Follow figure 1.16 when the back of the skin is not accessible. The scarf slope of 1 in 12 shown in both figures is the steepest slope permitted for all species of plywood. If the radius of curvature of the skin at all points on the trimmed opening is greater than 100 times the skin thickness, a scarf patch may be installed.

Scarf cuts in plywood may be made by hand plane, spoke shave, scraper, or accurate sandpaper block. Rasped surfaces, except at the corners of scarf patches and sawed surfaces, are not recommended as they are likely to be rough or inaccurate.

Nail-strip gluing is often the only method available for gluing scarf joints in plywood when used in repair work; therefore, it is es-

sential that all scarf joints in plywood be backed with plywood or solid wood to provide adequate nailholding capacity. The face grain direction of the plywood patch should be the same as that of the original skin.

a. Scarf Patches (Back of Skin Accessible). When the back of a damaged plywood skin is accessible (such as a fuselage skin), it should be repaired with scarf patches following the details shown in figure 1.15. Whenever possible, the edge of the patch should be supported as shown in section C–C. When the damage follows or extends to a framing member, the scarf may be supported as shown in section B–B.

Damages that do not exceed 25 times the skin thickness in diameter after being trimmed to a circular shape, and if the trimmed opening is not nearer than 15 times the skin thickness to a framing member, may be repaired as shown in figure 1.15, section D–D. The backing block is carefully shaped from solid wood and fitted to the inside surface of the skin, and is temporarily held in place with nails. A hole, the exact size of the inside circle of the scarf patch, is made in the block, and is centered over

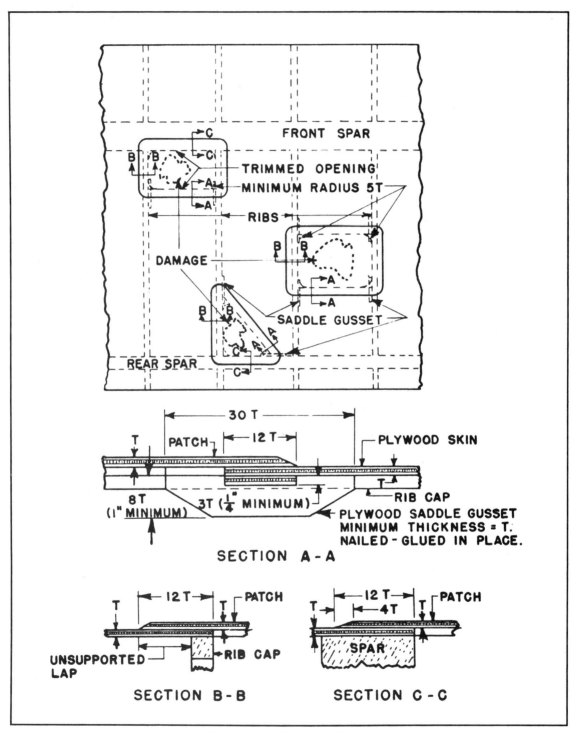

FIGURE 1.14.—Surface patches.

18

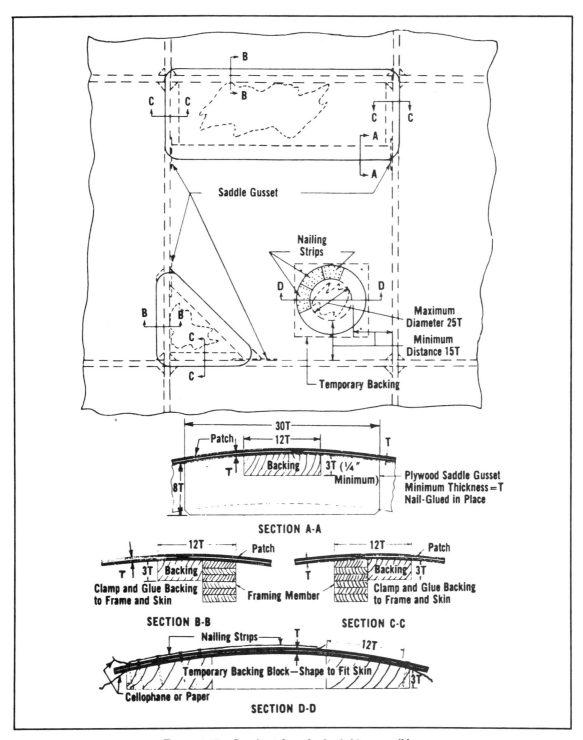

Saddle Gusset

Nailing Strips

Maximum Diameter 25T

Minimum Distance 15T

Temporary Backing

30T

Patch

12T

T

Backing

3T (¼" Minimum)

T

8T

Plywood Saddle Gusset Minimum Thickness = T Nail-Glued in Place

SECTION A-A

12T

Patch

T

3T

Backing

Clamp and Glue Backing to Frame and Skin

Framing Member

SECTION B-B

12T

Patch

Backing

3T

T

Clamp and Glue Backing to Frame and Skin

SECTION C-C

Nailing Strips

T

12T

Temporary Backing Block—Shape to Fit Skin

3T

Cellophane or Paper

SECTION D-D

FIGURE 1.15.—Scarf patches—back of skin accessible.

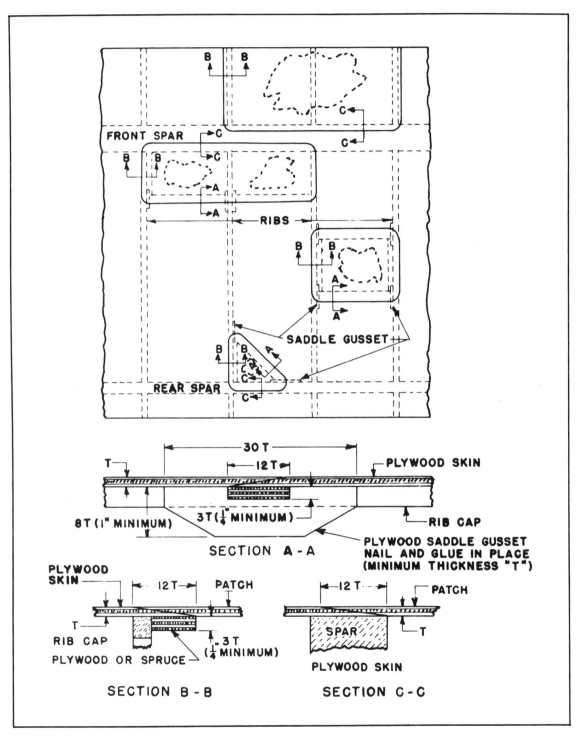

FIGURE 1.16.—Scarf patches—back of skin not accessible.

the trimmed area of damage. The block is removed, after the glue on the patch has set, and leaves a flush surface to the repaired skin.

b. Steps in Making Scarf Patch (Back of Skin Not Accessible).

(1) After removing damaged sections, install backing strips, as shown in figure 1.16, along all edges that are not fully backed by a rib or a spar. To prevent warping of the skin, backing strips should be made of a soft-textured plywood, such as yellow poplar or spruce rather than solid wood. All junctions between backing strips and ribs or spars should have the end of the backing strip supported by a saddle gusset of plywood.

(2) If needed, nail and glue the new gusset plate to rib. It may be necessary to remove and replace the old gusset plate by a new saddle gusset; or, it may be necessary to nail a saddle gusset over the original.

(3) Attach nailing strips to hold backing strips in place while the glue sets. Use bucking bar where necessary to provide support for nailing. Unlike the smaller patches made in a continuous process, work on the airplane must wait while the glue, holding the backing strips, sets. After setting, complete finishing in usual manner.

24. PLUG PATCHES. Two types of plug patches, oval and round, may be used on plywood skins provided the damage can be covered by the patches whose dimensions are given in figures 1.17 and 1.18. As the plug patch is strictly a skin repair, it should be used only for damage that does not involve the supporting structure under the skin. Oval patches must be prepared with the face grain carefully oriented to the same direction as the original skin. Orientation of the face grain direction of the round plug patch to that of the skin surface is no problem,

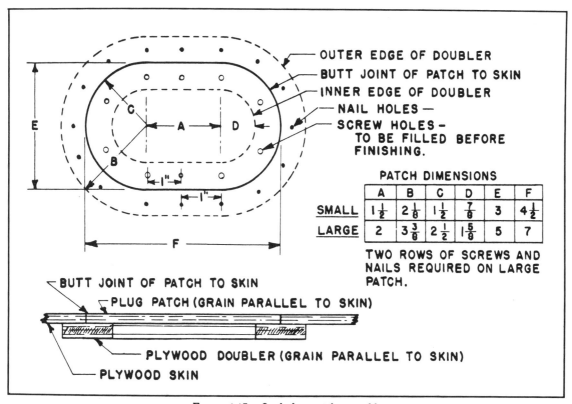

OUTER EDGE OF DOUBLER
BUTT JOINT OF PATCH TO SKIN
INNER EDGE OF DOUBLER
NAIL HOLES
SCREW HOLES -
TO BE FILLED BEFORE FINISHING.

PATCH DIMENSIONS

	A	B	C	D	E	F
SMALL	$1\frac{1}{2}$	$2\frac{1}{8}$	$1\frac{1}{2}$	$\frac{7}{8}$	3	$4\frac{1}{2}$
LARGE	2	$3\frac{3}{8}$	$2\frac{1}{2}$	$1\frac{5}{8}$	5	7

TWO ROWS OF SCREWS AND NAILS REQUIRED ON LARGE PATCH.

BUTT JOINT OF PATCH TO SKIN
PLUG PATCH (GRAIN PARALLEL TO SKIN)
PLYWOOD DOUBLER (GRAIN PARALLEL TO SKIN)
PLYWOOD SKIN

FIGURE 1.17.—Oval plug patch assembly.

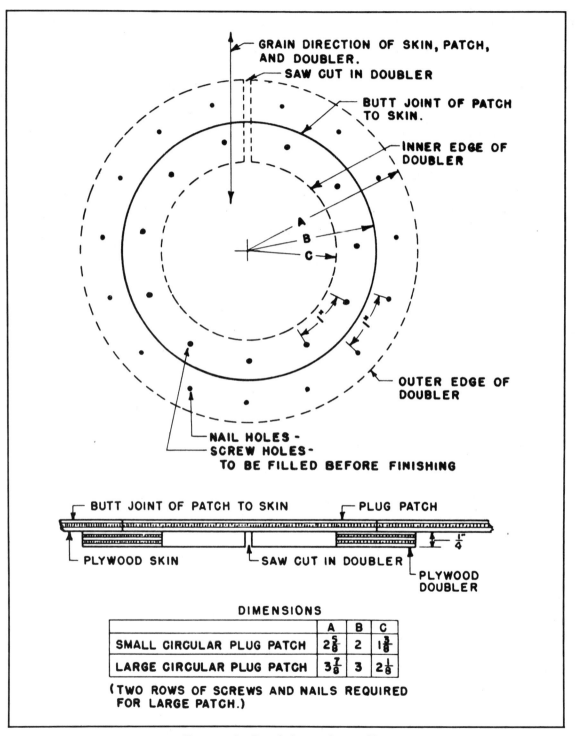

GRAIN DIRECTION OF SKIN, PATCH, AND DOUBLER.

SAW CUT IN DOUBLER

BUTT JOINT OF PATCH TO SKIN.

INNER EDGE OF DOUBLER

A
B
C

OUTER EDGE OF DOUBLER

NAIL HOLES —
SCREW HOLES —
TO BE FILLED BEFORE FINISHING

BUTT JOINT OF PATCH TO SKIN

PLUG PATCH

PLYWOOD SKIN

SAW CUT IN DOUBLER

PLYWOOD DOUBLER

$\frac{1''}{4}$

DIMENSIONS

	A	B	C
SMALL CIRCULAR PLUG PATCH	$2\frac{5}{8}$	2	$1\frac{3}{8}$
LARGE CIRCULAR PLUG PATCH	$3\frac{7}{8}$	3	$2\frac{1}{8}$

(TWO ROWS OF SCREWS AND NAILS REQUIRED FOR LARGE PATCH.)

FIGURE 1.18.—Round plug patch assembly.

as the round patch may be rotated until grain directions match.

a. Steps in Making Oval Plug Patch.

(1) Explore the area about the hole to be sure it lies at least the width of the oval doubler from a rib or a spar. Refer to figure 1.17 for repair details.

(2) Lay a previously prepared oval plug patch over the damage and trace the patch. Saw to the line and trim the hole edges with a knife and sandpaper.

(3) Mark the exact size of the patch on one surface of the oval doubler and apply glue to the area outside the line. The oval doubler should be made of some soft-textured plywood, such as yellow poplar or spruce. Insert doubler through the hole and bring it, glue side up, to the underside of the skin with its pencil outline of the patch matching the edges of the hole. If the curvature of the surface to be repaired is greater than a rise of 1/8 inch in 6 inches, the doubler should be preformed by hot water or steam bending to the approximate curvature.

(4) Apply nailing strips outlining the hole to apply glue pressure between doubler and skin. Use bucking bar to provide support for nailing. When two rows of nails are used, stagger nail spacing.

(5) Apply glue to remaining surface and to an equivalent surface on the patch.

(6) Lay the patch in position over the dou-bler, and screw the pressure plate to the patch assembly using a small nail to line up the holes that have been previously made with patch and plate matching. No. 4 roundhead screws are used. Lead holes in the plywood doubler are not necessary. Waxed paper or cellophane between the plate and patch prevents glue from sealing the plate to the patch. No clamps or further pressure need be applied as the nailing strips and screws exert ample pressure. Hot sandbags, however, may be laid over the patch to speed the setting of the glue. Finish in the usual manner.

b. Round Plug Patch. The steps in making a round plug patch shown in figure 1.18 are identical with those for making the oval patch except the insertion of the doubler. In using the round patch, where access if from only one side, the round doubler cannot be inserted unless it has been split.

25. FABRIC PATCH. Small holes not exceeding 1 inch in diameter, after being trimmed to a smooth outline, may be repaired by doping a fabric patch on the outside of the plywood skin. The edges of the trimmed hole should first be sealed and the fabric patch should overlap the plywood skin by at least 1 inch. Holes nearer than 1 inch to any frame member, or in the leading edge or frontal area of the fuselage, should not be repaired with fabric patches.

26.–36. RESERVED.

Section 2. FINISHING WOOD STRUCTURES

37. GENERAL. Any repair to spars, ribs, skin surfaces, or other structural parts of the airframe involves finishing as the final step of the job. The time and effort spent during the preparatory phase of the refinishing process will be reflected in the appearance of the finished surface. Adherence to the instructions issued by the finish manufacturer is necessary to obtain the appearance desired and protective characteristics for the product used.

38. PRECAUTIONS TO BE OBSERVED. When making repairs, avoid excessive contamination of surfaces with glue squeezeout at joints and on all surfaces. Excess glue should always be removed before applying finish. Because paints and glues are incompatible, even a slight amount of glue underneath the finish may cause premature deterioration.

a. Soiling substances, such as oil and grease,

should be removed as completely as possible. Naphtha may be used to sponge off oil and grease. Markings that are made by grease pencils or lumber crayons containing wax are harmful and should be removed, but marks made by ordinary soft graphite pencils and nonblotting stamp pad inks may be safely finished over. All dust, dirt, and other solid particles should be cleaned off.

b. *Sawdust, shavings,* and chips must be removed from enclosed spaces before they are sealed off by replacement of skin. A vacuum cleaner is useful for such cleaning.

c. *Since no satisfactory gluable sealer* has yet been developed, it is necessary to avoid applying sealer over the areas where glue will be applied. Mark off areas to receive glue, allowing an additional 1/4 inch on each side of the glue area to provide for misalinement when mating the parts. It is preferable to leave some unsealed areas rather than risk weakening the glue joint by accidental overlap of the sealer into the glued areas.

d. *Finish is likely to crack* when applied over flush-driven nails and screws. To avoid this, a strip of tape may be applied over the heads after application of sealer and before the final finish is applied.

e. *Fill all holes* left from nail-strip gluing or countersunk nails and screws with a wood filler before finishing the surface. It may be necessary to cover with a patching putty the slight depressions left after applying filler, if a completely smooth surface is desired; but, as a rule, patching putty may be dispensed with safety.

f. *Treat surfaces* which are likely to come in contact with fabric during the doping process with a dope-proof paint, cellophane tape, etc., to protect them against the action of the solvents in the dope.

39. FINISHING OF INTERIOR SURFACES. Finish repaired ribs, spars, interior of plywood skin, and other internal members, including areas of contact between metal and wood, by applying at least two coats of spar varnish. Protect built-up box spars and similar closed structures on the interior by at least one heavy coat of spar varnish or lionoil. Where better protection is required, as on the surfaces of wheel wells and the bottoms of hulls below the floor boards, an additional coat of aluminized sealer consisting of 12 to 16 ounces of aluminum paste per gallon of sealer may be applied.

40. FINISHING OF EXTERIOR SURFACES. Exterior surfaces should first be sealed with at least two coats of sealer or spar varnish. The surface finish should then be completed by the application of enamel, aluminized varnish, or other special finish as required to duplicate the original finish. If dope or lacquer is used to complete the finish, the sealer coats should be dope-proof. Spar varnish or sealer conforming to Specification MIL–V–6894 is satisfactory.

41. FINISHING OF END GRAIN SURFACES. End grain surfaces, such as edges of plywood skins and holes in spars and other primary structural members, require careful protection. Sand these surfaces smooth. Apply two coats of a highly pigmented sealer, or one coat of wood filler, and one coat of clear sealer to end grain interior surfaces and cut holes. Exterior end grain surfaces (except those covered with doped fabric) require an additional (third) coat of clear sealer. A final coat of aluminized varnish may be applied to end grain surfaces. If the surfaces are to be finished with dope or lacquer, a dope-proof sealer similar to Specification MIL–V–6894 should be used.

Exposed end grain includes such surfaces as those around ventholes, inspection holes, fittings, and exposed scarfed or tapered surfaces such as those of tapered blocking.

42. FINISHING WITH FABRIC OR TAPE. To refinish with fabric or tape, it is first necessary to insure that paint has been removed from an area greater than that to be covered by the fabric.

a. *Apply two brush coats* of a dope-proof sealer similar to Specification MIL–V–6894, allowing the first coat to dry 2 hours and the second coat at least 6 hours. Follow with one coat of clear dope, and allow it to dry 45 minutes. Apply a second coat of clear dope and lay into the wet film a piece of pinked-edge airplane cloth. All air bubbles should be worked out by brushing to insure maximum adherence. Allow this to dry 45 minutes. Apply one brush coat to insure proper penetration, and at least one spray coat of clear dope, allowing each to dry 45 minutes. The dried spray coat may be sanded with fine sandpaper to obtain a smoother finish. Complete the refinishing of the surface by application of lacquer, enamel, or aluminized varnish as required to match the adjacent area.

b. *The size of the fabric patch* should be such as to extend at least 1/2 inch on each side of any crack or group of cracks, at least 1 inch on each side of a scarfed joint glue line, and at least 2 inches beyond any edge of a skin patch to insure proper adhesion.

43.–53. RESERVED.

Comment: As a practical matter, aircraft-grade spruce is your best choice—unless, of course, you are making a repair to a structure framed from other wood. Make certain that it carries the inspector's stamp establishing that it is "Certified, Inspected, Aircraft Grade." Otherwise you have no assurance that the quality or moisture content will be acceptable. In "lumberyard" spruce it seldom is.

A reliable source for aircraft spruce is the Posey Manufacturing Company, Hoquiam, WA 98550.

Always order spruce surfaced on both sides. If it is to be used for wing spars, so state on your order, and order to your required finish dimensions. Wing rib stock should be ordered as "flat stock," surfaced on both sides, and in random widths and lengths, stating your minimum length requirements.

No one expects today's aircraft mechanic to be an accomplished woodworker. Except for the Bellanca Viking wing (Figure 1.19) and those of the early Mooney, very little wood has been used in production aircraft since WWII. A lot of homebuilt airplanes are wood-framed, but even the amateur aircraft builders have turned to metal and composites in recent years. The Pop Riveter, plus designs without complex curves, have allowed the amateur plane builder to switch to all-metal structures, while the fiberglass and foam airframes (some with wood basic structures) appear to be gaining in popularity.

However, antique and classic fabric-covered airplanes (Figs. 1.20, 1.21) are being restored and refurbished wherever they can be found—and not only by collectors, but also by people seeking low-cost fun flying, with a minimum of avionics, from pasture airports. Many of these machines contain a lot of wood.

Note to the amateur aircraft builder: We cannot overstate the importance of using only inspected, aircraft-grade wood (wood that is *so stamped*; don't take anyone's word for it). It is poor economy to risk loss of your time, labor, and money using substandard materials that may shrink or warp and that may result in components that will not be signed off by the aircraft inspector.

Store your wood flat in a dry place, and not in contact with a cement floor. Protect it from oil and grease.

TOOLS

The woodworking power tools you should have depends upon the amount of such work you expect to do. Investment in a table saw can hardly be justified

Figure 1.19.—The Bellanca Viking wing is wood-framed with plywood covering.

Figure 1.20.—The classic Beechcraft Model 17 "Staggerwing" has wood-framed
wings and wooden fixed tail surfaces, along with elaborate wood formers in the fuselage.

for a single product. It is necessary for ripping cap-strips, stringers, etc., but if you are only going to perform those operations once (or once in a blue moon) it's more practical to hire them done. The same applies to a power planer and router. Prices start at about $350.

You must have a drill press, or at least a stand to which you can attach an electric drill as a substitute for a drill press. Keep drill bits sharp. Drill press prices start at $80 (⅜-inch chuck) and go to about $400 (½-inch chuck). A stand that mounts your hand-held electric drill and converts it into a drill press is priced at $30.

A 12-inch band saw, with both ½ and 3/16th-inch wide blades, is extremely useful for a wide range of aircraft woodworking tasks. We'd classify it as another "must have" tool. Prices range from $350 to $425, and blades are about $10 each.

A medium-sized bench vise, solidly mounted, is essential. You can get a regular wood vise, which is useful only for woodworking, for $14, or you can use an ordinary shop vise by placing thin pieces of scrap wood against each jaw to protect the pieces being worked. Good medium-sized shop vises range in price from $35 to $90.

Necessary hand tools are: Both a rip saw and crosscut saw at $15 to $20 each; a medium-sized plane, $23; a couple of wood chisels, ½ inch and one inch, $3 each; a pair of rasp-type files, half-round, one coarse and one medium, $3 to $6 each; a carpenter's brace and bit is handy, though not really essential. The brace is $18, and wood bits are $5 to $10 each. A magnetized tack hammer is necessary and will cost about $5. You will need approximately 10 C-clamps in two-inch and six-inch sizes, which will be priced at $2.50 and $6.50 each, respectively. You will also need

Figure 1.21.—Most
antique aircraft, such as this mint condition DeHavilland Gypsy Moth, will have
wooden wings. Almost all production aircraft
had switched from wood to tubular steel fuselages by
the mid-twenties. Some homebuilts are still "all-wood."

two pairs of parallel clamps at $10.85 per pair.

Finally, a good tape ruler is essential and will cost $3.50 for a six-footer, $7.50 for an eight-foot tape. A square protractor will be about $7, a set of trammell points with bar, $25, and a sheet metal hammer along with a rounded bucking bar, $6 and $8 respectively.

WOOD-FRAMED FUSELAGES

It is highly unlikely that you will ever encounter a production airplane with a wood-framed fuselage because those that remain have long since been restored. But there are some all-wood homebuilts because wood is actually an excellent airframe material. It is just as strong as metal, is more flexible, and will last just as long. It was abandoned by commercial aircraft manufacturers because it did not lend itself to mass production techniques. Wooden airframes must be completely handbuilt.

Wood-framed fuselages are usually built up of ¾-inch to ⅞-inch square spruce. Each fuselage side is assembled in a jig, the jig normally consisting of a flat surface (often plywood sheets) to which small blocks are attached. These serve as guides to position each structural piece in conformance with the plans. This method is the same as that used in building flying model airplanes, the blocks serving the same purpose as the pins used in model building. Plywood gussets, attached with cement-coated aircraft nails (#20) and

Weldwood resin glue, secure each joint.

When making the jig, do not place the form blocks next to joints. The old modelers' trick of placing waxed paper on the jig beneath glued joints will prevent excess glue from bonding the structure to the jig at those points. The fuselage gussets should be made from ⅛-inch birch plywood, unless you are making a repair and find something different in the original structure.

When making repairs to a wood fuselage, always repair/rebuild as per original. If that is not possible, or if you have a good reason for wanting to do things a different way, *always* consult an aircraft inspector at the nearest FAA General Aviation District Office (GADO). Proceed on your own without his okay and you may have to do the whole thing over.

The same applies if you are an amateur plane builder working on a homebuilt. In such an event you should have discussed the project with the GADO people before cutting the first piece of wood. You can do yourself an even bigger favor by talking with the GADO inspector before purchasing your plans, because he will have had experience with a lot of homebuilts and will know their histories and problem areas. His advice can be very useful. Another consideration is the effect this early visit will have on your future relationship with that office. The GADO people don't like surprises, and the amateur builder (or licensed aircraft mechanic, for that matter) who ignores GADO until forced to call upon them for approval of a project is in danger of receiving the same kind of consideration he has showed them. Work with them and they'll work with you.

A separage jig will be required in which to assemble the cross pieces of top and bottom to the two previously constructed sides. Wetting or steaming of the structure is not necessary to bring the two sides together at the rudder post. Aircraft grade spruce is flexible enough to conform to the curves in any properly proportioned fuselage. Steaming of the wood and sharp bends weaken the structure.

The fuselage formers, those pieces fastened to the basic frame to provide a rounded contour, are made of 3/16-inch or ¼-inch aircraft or marine plywood, surfaced on both sides. The longitudinal stringers that attach to the formers are usually ¼-× ¾-inch spruce strips fitted edgewise to notches in the formers. The spaces between each notch should be flattened or dished-out slightly so that the fabric cover will not come in contact with the formers. The stringers are not fitted flush into the formers, but protrude ¼-inch from the ½-inch deep notches.

The formers will, of course, contain lightening holes made with the proper size hole-saw blades in your drill press. The sizes and number of lightening holes will be determined by the size of the formers. Some formers may be so narrow that few, if any, lightening holes are necessary. In any event, the idea is to save as much weight as possible without weakening the former.

Cockpit floorboards of 3/16-inch plywood are recommended; this will give sufficient strength without adding excess weight.

Other plywood in the cockpit area is usually ⅛-inch. Many homebuilts with wood-framed fuselages are plywood covered from the firewall to the rear of the cockpit.

Finally, some experienced aircraft woodworkers advise that top longerons not be installed as each fuselage side is assembled in the jig. They build the top of the fuselage in a top/bottom jig. Then they attach the two sides to the top, with the aid of bar clamps, while the bottom cross pieces are installed with the structure in the top/bottom jig.

WINGS

Spruce is superior to any of the other approved woods for wing spars (beams) when strength, workability, consistency, and dependable glued joints are all taken into consideration.

The preceding section of 43.13 obviously assumes that the mechanic is familiar with the several types of wooden spars, but that may not always be the case. A box spar, often used in cantilever wings (wings without external bracing) is hollow. It is built up of top and bottom pieces of spruce faced on each side with plywood. It is not completely hollow; blocks of spruce are secured inside at fitting or attachment points.

Solid laminated spars are built up of spruce strips bonded together after the fashion of laminated wooden propellers. Often, the reason for going to a laminated spar is the unavailability of a flawless single piece of spruce of the proper size.

Some old airplanes have solid, single-piece spars that are routed out on each face to produce a sort of I-beam cross section. But the weight thus saved is negligible, and will not justify the labor/cost required. It is unlikely that you will have the equipment or the skill to perform such an operation yourself. If you are rebuilding such a wing and a new spar is called for, you may substitute a solid or laminated spar without the routed faces. You may also substitute spruce for spars made of other woods. When such changes are desirable, it is probably the best to clear them in advance with the GADO inspector.

Another type of wooden I-beam spar that was used in old production aircraft (and perhaps some current homebuilts) is a solid, comparatively narrow beam reinforced along the top and bottom on each face with plywood or spruce strips.

When reinforcing plates are to be added to the spar at strut attachment or other stress points, these plates should be feathered as per figure 1.1. This spreads stresses and does not leave a clearly defined edge at each end of the plate where stress would tend to concentrate.

Due to the positioning of fittings on the spar, most spars will have a top and bottom. Make sure that you don't get the spar upside down while working with it. Also make sure that the wood is kept clean. Don't handle it with greasy hands, and don't scribe it with a sharp instrument; mark it with pen or pencil.

Bolt holes in the spar must be made with care and in a drill press. You cannot hand-drill and expect to get a perfectly round hole at an exact 90-degree angle to the face.

WING RIBS

Some of the single-place homebuilts of low horsepower—that is, airplanes with small wing ribs—have ribs cut from sheets of aircraft-grade plywood. This makes rib construction fast and easy, because they are cut out with a band saw and lightening holes are added with the drill press. Depending on the thickness of the plywood rib, capstrips may or may not be added.

Wooden ribs may also be built up in a jig using spruce strips as small as ¼-inch square. Use whatever size is called for in the plans, and replace as per original for a repair.

The jig should be made of ⅝ to ¾-inch plywood to ensure that it offers a perfectly flat surface. The guide blocks attached to the jig must be very carefully placed to make sure that the ribs are shaped exactly according to plan, and should be slightly less thick than the structural pieces they hold in place to facilitate the nailing and gluing of joints and gussets.

Some ribs with a fairly deep curve forward of the front spar will require that the upper capstrips be soaked in water (or steamed) in order to fit into the jig without danger of breaking. It is usually easier to slide the top capstrip into the jig from the rear. You may have to drive it in with light taps of a "skinhead" mallet.

Rib gussets are normally made of 1/16-inch plywood (although we recall encountering some made of a very stiff processed paper, in the wings of a 1940 Aeronca Chief, a few years ago). The gussets, too, are cut out on the band saw, making about ten of them per cut with the gusset material held together with a few nails.

Attach the gussets with glue and a minimum number of 20-gauge nails spaced about ½-inch apart. Do not attempt to remove the nails after the glue has set. The weight thus saved would not justify the effort or the potential for damage to the ribs.

The capstrips and truss pieces should be cut so that the grain of the wood is vertical. This provides maximum resistance to warping after the cover goes on the wing. (Properly installed fabric covering will not be over-taut. We will discuss fabric installation and finishing in a subsequent section.)

When assembling the ribs in the jig, always omit the vertical truss piece of each rib that is next to the rear face of the front spar, and omit both vertical trusses adjacent to the rear spar faces. These pieces will be installed after the wing has been trammeled ("squared"). Otherwise, you are likely to find that the spaces for the spars in each rib are not exact and that some ribs are slightly deformed by the trammeling process. Another consideration is that you will not be able to slide the ribs over the spars' reinforcing plates if these vertical trusses are in place.

If you are working with ribs sawed from plywood sheets, the only way to allow for a proper fit to the spars is to cut the rib spar openings slightly oversize and then, after assembly and trammeling, install reinforcing blocks on each side of each rib for secure attachment to the spars.

Ash was the favorite wood for wingtip bows and center section trailing edges during the biplane era. The craftsmen of those days steamed and carefully shaped these components from single pieces of wood. Replacing such pieces, it is probably easier (and legal) to make a jig and build up tip bows and curved center section trailing edges by laminating narrow strips of spruce. The curves will take up a surprising amount of

material, so make sure that the strips are of sufficient length before applying the glue.

WING ASSEMBLY

The wing will be assembled upside down, so very carefully mark the position of each rib on the bottoms of the spars with pen or pencil. Also mark the exact centerline of each compression member attach fitting. It is usually easier to install the wing root compression member first, because this will hold the spars upright while the ribs are slipped over the spars, starting with the inboard ribs and working outward toward the wingtip. This means, of course, that all of the ribs, except the butt or wing root rib, are slipped over the spars from the wingtip. The tip rib will not be installed until after the wing is trammeled since it is outboard of the last compression member.

With the ribs located loosely on the spars, the metal fittings for the compression members are bolted in place. Then install the compression members, repeatedly measuring the center-to-center distance between front and rear spar to make sure that the spars are parallel. Wide, flat washers of no more than 1/16 inch thickness may be used to shim the compression members in order to maintain the exact measurement between the spars. Use washers of wide area in order to avoid crushing the wood.

Most wood-framed wings will contain wire bracing between the spars, and these wires will each have some means of adjustment such as a turnbuckle or threaded barrel. These wires are installed next, and tightened only enough to remove any slack.

Next, the wing may be trammeled. The trammeling points will be located where the longitudinal centerline of the spar is intersected by a line extending across the spar from the centerline of each compression member. Maybe we'd better explain that more fully: We're looking at the spars' bottom edges. A line drawn down the center of the bottom edge from wing root to wingtip is intersected, at right angles, by lines extended across the bottom edge of the spars, which are extensions of the centerlines of the compression members. Those intersections are the trammeling points.

The object is to square each bay (the space between two compression members) by adjusting the tension of the brace wires. These wires, by the way, are called "drag" and "anti-drag" wires. A bay is squared when the diagonal distances between front and rear spar trammel points are equal in that bay.

You may use a ruler for this operation, but a regular trammel bar four to six feet in length, with sliding points on each end, is better.

The tension on the wires should be equal, and if you do or expect to do very much of this kind of work, a tensiometer for determining wire tension is a worthwhile investment. Experienced craftsmen can pluck these wires with a finger and judge by sound when they have them all of equal and proper tension. Tape the wires where they cross each other to prevent wear or chafing from vibration. And, of course, safety the turnbuckles after the final adjustments are made.

Now, at last, you are ready to secure the ribs to the spars with glue and 20-gauge nails (½ to ¾-inch in length, depending upon the size of the capstrips).

If the wing has false ribs (partial ribs that extend only from the front spar forward), these go on next, and are followed by the spanwise spruce strip glued and nailed (1 ¼ inch nails into the notches in the leading edges of the wing ribs).

With the spanwise leading edge strip in place, you may turn the wing structure right side up to install a wing walk if this happens to be a biplane lower panel.

Wing walks are usually made of 3/16-inch plywood attached to the tops of the wing root rib and the next inboard rib and supported beneath by several ¾ to one-inch square braces fitted between these two ribs. If the walk extends beyond the front spar to the leading edge, that portion may have to be steamed in order to make it conform to the wing curve. The two inboard ribs are often solid plywood and the top edges of these ribs, where the walk is to be attached, may be cut down 3/16-inch to make the walk level with the wing's fabric cover.

You may also want to cover the space between the two inboard ribs on the bottom of the wing with 1/16-inch plywood to protect the lower surface from debris picked up by the landing gear. Always install drain holes at low points in such boxed structures, and varnish the interior before closing.

The wingtip bow may be installed next. It is usually supported by one or two pairs of ½-inch (approximately, depending on wing size) square spruce braces that extend from near the center of the bow to the upper and lower junctions formed by the tip rib and the spars.

If the leading edge of the wing is covered with shaped aluminum, it is attached by nailing to the bottom of the front spar and then pulling it snugly around the leading edge to be nailed to the top edge of the front spar. Nailing strips glued to the top of the spar between each rib allow a smooth surface. Bend down the edges of the metal so that they do not chafe the fabric cover. Varnish the wing structure before attaching this component. At least two coats of marine spar varnish or Varathane are required.

If the leading edge is plywood-covered, usually 1/16 inch, the top surface may have to be wetted in order to make this piece conform to the proper shape and fit snugly. Nail first to the leading edge spanwise strip, then up over each rib, and then to the nailing strips between each rib. Varnish the inside surfaces of this component.

The trailing edge aluminum is purchased preformed. It is attached to each rib with a soft rivet. Take care to keep the trailing edge straight by measuring the distance from the rear spar face before drilling each rivet hole.

GENERAL

A primary rule to follow when constructing a homebuilt airplane is to build according to the plans. You should discuss the plans with the GADO people before starting the project. Thereafter, any deviation from the plans demands prior consultation with GADO. Make a structural change of your own design and you may be in for an unpleasant (and costly) surprise when the inspector is called to sign off of the airframe prior to its final covering.

The rules to follow in restoring/refurbishing/repairing a production airplane are:

1. Always duplicate the original structure if possible.

2. Adhere to 43.13 standards.

3. If you are not an FAA-licensed airframe mechanic, you must work under the direct supervision of an AP who has aircraft woodworking experience.

4. If you are a licensed airframe mechanic, but without aircraft woodworking experience, you should proceed under the supervision of an AP or IA (the latter being an AP with inspection authorization) who is qualified in this area. Actually, this is one of those rather gray areas in the FARs. The regulations do require that licensed mechanics have instruction/experience in specialized repair procedures, but do not spell out all possible situations. Common sense is one's best guide—backed by consultation with the nearest GADO. Work with the GADO inspector (examiner) and he will work with you. He's human.

The above reminds us of another point that should be made about homebuilt aircraft. Some homebuilt plans are inadequate and not sufficiently detailed. The builder is forced to ad lib. When such deficiency involves the structural integrity of the airframe or could affect aircraft performance, one's solution is best cleared with the GADO inspector.

Aircraft Metal Structures

(Reprinted from FAA 43.13, Chapter 2)

Section 1. REFERENCES AND PRECAUTIONARY MEASURES

55. FLUTTER AND VIBRATION PRECAUTIONS. To prevent the occurrence of severe vibration or flutter of flight control surfaces during flight, precautions must be taken to stay within the design balance limitations when performing maintenance or repair.

a. *Balance Changes.* The importance of retaining the proper balance and rigidity of aircraft control surfaces cannot be underestimated. As a general rule, repair the control surface in such a manner that the structure is identical to the original so that the weight distribution is not affected in any way. In order to preclude the occurrence of flutter of the control surface in flight, a degree of static and/or dynamic balance is established for each model of aircraft. Under certain conditions, counter-balance weight is added forward of the hinge line to maintain balance. Remove or add balance weight only when necessary in accordance with the manufacturer's instructions, or obtain FAA approval. Flight testing may be required.

Failure to check and retain control surface balance within the original or maximum allowable value could result in a serious flight hazard.

b. *Materials and Construction Techniques.* The development of new materials and techniques has made possible the use of control surfaces of less mass weight for a given area than some aircraft of older design. The effect of repair or weight change on the balance and center of gravity is proportionately greater on lighter surfaces than on the older designs. Since control surfaces on some models are balanced for flutter-free operation up to maximum speed for which the aircraft was originally designed, special attention, therefore, must be given to such surfaces relative to the effects of structural repairs and rework on their balance condition.

c. *Painting and Refinishing.* Special emphasis is directed to the effect indiscriminate application of extra coats of dope or paint has on the balance of control surfaces. Proper maintenance of control surface balance may require removal of dope or paint, down to the base coat, prior to application of finish coats. Consult the aircraft manufacturer's instructions relative to finishing and balance of control surfaces.

d. *Trapped Water or Ice*. Instances of flutter have occurred from unbalanced conditions caused by the collection of water or ice within the surface. Therefore, ventilation and drainage provisions must be checked and retained when maintenance is being done. Certain construction designs do not provide for ventilation and may collect moisture through condensation which will affect balance. In the event this condition is found, refer to the manufacturer's instructions for moisture removal.

e. *Trim Tab Maintenance*. In addition to unbalanced control surface, loose or vibrating trim tabs will increase wear of actuating mechanisms and hinge points which may develop serious flutter conditions. Most trim tabs are not balanced separately from the control surface. Minimum tab flutter is maintained through rigid actuating mechanisms. Trim tabs and their actuating mechanism are constructed as lightly as possible to keep the weight aft of the hinge line of the control surface as low as possible. Actuating mechanisms are highly susceptible to wear, deformation, and fatigue failures because of the buffeting nature of airflow over the tab mechanism. Trailing-edge play of the tab may increase, through wear of the mechanism, to an unsafe condition. Careful inspection of the tab and its mechanism should be conducted during overhaul and inspection periods. Compared to other systems on the aircraft, only a minor amount of tab-mechanism wear can be tolerated. In the absence of a specified limit for tab trailing

edge movement in the manufacturer's manual, it is acceptable to use a limit of 2 1/2% of the chord, measured at the trailing edge of the tab. For example, a tab that has a chord of 4" would have a maximum permissible free play of 4" x .025 or 0.100 inches (total motion up and down) measured at the trailing edge. Correct any free play in excess of this amount. Care must also be exercised during repair or rework to prevent stress concentration points or areas which could increase the fatigue susceptibility of the trim tab system.

56. BRAZING. Brazing may be used for repairs to primary aircraft structures only if brazing was originally approved for the particular application. Brazing is not suitable for repair of welds in steel structures due to lower strength values of the brazed joint as compared to welded joints. Brazing may be used in the repair of secondary structures.

Due to the large number of brazing alloys used, it is difficult to be certain that the material selected for repairing a brazed joint will result in a joint having the same strength characteristics as the original. In cases where it is necessary to apply copper alloy brazing material, more than once on a steel surface, and particularly if temperatures over 2,000° F. are reached, there is a possibility that brazing metal may penetrate between the grains in the steel to an extent that may cause cracking. Copper brazing of steel is normally accomplished in a special furnace having a controlled atmosphere, and at a temperature so high that field repairs are seldom feasible. If copper brazing is attempted without a controlled atmosphere, the copper will probably not completely flow and fill the joint. Therefore, copper brazing in any other than appropriately controlled conditions is not recommended.

57.–67. RESERVED.

Section 2.   WELDING

68. GENERAL. This section covers weld repairs to aircraft and component parts thereof with the exception of welding on powerplants and

propellers which is provided in chapters 12 and 14 respectively. Observe the following when using such equipment as tungsten inert gas (TIG), metal inert gas (MIG), plasma arc, shield carbon arc, and oxygen-acetylene gas.

a. Equipment Selection. Use the welding equipment manufacturers' information to determine if the equipment will satisfy the requirements for the type of welding operation being undertaken. Disregarding such detailed operating instructions may cause substandard welds. For example, when using TIG equipment, a weld can be contaminated with tungsten if the proper size electrode is not used when welding with direct current reverse polarity. Another example, the depletion of the inert gas supply below the critical level causes a reduction in the gas flow and will increase the danger of atmospheric contamination.

(1) Electric welding equipment versatility requires careful selection of the type current and polarity to be used. Since the composition and thickness of metals are deciding factors, the selection may vary with each specific application. Metals having refractory surface oxide films, i.e., magnesium alloys and aluminum and its alloys, are generally welded with A.C., while D.C. is used for carbon, low alloy, noncorrodible, and heat-resisting steels, copper, etc. General recommendations covering current and polarity are shown in figure 2.1.

(2) Oxygen-acetylene gas equipment is suitable for welding most metals. It is not, however, the best method to use on such materials as stainless steels, magnesium, and aluminum alloys because of base metal oxidization, distortion, and loss of ductility.

NOTE: When oxyacetylene is used, all flux must be removed, as it may cause corrosion.

b. Accurately Identify the Type of Material to be Repaired. If positive identification is not possible, contact the aircraft manufacturer or subject the item to a metallurgical laboratory analysis. Before any welding is attempted, carefully consider the weldability of the alloy since all alloys are not readily weldable. The following steels are readily weldable: plain carbon of the 1000 series, nickel steel of the SAE 2300 series, chrome-nickel alloys of the SAE 3100 series, chrome-molybdenum steels of

FIGURE 2.1.—Current and polarity selection for inert gas welding.

MATERIAL	ALTERNATING CURRENT* With High-Frequency Stabilization	DIRECT CURRENT STRAIGHT Polarity	DIRECT CURRENT REVERSE Polarity
Magnesium up to 1/8 in. thick	1	N.R.	2
Magnesium above 3/16 in. thick	1	N.R.	N.R.
Magnesium Castings	1	N.R.	2
Aluminum up to 3/32 in. thick	1	N.R.	2
Aluminum over 3/32 in. thick	1	N.R.	N.R.
Aluminum Castings	1	N.R.	N.R.
Stainless Steel	2 *	1	N.R.
Brass Alloys	2 *	1	N.R.
Silicon Copper	N.R.	1	N.R.
Silver	2	1	N.R.
Silver Cladding	1	N.R.	N.R.
Hard-facing	1	1	N.R.
Cast Iron	2 *	1	N.R.
Low Carbon Steel, 0.015 to 0.030 in.	2**	1	N.R.
Low Carbon Steel, 0.030 to 0.125 in.	N.R.	1	N.R.
High Carbon Steel, 0.015 to 0.030 in.	2 *	1	N.R.
High Carbon Steel, 0.030 in. and up	2 *	1	N.R.

1. Recommended   2. Acceptable   N.R. Not Recommended

*Where A.C. is recommended as second choice, use approximately 25% higher current than is recommended for DCSP.

**Do not use A.C. on tightly jigged part.

the SAE 4100 series, and low nickel-chrome-molybdenum steel of the SAE 8600 series.

c. Preparation for Welding. Hold elements to be welded in a welding jig or fixture which is sufficiently rigid to prevent misalinement due to expansion and contraction of the heated material and which positively and accurately position the pieces to be welded.

d. Cleaning Prior to Welding. Clean parts to be welded with a wire brush or other suitable methods. When cleaning with a wire brush, do not use a brush of dissimilar metal; for example, brass or bronze on steel. The small deposit left by a brass or bronze brush will materially weaken the weld and may cause cracking or subsequent failure of the weld. In case members were metallized, the surface metal may be removed by careful sandblasting followed by a light buffing with emery cloth.

e. Condition of Complete Weld. Make sure that:

(1) The finished weld has a smooth seam and is uniform in thickness;

(2) The weld metal is tapered smoothly into the base metal;

(3) No oxide has formed on the base metal at a distance of more than 1/2 inch from the weld;

(4) The weld shows no signs of blowholes, porosity, or projecting globules;

(5) The base metal shows no signs of pitting, burning, cracking, or distortion;

(6) The depth of penetration insures fusion of base metal and filler rod; and

(7) Welding scale is removed by wire brushing or sandblasting.

f. Practices to Guard Against. Do not file welds in an effort to make a smooth-appearing job, as such treatment causes a loss of strength. Do not fill welds with solder, brazing metal, or any other filler. When it is necessary to reweld a joint which was previously welded, remove all old weld material before rewelding. Avoid welding over a weld because reheating may cause the material to lose its strength and be-

come brittle. Never weld a joint which has been previously brazed.

g. Torch Size (Oxyacetylene Welding). The size of the torch tip depends upon the thickness of the material to be welded. Commonly used sizes proved satisfactory by experience are:

Thickness of steel (in inches)	Diameter of hole in tip	Drill size
0.015 to 0.031	0.026	71
0.031 to 0.065	.031	68
0.065 to 0.125	.037	63
0.125 to 0.188	.042	58
0.188 to 0.250	.055	54
0.250 to 0.375	.067	51

h. Welding Rods and Electrodes. Use welding rods and electrodes that are compatible with the materials to be welded. Welding rods and electrodes for various applications have special properties suitable for the application intended. Figure 2.3 shows the allowable strength for the weld metal. Figure 2.2 lists specifications for corresponding metals, and the applicable specification will identify the use of A.C. or D.C., straight or reverse polarity.

i. Rosette Welds. Rosette welds are generally employed to fuse an inner reinforcing tube (liner) with the outer member. Where a rosette weld is used, drill the hole, in the outside tube only, of a sufficient size to insure fusion of the inner tube. A hole diameter of approximately one-fourth the tube diameter of the outer tube serves adequately for this purpose. In cases of tight-fitting sleeves or inner liners, the rosettes may be omitted.

j. Heat-Treated Members. Certain structural parts may be heat-treated and therefore could require special handling. In general, the more responsive an alloy steel is to heat treatment, the less suitable it is for welding because of its tendency to become brittle and lose its ductility in the welded area. Weld the members which depend on heat treatment for their original physical properties, using a welding rod suitable for producing heat-treated values comparable to those of the original members (see paragraph 68h). After welding, reheat-treat

FIGURE 2.2.—Specifications guide for welding metals.

Material To Be Welded	Electric Welding	Tungsten Inert Gas (TIG)	Metal Inert Gas (MIG)	Shield Carbon—ARC	Oxygen Acetylene
Medium & High Tensile Steel. Stress Relieved	MIL-E-22200/1 MIL-9018	MIL-E-23765/1B Class MIL-E-705-2	MIL-E-23765/1B Class MIL-E-705-4	NONE	MIL-R-908A Class 1
High Carbon Steel	MIL-E-7018 MIL-E-22200	MIL-E-23765/1B Class MIL-E-705-2	MIL-E-23765/1B Class MIL-E-705-6	MIL-R-CUS1-A	MIL-R-908A Class 1
Low and Medium Carbon Steel	MIL-E-15599-C [1]	MIL-E-23765/1B Class MIL-E-705-2	MIL-E-23765/1B Class MIL-E-705-6	MIL-R-CUS1-A	MIL-R-5632 Class 1
Aluminum and Aluminum Alloy	MIL-E-15997A	QQR-566 MIL-E-16053-K [3]	QQR-566 MIL-E-16053-K [3]	QQR-566 [2]	QQR-566 [2]
Stainless Alloys	MIL-E-6844 M-L-E-22200 [3]	MIL-R-5031B [3]	MIL-R-5031B [3]	MIL-R-5031B [3]	MIL-R-5031B [3]
Copper and Nickel Alloys	NONE	QQR-571A [4]	MIL-E-21659 [4]	QQR-571A [4]	QQR-571A [4]
Magnesium Alloys	NONE	MIL-R-6944 Specify Alloy	MIL-W-18326 Specify Alloy	NONE	MIL-R-6944 Specify Alloy
Hard Surface Filler	MIL-E-19141 (Refer to A.W.S A5.13 or ASTM-A399)	MIL-E-19141 (Refer to A.W.S A5.13 or ASTM-A399)	MIL-E-19141 (Refer to A.W.S. A5.13 or ASTM-A399)	MIL-E-19141 (Refer to A.W.S. A5.13 or ASTM-A399)	MIL-19141 (Refer to A.W.S. A5.13 or ASTM-A399)

[1] Specify MIL Type 6010, 6011, 6012, 6013, 6020, 6024, 6027—Same as A.W.S. Number for type.

[2] Specify Aluminum Alloy by Aluminum Assoc. Number e.g.: Type 1100, 5083, etc.

[3] Specify Alloy by A.I.S.I. Number e.g.: 304, 316, 342, etc.

[4] Specify type per A.W.S. A5.6-66 or ASTM B-225-66.

A.W.S. American Welding Society
ASTM American Society for Testing Materials
A.I.S.I. American Iron and Steel Institute (SAE).

FIGURE 2.3.—Strengths of welded joints.

Material	Heat treatment subsequent to welding	Welding rod or electrode	Ultimate stress in shear × 1000	Ultimate tensile stress × 1000
Carbon and Alloy steels	None	MIL–R–5632, Class I MIL–E–15599, Classes E–6010 & E–6013	32 32	51 51
Alloy steels	None	MIL–R–5632, Class 2	43	72
Alloy steels	Stress relieved	MIL–E–6843, Class 10013 MIL–E–18038, Class E–10015 & E–10016	50	85
Alloy steels	Stress relieved	MIL–E–18038, Class E–12015 & E–12016	60	100

such members to the manufacturer's specifications.

69. STEEL PARTS NOT TO BE WELDED.

a. Brace Wires and Cables. Do not weld airplane parts whose proper function depends upon strength properties developed by cold-working. Among parts in this classification are streamlined wires and cables.

b. Brazed and Soldered Parts. Do not weld brazed or soldered parts as the brazing mixture or solder will penetrate the hot steel and weaken it.

c. Alloy Steel Parts. Do not weld alloy steel parts such as aircraft bolts, turnbuckle ends, etc., which have been heat-treated to improve their mechanical properties.

70. REPAIR OF TUBULAR MEMBERS.

a. Inspection. Prior to repairing tubular members, carefully examine the structure surrounding any visible damage to insure that no secondary damage remains undetected. Secondary damage may be produced in some structure remote from the location of the primary damage by the transmission of the damaging load along the tube. Damage of this nature usually occurs where the most abrupt change in direction of load travel is experienced. If this damage remains undetected, subsequent normal loads may cause failure of the part.

b. Location and Alinement of Welds. Unless otherwise noted, welded steel tubing may be spliced or repaired at any joint along the length of the tube. Pay particular attention to the proper fit and alinement to avoid distortion.

c. Members Dented at a Cluster. Repair dents at a steel-tube cluster-joint by welding a specially formed steel patch plate over the dented area and surrounding tubes, as shown in figure 2.4. To prepare the patch plate, cut a section of steel sheet of the same material and thickness as the heaviest tube damaged. Trim the reinforcement plate so that the fingers extend over the tubes a minimum of 1.5 times the respective tube diameter as shown in the figure. Remove all the existing finish on the damaged cluster-joint area to be covered by the reinforcement plate. The reinforcement plate may be formed before any welding is attempted, or it may be cut and tack-welded to one or more of the tubes in the cluster-joint, then heated and formed around the joint to produce a smooth contour. Apply sufficient heat to the plate while forming so that there is generally a gap of no more than 1/16 inch from the contour of the joint to the plate. In this operation avoid unnecessary heating, and exercise care to prevent damage at the point of the angle formed by any two adjacent fingers of the plate. After the plate is formed and tack-welded to the cluster-joint, weld all the plate edges to the cluster-joint.

d. Members Dented in a Bay. Repair dented, bent, cracked, or otherwise damaged tubular members by using a split-sleeve reinforcement;

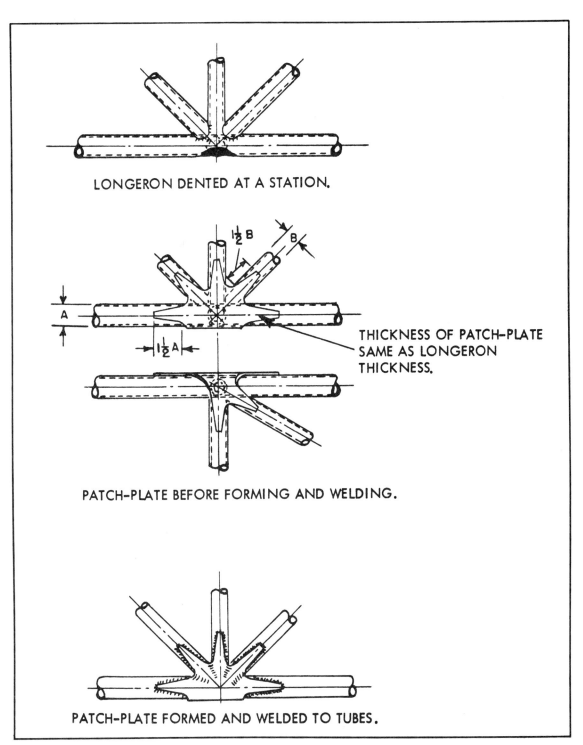

LONGERON DENTED AT A STATION.

$1\frac{1}{2}$ B

B

A

$1\frac{1}{2}$ A

THICKNESS OF PATCH-PLATE
SAME AS LONGERON
THICKNESS.

PATCH-PLATE BEFORE FORMING AND WELDING.

PATCH-PLATE FORMED AND WELDED TO TUBES.

FIGURE 2.4.—Members dented at a cluster.

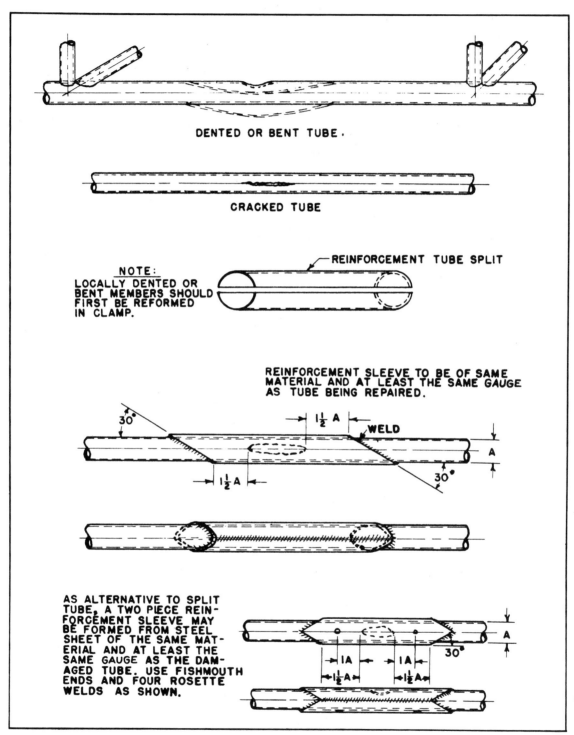

DENTED OR BENT TUBE.

CRACKED TUBE

REINFORCEMENT TUBE SPLIT

NOTE:
LOCALLY DENTED OR BENT MEMBERS SHOULD FIRST BE REFORMED IN CLAMP.

REINFORCEMENT SLEEVE TO BE OF SAME MATERIAL AND AT LEAST THE SAME GAUGE AS TUBE BEING REPAIRED.

30°
$1\frac{1}{2}$ A
WELD
A
$1\frac{1}{2}$ A
30°

AS ALTERNATIVE TO SPLIT TUBE, A TWO PIECE REINFORCEMENT SLEEVE MAY BE FORMED FROM STEEL SHEET OF THE SAME MATERIAL AND AT LEAST THE SAME GAUGE AS THE DAMAGED TUBE. USE FISHMOUTH ENDS AND FOUR ROSETTE WELDS AS SHOWN.

A
30°
1A
1A
$1\frac{1}{2}$ A
$1\frac{1}{2}$ A

FIGURE 2.5.—Members dented in a bay—repairs by welded sleeve.

40

carefully straighten the damaged member; and in the case of cracks, drill No. 40 (0.098) stopholes at the ends of the crack.

71. REPAIR BY WELDED SLEEVE. This repair is outlined in figure 2.5. Select a length of steel tube sleeve having an inside diameter approximately equal to the outside diameter of the damaged tube and of the same material, and at least the same wall thickness. Diagonally cut the sleeve reinforcement at a 30° angle on both ends so that the minimum distance of the sleeve from the edge of the crack or dent is not less than 1 1/2 times the diameter of the damaged tube. Cut through the entire length of the reinforcement sleeve, and separate the half-sections of the sleeve. Clamp the two sleeve sections to the proper positions on the affected areas of the original tube. Weld the reinforcement sleeve along the length of the two sides, and weld both ends of the sleeve to the damaged tube as shown in the figure. The filling of dents or cracks with welding rod in lieu of reinforcing the member is not acceptable.

72. REPAIR BY BOLTED SLEEVE. Do not use bolted sleeve repairs on welded steel tube structure unless specifically authorized by the manufacturer or the FAA. The tube area removed by the boltholes in this types of repair may prove critical.

73. WELDED-PATCH REPAIR. Dents or holes in tubing may be repaired by a welded patch of the same material and one gauge thicker, as shown in figure 2.6 provided:

   a. *Dented Tubing.*

   (1) Dents are not deeper than 1/10 of tube diameter, do not involve more than 1/4 of the tube circumference, and are not longer than tube diameter.

   (2) Dents are free from cracks, abrasions, and sharp corners.

   (3) The dented tubing can be substantially reformed without cracking before application of the patch.

   b. *Punctured Tubing.* Holes are not longer than tube diameter and involve not more than 1/4 of tube circumference.

74. SPLICING TUBING BY INNER SLEEVE METHOD. If the damage to a structural tube is such that a partial replacement of the tube is necessary, the inner sleeve splice shown in figure 2.7 is recommended, especially where a smooth tube surface is desired. Make a diagonal cut when removing the damaged portion of the tube and remove the burr from the edges of the cut by filing or similar means. Diagonally cut a replacement steel tube of the same material and diameter, and at least the same wall thickness, to match the length of the removed portion of the damaged tube. At each end of the replacement tube allow a 1/8-inch gap from the diago-

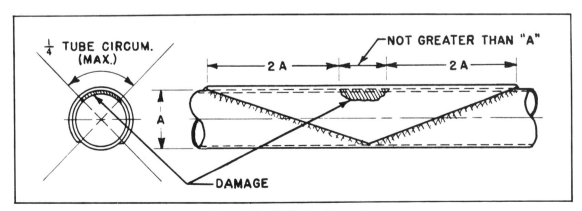

FIGURE 2.6.—Welded patch repair.

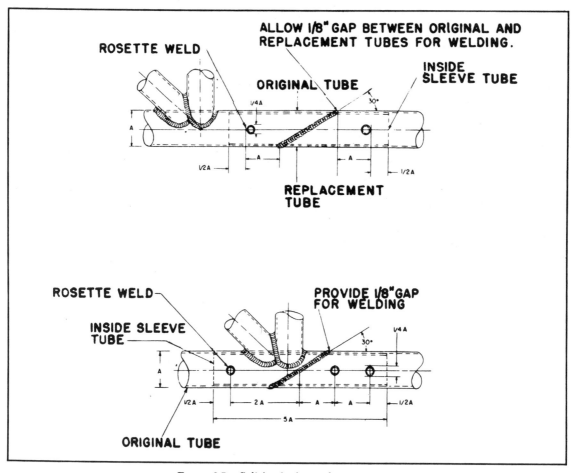

FIGURE 2.7.—Splicing by inner sleeve method.

nal cuts to the stubs of the original tube. Select a length of steel tubing of the same material, and at least the same wall thickness, and of an outside diameter, equal to the inside diameter of the damaged tube. Fit this innersleeve tube material snugly within the original tube, with a maximum diameter difference of 1/16 inch. From this inner-sleeve tube material cut 2 sections of tubing, each of such a length that the ends of the inner sleeve will be a minimum distance of 1 1/2-tube diameters from the nearest end of the diagonal cut.

If the inner sleeve fits very tightly in the replacement tube, chill the sleeve with dry ice or in cold water. If this is insufficient, polish down the diameter of the sleeve with emery cloth. Weld the inner sleeve to the tube stubs through the 1/8-inch gap, forming a weld bead over the gap.

75. SPLICING TUBING BY OUTER SLEEVE METHOD.
If partial replacement of a tube is necessary, make the outer sleeve splice using a replacement tube of the same diameter. Since the outer sleeve splice requires the greatest amount of welding, it should be used only when the other splicing methods are not suitable. Information on the replacement by use of the welded outside sleeve method is given in figures 2.8 and 2.9.

Remove the damaged section of a tube utilizing a 90° cut. Cut a replacement steel tube of

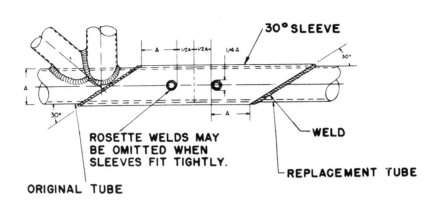

30° SLEEVE

ROSETTE WELDS MAY
BE OMITTED WHEN
SLEEVES FIT TIGHTLY.

ORIGINAL TUBE

WELD

REPLACEMENT TUBE

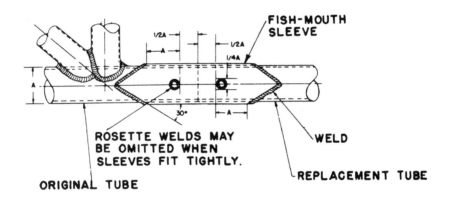

FISH-MOUTH
SLEEVE

ROSETTE WELDS MAY
BE OMITTED WHEN
SLEEVES FIT TIGHTLY.

ORIGINAL TUBE

WELD

REPLACEMENT TUBE

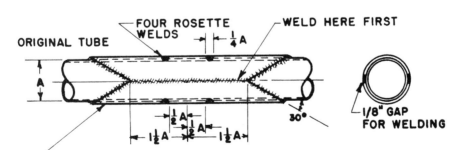

FOUR ROSETTE
WELDS

WELD HERE FIRST

ORIGINAL TUBE

1/8" GAP
FOR WELDING

ALTERNATIVE SPLIT SLEEVE SPLICE ~
IF OUTSIDE DIAMETER OF ORIGINAL TUBE IS LESS THAN 1 INCH, SPLIT
SLEEVE MAY BE MADE FROM STEEL TUBE OR SHEET STEEL. USE SAME
MATERIAL OF AT LEAST THE SAME GAUGE. FOR ORIGINAL TUBE
DIAMETERS OF 1 INCH AND OVER, USE SHEET STEEL ONLY.

FIGURE 2.8.—Splicing by outer sleeve method—replacement by welded outside sleeve.

43

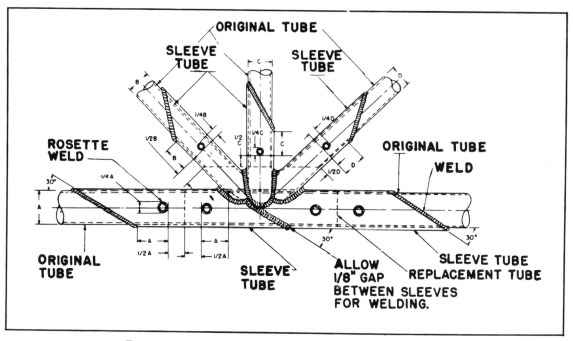

FIGURE 2.9.—Tube replacement at a station by welded outer sleeves.

the same material, diameter, and at least the same wall thickness to match the length of the removed portion of the damaged tube. This replacement tube must bear against the stubs of the original tube with a total tolerance not to exceed 1/32 inch. The outer sleeve tube material selected must be of the same material and at least the same wall thickness as the original tube. The clearance between inside diameter of the sleeve and the outside diameter of the original tube may not exceed 1/16 inch. From this outer sleeve tube material, cut diagonally (or fishmouth) 2 sections of tubing, each of such length that the nearest end of the outer sleeve is a minimum distance of 1 1/2-tube diameters from the end of the cut on the original tube. Use a fishmouth sleeve wherever possible. Remove the burr from the edges of the sleeves, replacement tube, and the original tube stubs. Slip the two sleeves over the replacement tube, aline the replacement tube with the original tube stubs, and slip the sleeves out over the center of each joint. Adjust the sleeves to suit the area and to provide maximum reinforcement. Tackweld the two sleeves to the replace-

ment tube in two places before welding. Apply a uniform weld around both ends of one of the reinforcement sleeves and allow the weld to cool; then, weld around both ends of the remaining reinforcement tube. Allow one sleeve weld to cool before welding the remaining tube to prevent undue warping.

76. SPLICING USING LARGER DIAMETER REPLACEMENT TUBES. The method of splicing structural tubes, as shown in figure 2.10, requires the least amount of cutting and welding. However, this splicing method cannot be used where the damaged tube is cut too near the adjacent cluster-joints, or where bracket-mounting provisions make it necessary to maintain the same replacement tube diameter as the original. As an aid in installing the replacement tube, squarely cut the original damaged tube leaving a minimum short stub equal to 2 1/2-tube diameters on one end and a minimum long stub equal to 4 1/2-tube diameters on the other end. Select a length of steel tube of the same material and at least the same wall thickness, having an inside diameter approximately equal to

44

the outside diameter of the damaged tube. Fit this replacement tube material snugly about the original tube with a maximum diameter difference of 1/16 inch. From this replacement tube material, cut a section of tubing diagonally (or fishmouth) of such a length that each end of the tube is a minimum distance of 1 1/2-tube diameters from the end of the cut on the original tube. Use a fishmouth cut replacement tube wherever possible. Remove the burr from the edges of the replacement tube and original tube stubs. If a fishmouth cut is used, file out the sharp radius of the cut with a small round file. Spring the long stub of the original tube from the normal position, slip the replacement tube over the long stub, then back over the short stub. Center the replacement tube between the stubs of the original tube. In several places tack-weld one end of the replacement tube, then weld completely around the end. In order to prevent distortion, allow the weld to cool completely, then weld the remaining end of the replacement tube to the original tube.

77. REPAIRS AT BUILT-IN FUSELAGE FITTINGS. Make splices in accordance with the methods described in paragraphs 70 through 75. Repair built-in fuselage fittings in the manner shown in figure 2.11. The following paragraphs outline the different methods as shown in the figure:

a. *Tube of Larger Diameter Than Original.* A tube (sleeve) of larger diameter than original is used in the method shown in figure 2.11(A). This necessitates reaming the fitting holes (at longeron) to a large diameter. The forward splice is to be a 30° scarf splice. Cut the rear longeron (right) approximately 4 inches from the centerline of the joint and a spacer 1 inch long fitted over the longeron. Edge-weld this spacer and longeron; make a tapered "V" cut approximately 2 inches long in the aft end of the outer sleeve and swage the end of the outer sleeve to fit the longeron and weld.

b. *Tube of Same Diameter as Original.* In the method shown in figure 2.11(B) the new sec-

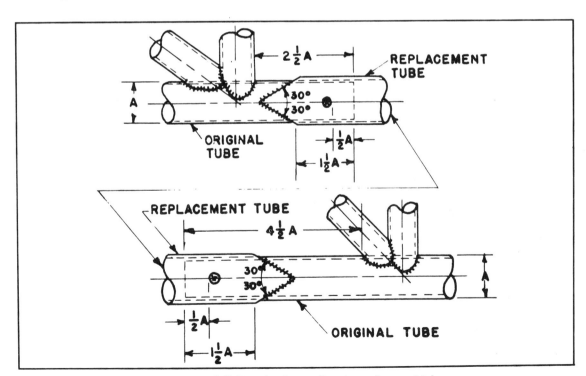

FIGURE 2.10.—Splicing using larger diameter replacement tube.

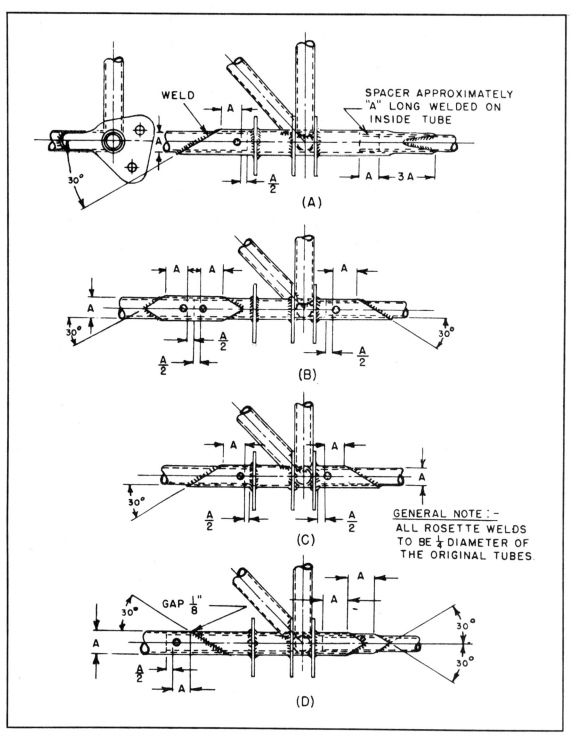

FIGURE 2.11.—Repairs at built-in fuselage fittings.

tion is the same size as the longeron forward (left) of the fitting. The rear end (right) of the tube is cut at 30° and forms the outside sleeve of the scarf splice. A sleeve is centered over the forward joint as indicated.

c. *Simple Sleeve.* It is assumed the longeron is the same size on each side of the fitting in this case, figure 2.11(C), and it is repaired by a simple sleeve of larger diameter than the longeron.

d. *Large Difference in Longeron Diameter Each Side of Fitting.* Figure 2.11(D) assumes that there is 1/4 inch difference in the diameter of the longeron on the two sides of the fitting. The section of longeron forward (left) of the fitting is cut at 30°, and a section of tubing of the same size as the tube and of such length as to extend well to the rear (right) of the fitting is slipped through it. One end is cut at 30° to fit the 30° scarf at left and the other end fishmouthed as shown. This makes it possible to insert a tube of such diameter as to form an inside sleeve for the tube on the left of the fitting and an outside sleeve for the tube on the right of the fitting.

78. ENGINE MOUNT REPAIRS. All welding on an engine mount should be of the highest quality, since vibration tends to accentuate any minor defect. Engine-mount members should preferably be repaired by using a larger diameter replacement tube telescoped over the stub of the original member and using fishmouth and rosette welds. However, 30° scarf welds in place of the fishmouth welds will be considered acceptable for engine-mount repair work.

a. *Check of Alignment.* Repaired engine mounts must be checked for accurate alignment. When tubes are used to replace bent or damaged ones, the original alignment of the structure must be maintained. This can be done by measuring the distance between points of corresponding members that have not been distorted, and by reference to the manufacturer's drawings.

b. *Cause for Rejection.* If all members are out of alinement, reject the engine mount and re-place by one supplied by the manufacturer or one which was built to conform to the manufacturer's drawings. The method of checking the alignment of the fuselage or nacelle points should be requested from the manufacturer.

c. *Engine Mount Ring Damage.* Repair minor damage, such as a crack adjacent to an engine attachment lug, by rewelding the ring and extending a gusset or a mounting lug past the damaged area. Engine mount rings which are extensively damaged must not be repaired, unless the method of repair is specifically approved by an authorized representative of the FAA, or the repair is accomplished in accordance with FAA approved instructions furnished by the aircraft manufacturer.

79. LANDING GEAR REPAIR.

a. *Round Tube Construction.* Repair landing gears made of round tubing using standard repairs and splices as shown in figures 2.5 and 2.11.

b. *Streamline Tube Construction.* Repair landing gears made of streamlined tubing by either one of the methods shown in figures 2.12 and 2.15.

c. *Axle Assemblies.* Representative types of repairable and nonrepairable landing gear axle assemblies are shown in figure 2.16. The types as shown in A, B, and C of this figure are formed from steel tubing and may be repaired by the applicable method shown in figures 2.5 thru 2.15 in this Advisory Circular. However, it will always be necessary to ascertain whether or not the members are heat treated.

The axle assembly as shown in figure 2.16(D) is, in general, of a nonrepairable type for the following reasons:

(1) The axle stub is usually made from a highly heat-treated nickel alloy steel and carefully machined to close tolerances. These stubs are usually replaceable and should be replaced if damaged.

(2) The oleo portion of the structure is generally heat-treated after welding and is per-

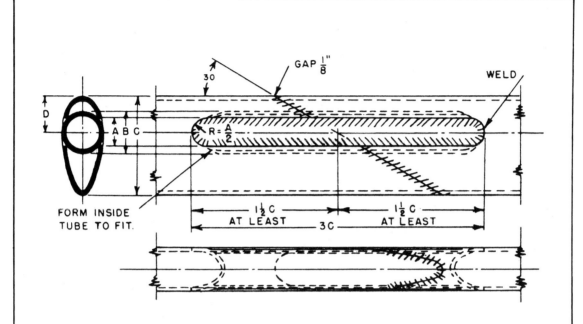

A – SLOT WIDTH (ORIGINAL TUBE)
B – OUTSIDE DIAMETER (INSERT TUBE)
C – STREAMLINE TUBE LENGTH OF MAJOR AXIS

S.L. SIZE	A	B	C	D
1"	3/8"	9/16"	1.340"	.496"
1- 1/4	3/8	11/16	1.670	.619
1- 1/2	1/2	7/8	2.005	.743
1- 3/4	1/2	1	2.339	.867
2	1/2	1-1/8	2.670	.991
2- 1/4	1/2	1- 1/4	3.008	1.115
2- 1/2	1/2	1- 3/8	3.342	1.239

ROUND INSERT TUBE (B) SHOULD BE AT LEAST OF SAME
MATERIAL AND ONE GAUGE THICKER THAN ORIGINAL
STREAMLINE TUBE (C).

FIGURE 2.12.—Streamline tube splice using round tube (applicable to landing gears).

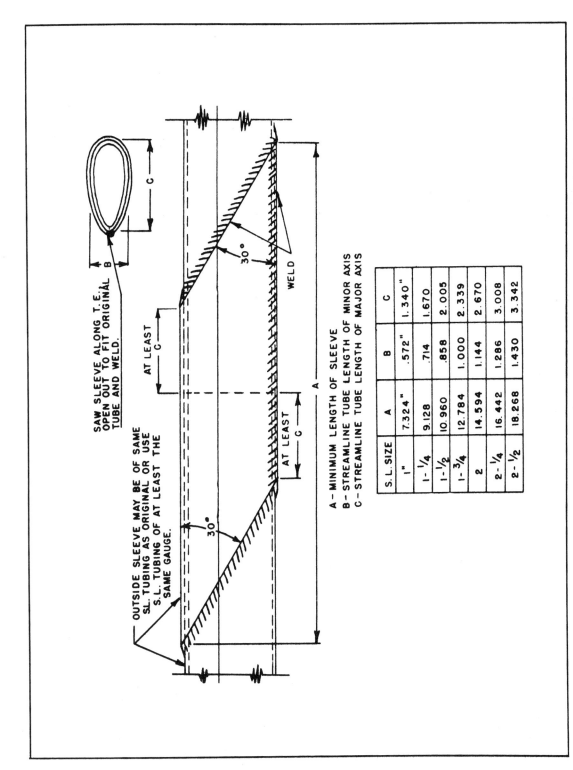

SAW SLEEVE ALONG T.E.
OPEN OUT TO FIT ORIGINAL
TUBE AND WELD.

OUTSIDE SLEEVE MAY BE OF SAME
S.L. TUBING AS ORIGINAL OR USE
S.L. TUBING OF AT LEAST THE
SAME GAUGE.

WELD

A — MINIMUM LENGTH OF SLEEVE
B — STREAMLINE TUBE LENGTH OF MINOR AXIS
C — STREAMLINE TUBE LENGTH OF MAJOR AXIS

S.L.SIZE	A	B	C
1"	7.324"	.572"	1.340"
1-¼	9.128	.714	1.670
1-½	10.960	.858	2.005
1-¾	12.784	1.000	2.339
2	14.594	1.144	2.670
2-¼	16.442	1.286	3.008
2-½	18.268	1.430	3.342

FIGURE 2.13.—Streamline tube splice using split sleeve (applicable to wing and tail surface brace struts and other members).

49

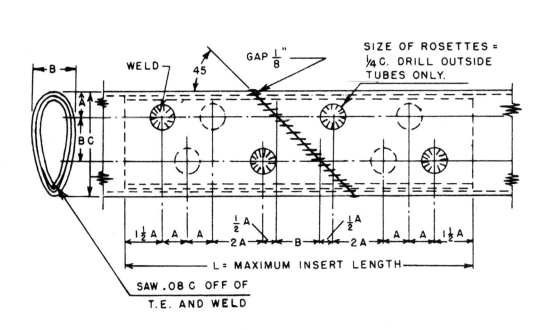

INSERT TUBE IS OF SAME STREAMLINE TUBING AS ORIGINAL.

A IS $\frac{2}{3}$ B

B IS MINOR AXIS LENGTH OF ORIGINAL STREAMLINE TUBE
C IS MAJOR AXIS LENGTH OF ORIGINAL STREAMLINE TUBE

S. L. SIZE	A	B	C	L
1 "	.382	.572	1.340	5.16
1 1/4	.476	.714	1.670	6.43
1 1/2	.572	.858	2.005	7.72
1 3/4	.667	1.000	2.339	9.00
2	.763	1.144	2.670	10.30
2 1/4	.858	1.286	3.008	11.58
2 1/2	.954	1.430	3.342	12.88

FIGURE 2.14.—Streamline tube splice using split insert (applicable to landing gears).

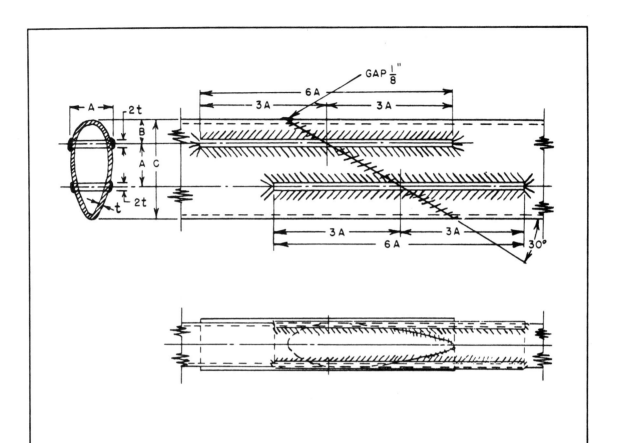

A- STREAMLINE TUBE LENGTH OF MINOR AXIS, PLATE WIDTHS.
B- DISTANCE OF FIRST PLATE FROM LEADING EDGE, $\frac{2}{3}$ A.
C- STREAMLINE TUBE LENGTH OF MAJOR AXIS.

S.L. SIZE	A	B	C	6A
1"	.572	.382	1.340	3.43
1-¼	.714	.476	1.670	4.28
1-½	.858	.572	2.005	5.15
1-¾	1.000	.667	2.339	6.00
.2	1.144	.762	2.670	6.86
2-¼	1.286	.858	3.008	7.72
2-½	1.430	.954	3.342	8.58

FIGURE 2.15.—Streamline tube splice using plates (applicable to landing gears).

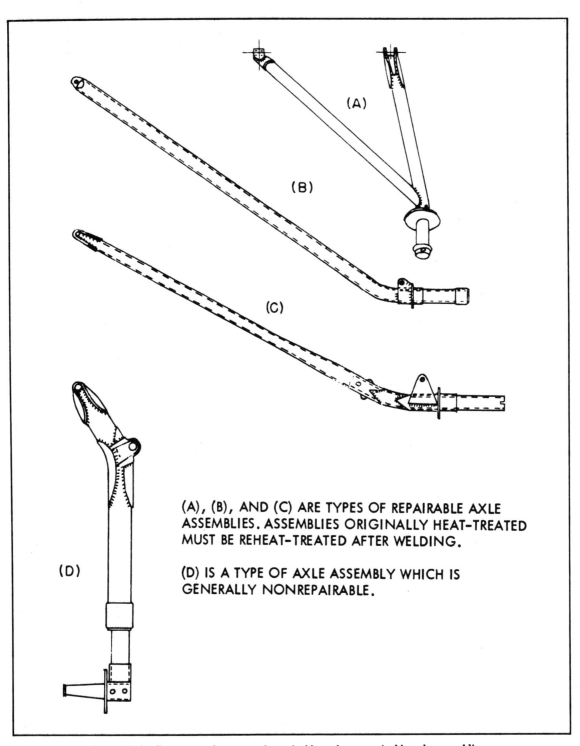

(A), (B), AND (C) ARE TYPES OF REPAIRABLE AXLE
ASSEMBLIES. ASSEMBLIES ORIGINALLY HEAT-TREATED
MUST BE REHEAT-TREATED AFTER WELDING.

(D) IS A TYPE OF AXLE ASSEMBLY WHICH IS
GENERALLY NONREPAIRABLE.

FIGURE 2.16.—Representative types of repairable and nonrepairable axle assemblies.

fectly machined to assure proper functioning of the shock absorber. These parts would be distorted by welding after machining.

80. BUILT-UP TUBULAR WING OR TAIL SURFACE SPARS.

Repair built-up tubular wing or tail surface spars by using any of the applicable splices and methods of repair shown in figures 2.5 through 2.15 provided the spars are not heat-treated. In the case of heat-treated spars, the entire spar assembly would have to be re-heat-treated to the manufacturer's specifications after completion of the repair. In general, this will be found less practicable than replacing the spar with one furnished by the manufacturer.

81. WING AND TAIL BRACE STRUTS.

In general, it will be found advantageous to replace damaged wing-brace struts made either from rounded or streamlined tubing with new members purchased from the original manufacturer. However, there is no objection from an airworthiness point of view to repairing such members in a proper manner. An acceptable method, in case streamlined tubing is used, will be found in figure 2.13. Repair similar members made of round tubes using a standard splice, as shown in figures 2.5, 2.7, or 2.8.

a. *Location of Splices.* Steel brace struts may be spliced at any point along the length of the strut, provided the splice does not overlap part of an end fitting. The jury strut attachment is not considered an end fitting; therefore, a splice may be made at this point. The repair procedure and workmanship should be such as to minimize distortion due to welding and the necessity for subsequent straightening operations. Observe every repaired strut carefully during initial flights to ascertain that the vibration characteristics of the strut and attaching components are not adversely affected by the repair. A wide range of speed and engine-

power combination must be covered during this check.

(1) **Fit and Alignment.** When making repairs to wing and tail surface brace members, pay particular attention to proper fit and alinement to avoid distortion.

82. REPAIRS TO WELDED PARTS.

Repairs to welded assemblies may be made by:

a. *Replacing welded joints*—cutting out the welded joint and replacing it with one properly gusseted, or

b. *Replacing weld deposit*—chipping out the metal deposited by the weld process and re-welding after properly reinforcing the joint by means of inserts or external gussets.

83. STAINLESS STEEL STRUCTURE.

Repair structural components made from stainless steel, particularly the "18–8" variety (18 percent chromium, 8 percent nickel), joined by spot welding in accordance with the instructions furnished by the manufacturer. Substitution of bolted or riveted connections for spot-welded joints are to be specifically approved by an authorized representative of the FAA.

a. *Secondary Structural and Nonstructural Elements.* Repair such elements as tip-bows or leading and trailing edge tip-strips of wing-and-control surfaces by soldering with a 50–50 lead-tin solder or a 60–40 alloy of these metals. For best results use a flux of phosphoric acid (syrup). Since the purpose of flux is to attack the metal so that the soldering will be effective, remove excess flux by washing the joint. Due to the high-heat conductivity of the stainless steel, use a soldering iron large enough to do the work properly. Repair leaky spot-welded seams in boat hulls, fuel tanks, etc., in a similar manner.

84.–94. RESERVED.

Comment: The foregoing section of 43.13 is, of course, addressed to licensed airframe mechanics who know how to weld. If you are an amateur plane

builder, several points should be made concerning the art/skill of welding:

If you intend to build an airplane with a welded

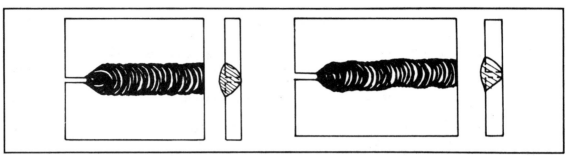

Figure 2.16A.—Examples of good welds (see text).

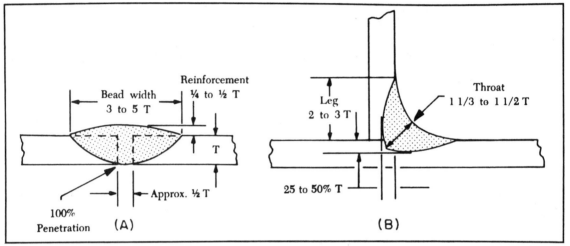

Figure 2.16B.—(A) Butt weld, and (B) fillet weld, showing width and depth of bead.

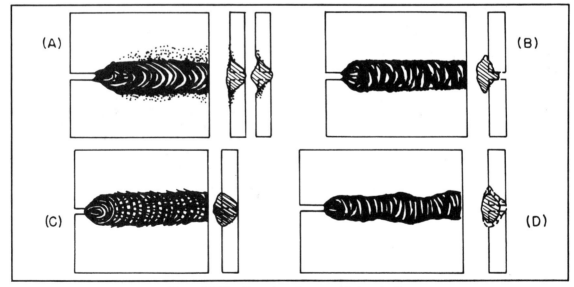

Figure 2.16C.—Examples of poor welds (see text).

steel fuselage, you have three options. You may attend welding classes at the nearest vo-tech school; you may hire a licensed AP to weld your airframe (and engine mount, landing gear, etc. Even "all wood" airplanes require some welding); or you may, if you belong to a local chapter of the Experimental Aircraft Association (EAA), find a fellow EAAer who is an experienced welder and is willing to do it for you. (To contact the nearest EAA chapter, write to the EAA at 3000, Poberezny Road, Oshkosh, WI 54901.)

Yes, it's possible to teach yourself enough about welding to handle the several welded components on an airplane, especially with a few hours' supervision by a competent welder. The equipment will cost in the neighborhood of $100 for an oxyacetylene (oxygen-acetylene) system, except for the tanks of oxygen and acetylene which may be rented at a cost of about $40.

Before ordering plans for a homebuilt employing a steel tube fuselage structure, we suggest that you check the current price of 4130 chrome moly steel tubing. It has steadily become more expensive during recent years.

A properly designed joint weld is stronger than the base metal that it joins. A good weld is uniform in width; the ripples are even and well feathered into the base metal, which shows no burn due to overheating. (See figure 2.16A.) The weld has good penetration and is free of gas pockets, porosity, or inclusions. The

Figure 2.16D.—Welded steel fuselage of the 1929 Great Lakes Sport Trainer.
Original engine was the Cirrus Mk III, a four-cylinder, in-line air-cooled powerplant of 90 hp.

edges of the bead illustrated on the right are not in a straight line, yet the weld is good, since penetration is excellent.

Penetration is the depth of fusion in a weld. Thorough fusion is the most important characteristic that contributes to a sound weld. Penetration is affected by the thickness of the material to be joined, the size of the filler rod, and how it is added. In a butt weld the penetration should be 100 percent of the thickness of the base metal. The width and depth of the bead for a butt weld and fillet weld are shown in figure 2.16B.

The weld shown in figure 2.16C (at A) was made too rapidly. The long and pointed appearance of the ripples was caused by an excessive amount of heat or an oxidizing flame. If the weld were cross-sectioned, it probably would reveal gas pockets, porosity, and slag inclusion.

Figure 2.16C (B) illustrates a weld that has im-proper penetration and cold laps caused by insufficient heat. It appears rough and irregular and its edges are not feathered into the base metal.

The puddle has a tendency to boil during the welding operation if an excessive amount of acetylene is used. This often leaves slight bumps along the center and craters at the finish of the weld. Cross-checks will be apparent if the body of the weld is sound. If this weld were cross-sectioned, pockets and porosity would be visible. Such a condition is shown in figure 2.16C at C.

A bad weld with irregular edges and considerable variation in the depth of penetration is shown in D of figure 2.16C. It often has the appearance of a cold weld.

For additional information on welding (figure 2.16D). See the Appendix, which is reprinted from FAA AC65-15.

Section 3.   METAL REPAIR PROCEDURES

95. RIVETED OR BOLTED STEEL TRUSS-TYPE STRUCTURES. Repairs to riveted or bolted steel truss-type structures should be made, employing the general principles outlined in the following paragraphs on aluminum alloy structures. Methods for repair of vital members should be specifically approved by a representative of the Federal Aviation Administration.

96. ALUMINUM ALLOY STRUCTURES. Extensive repairs to damaged stressed skin on monocoque types of aluminum alloy structures should preferably be made in accordance with specific recommendations of the manufacturer of the aircraft. In many cases, repair parts, joints, or reinforcements can be designed, and proof of adequate strength shown, without the calculation of the design loads and stresses, by properly considering the material and dimensions of the original parts and the riveted attachments. Examples illustrating the principles of this method as applied to typical repairs are given in this handbook, or may be found in textbooks on metal structures. An important point to bear in mind in making repairs on monocoque structures is that a repaired part must be as strong as the original with respect to all types of loads and general rigidity.

   a. Use of Annealed Alloys for Structural Parts. The use of annealed 2017 or 2024 for any structural repair of an aircraft is not considered satisfactory because of its poor corrosion-resisting properties.

   b. Hygroscopic Materials Improperly Moisture-Proofed. The use of hygroscopic materials improperly moisture-proofed, such as impregnated fabrics, or leather, and the like, to effect water-tight joints and seams is not an acceptable practice.

   c. Drilling Oversized Holes. Avoid drilling oversized holes or otherwise decreasing the effective tensile areas of wing-spar capstrips, wing, fuselage, or fin longitudinal stringers, or other highly stressed tensile members. Make all repairs or reinforcements to such members in accordance with factory recommendations or with the specific approval or a representative of the Federal Aviation Administration.

   d. Disassembly Prior to Repairing. If the parts to be removed are essential to the rigidity of the complete structure, support the remaining structure prior to disassembly in such a manner as to prevent distortion and permanent damage to the remainder of the structure.

When rivets are to be removed, weaken the rivet head by drilling. Use a drill of the same size as the rivet. Drilling must be exact center and to the base of the head only. After drilling, break off the head with a pin punch and carefully drive out the shank. Removal of rivet heads with a cold chisel and hammer is not recommended because skin damage and distorted rivet holes will probably result. Care must also be taken whenever screws must be removed for disassembly or removal of stress plates, access plates, fillets, etc., to avoid damage to adjoining structure. When properly used, impact wrenches can be effective tools for removal of screws; however, damage to adjoining structure may result from excessive vertical loads being applied through the screw axis. Excessive loads are usually related to improperly adjusted impact tools or attempting to remove screws that have seized from corrosion. Remove seized screw by drilling and use of a screw extractor. Structural cracks may appear in the doubler or tang that runs parallel to the line of anchor or plate nuts installed for securing access doors or plates. Inspect rivet joints adjacent to damaged structure for partial failure (slippage) by removing one or more rivets to see if holes are elongated or the rivets have started to shear.

97. SELECTION OF ALUMINUM FOR REPLACEMENT PARTS. In selecting the alloy, it is usually satisfactory to use 2024 in place of 2017 since the former is stronger. Hence, it will not be permissible to replace 2024 by 2017 unless the deficiency in strength of the latter material is compensated by an increase in material thickness, or the structural strength is substantiated by tests or analysis. Information on the comparative strength properties of these alloys, as well as 2014, 6061, 7075, etc., is contained in MIL–HDBK–5, *Metallic Materials and Elements for Flight Vehicle Structure*. The choice of temper depends upon the severity of the subsequent forming operations. Parts having single curvature and straight bend lines with a large bend radius may be advantageously formed from heat-treated material, while a part, such as a fuselage frame, would

have to be formed from soft, annealed sheet, and heat-treated after forming. Make sure sheet metal parts which are to be left unpainted are made of clad (aluminum coated) material. Make sure all sheet material and finished parts are free from cracks, scratches, kinks, tool marks, corrosion pits, and other defects which may be factors in subsequent failure.

a. Forming Sheet Metal Parts. Bend lines should preferably be made to lie at an angle to the grain of the metal (preferably 90°). Before bending, smooth all rough edges, remove burrs, and drill relief holes at the ends of bend lines and at corners, to prevent cracks from starting. For material in the heat-treated condition, the bend radius should be large. (See figure 2.17 for recommended bend radii.)

98. HEAT TREATMENT OF ALUMINUM ALLOY PARTS. All structural aluminum alloy parts are to be heat-treated in accordance with the heat-treatment instructions issued by the manufacturers of the materials. If the heat-treatment produces warping, straighten the parts immediately after quenching. Heat-treat riveted parts before riveting, to preclude warping and corrosion. When riveted assemblies are heated in a salt bath, the salt cannot be entirely washed out of the crevices, thus causing corrosion.

a. Quenching in Hot Water or Air. Quench material from the solution heat-treating temperature as rapidly as possible, with a minimum delay after removal from the furnace. Quenching in cold water is preferred, although less drastic chilling (hot or boiling water, air blast) is sometimes employed for bulk sections, such as forgings, to minimize quenching stresses.

b. Transferring Too Slowly From Heat-Treatment Medium to Quench Tank. Transfer of 2017 alloys from the heat-treatment medium to the quenchtank should be accomplished as quickly as possible. An elapsed time of 10 to 15 seconds will, in many cases, result in noticeably impaired corrosion resistance.

FIGURE 2.17.—Recommended radii for 90° bends in aluminum alloys.

Alloy and temper	Approximate sheet thickness (t) (inch)					
	0.016	0.032	0.064	0.128	0.182	0.258
2024–0 [1]	0	0–1t	0–1t	0–1t	0–1t	0–1t
2024–T3 [1][2]	1½t–3t	2t–4t	3t–5t	4t–6t	4t–6t	5t–7t
2024–T6 [1]	2t–4t	3t–5t	3t–5t	4t–6t	5t–7t	6t–10t
5052–0	0	0	0–1t	0–1t	0–1t	0–1t
5052–H32	0	0	½t–1t	½t–1½t	½t–1½t	½t–1½t
5052–H34	0	0	½t–1½t	1½t–2½t	1½t–2½t	2t–3t
5052–H36	0–1t	½t–1½t	1t–2t	1½t–3t	2t–4t	2t–4t
5052–H38	½t–1½t	1t–2t	1½t–3t	2t–4t	3t–5t	4t–6t
6061–0	0	0–1t	0–1t	0–1t	0–1t	0–1t
6061–T4	0–1t	0–1t	½t–1½t	1t–2t	1½t–3t	2½t–4t
6061–T6	0–1t	½t–1½t	1t–2t	1½t–3t	2t–4t	3t–4t
7075–0	0	0–1t	0–1t	½t–1½t	1t–2t	1½t–3t
7075–T6 [1]	2t–4t	3t–5t	4t–6t	5t–7t	5t–7t	6t–10t

[1] Alclad sheet may be bent over slight smaller radii than the corresponding tempers of uncoated alloy.
[2] Immediately after quenching, this alloy may be formed over appreciably smaller radii.

c. Reheating at Temperatures Above Boiling Water. Reheating of 2017 and 2024 alloys at temperatures above that of boiling water after heat treatment, and the baking of primers at temperatures above that of boiling water, will not be considered acceptable without subsequent complete and correct heat treatment, as such practice tends to impair the original heat treatment.

99. RIVETING.

a. Identification of Rivet Material. Identification of rivet material is contained in Chapter 5.

b. Replacement of Aluminum Alloy Rivets. All protruding head rivets (roundhead, flathead, and brazier head) may be replaced by rivets of the same type or by AN–470 Universal head rivets. Use flushhead rivets to replace flushhead rivets.

c. Replacement Rivet Size and Strength. Replace rivets with those of the same size and strength whenever possible. If the rivet hole becomes enlarged, deformed, or otherwise damaged, drill or ream the hole for the next large size rivet; however, make sure that the edge distance and spacings are not less than minimums listed in the next paragraph. Rivets may not be replaced by a type having lower strength properties, unless the lower strength is adequately compensated by an increase in size or a greater number of rivets.

d. Replacement Rivet-Edge Distances and Spacings for Sheet Joints. Rivet-edge distance is defined as the distance from the center of the rivet hole to the nearest edge of the sheet. Rivet spacing is the distance from the center of the rivet hole to the center of the adjacent rivet hole. The following prescribes the minimum edge distance and spacing:

(1) **Single row**—edge distance not less than 2 times the diameter of the rivet and spacing not less than 3 times the diameter of the rivet.

(2) **Double row**—edge distance and spacing not less than the minimums shown in figure 2.18.

(3) **Triple or multiple rows**—edge distance and spacing not less than the minimums shown in figure 2.18.

e. Use of 2117–T3 Aluminum Alloy Replacement Rivets. It is acceptable to replace 2017–T3 rivets of 3/16-inch diameter or less, and 2024–T4 rivets of 5/32-inch diameter or less with 2117–T3 rivets for general repairs, provided the replacement rivets are 1/32 inch greater in diam-

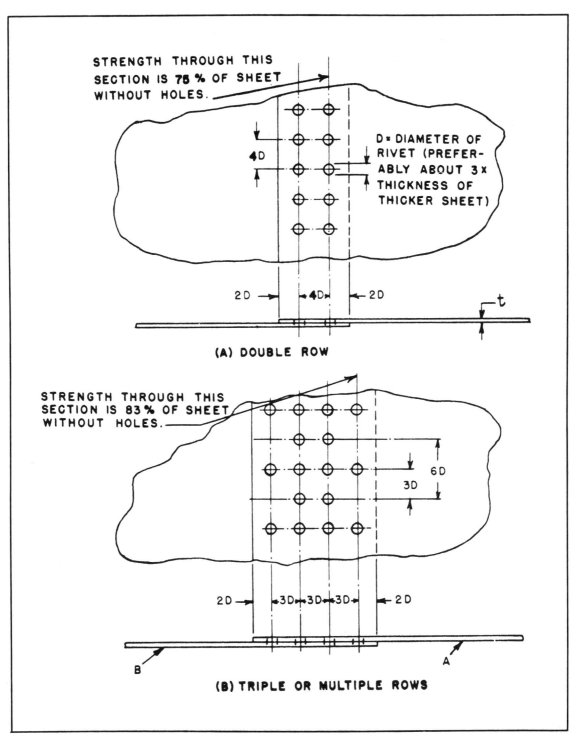

FIGURE 2.18.—Rivet hole spacing and edge distance for single-lap sheet splices.

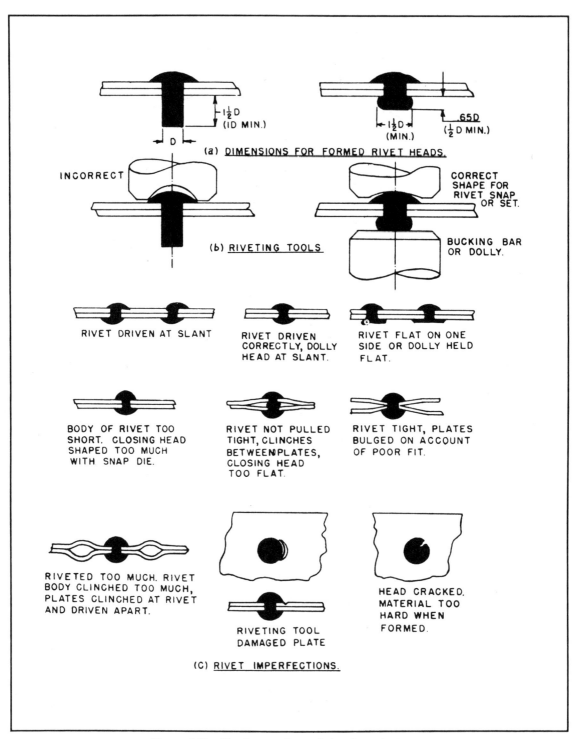

(a) DIMENSIONS FOR FORMED RIVET HEADS.

INCORRECT

CORRECT SHAPE FOR RIVET SNAP OR SET.

(b) RIVETING TOOLS

BUCKING BAR OR DOLLY.

RIVET DRIVEN AT SLANT

RIVET DRIVEN CORRECTLY, DOLLY HEAD AT SLANT.

RIVET FLAT ON ONE SIDE OR DOLLY HELD FLAT.

BODY OF RIVET TOO SHORT. CLOSING HEAD SHAPED TOO MUCH WITH SNAP DIE.

RIVET NOT PULLED TIGHT, CLINCHES BETWEEN PLATES, CLOSING HEAD TOO FLAT.

RIVET TIGHT, PLATES BULGED ON ACCOUNT OF POOR FIT.

RIVETED TOO MUCH. RIVET BODY CLINCHED TOO MUCH, PLATES CLINCHED AT RIVET AND DRIVEN APART.

RIVETING TOOL DAMAGED PLATE

HEAD CRACKED. MATERIAL TOO HARD WHEN FORMED.

(C) RIVET IMPERFECTIONS.

FIGURE 2.19.—Riveting practice and rivet imperfections.

eter than the rivets they replace and the edge distances and spacing are not less than the minimums listed in the preceding paragraph.

f. *Driving of Rivets*. The 2117 rivets may be driven in the condition received, but 2017 rivets above 3/16 inch in diameter and all 2024 rivets are to be kept either refrigerated in the "quenched" condition until driven, or be reheat-treated just prior to driving, as they would otherwise be too hard for satisfactory riveting. Dimensions for formed flat rivet heads are shown in figure 2.19, together with commonly found rivet imperfections.

g. *Blind-Type and Hollow Rivets*. Do not substitute hollow rivets for solid rivets in load-carrying members without specific approval of the application by a representative of the Federal Aviation Administration.

Blind rivets may be used in blind locations in accordance with the conditions listed in Chapter 5, provided the edge distances and spacings are not less than the minimum listed in paragraph 99d.

h. *New and Revised Rivet Patterns*. Design a new or revised rivet pattern for the strength required in accordance with the specific instructions in paragraphs 100e and 100j.

A general rule for the diameter of rivets used to join dural sheets is to use a diameter approximately 3 times the thickness of the thicker sheet. Do not use rivets where they would be placed in tension tending to pull the heads off. Back up a lap joint of thin sheets by a stiffening section.

100. REPAIR METHODS AND PRECAUTIONS FOR ALUMINUM STRUCTURE.
Carefully examine all adjacent rivets after the repair or alteration is finished to ascertain that they have not been harmed by operations in adjacent areas.

Drill rivet holes round, straight, and free from cracks. The rivet-set used in driving the rivets must be cupped slightly flatter than the rivethead as shown in figure 2.19. Rivets are to be driven straight and tight, but not over-driven or driven while too hard, since the fin-

ished rivet must be free from cracks. Information on special methods of riveting, such as flush riveting, usually may be obtained from manufacturer's service manuals.

a. *Splicing of Tubes*. Round or streamline tubular members may be repaired by splicing as shown in figure 2.20. Splices in struts that overlap fittings are not acceptable.

When solid rivets go completely through hollow tubes, their diameter must be at least one-eighth of the outside diameter of the outer tube. Rivets which are loaded in shear should be hammered only enough to form a small head, and no attempt made to form the standard roundhead. The amount of hammering required to form the standard roundhead often causes the rivet to buckle inside the tube. Satisfactory rivetheads may be produced in such installations by spinning, if the proper equipment is available. (Correct and incorrect examples of this type of rivet applications are incorporated in figure 2.20.)

b. *Repairs to Aluminum Alloy Members*. Make repairs to aluminum alloy members with the same material or with suitable material of higher strength. The 7075 alloy has greater tensile strength than other commonly used aluminum alloys such as 2014 and 2024, but is subject to somewhat greater notch sensitivity. In order to take advantage of its strength characteristics, pay particular attention to design of parts to avoid notches, small radii, large or rapid changes in cross sectional areas. In fabrication, exercise caution to avoid processing and handling defects, such as machine marks, nicks, dents, burrs, scratches, and forming cracks. Cold straightening or forming of 7075–T6 can cause cracking; hence, it may be advisable to limit this processing to minor cold straightening.

c. *Wing and Tail Surface Ribs*. Damaged aluminum alloy ribs either of the stamped sheetmetal type or the built-up type employing special sections, square or round tubing, may be repaired by the addition of suitable reinforcement. (Acceptable methods of repair are shown in figures 2.21 and 2.22.) These examples deal with types of ribs commonly found in

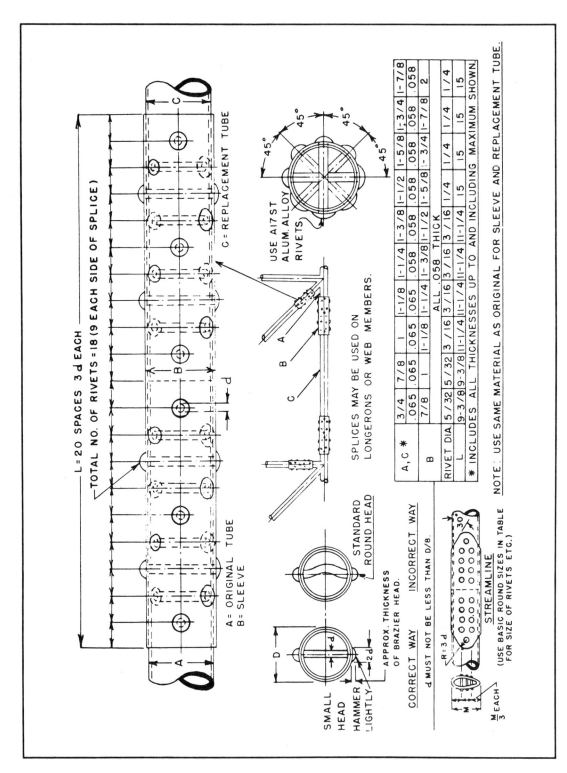

FIGURE 2.20.—Typical repair method for tubular members of aluminum alloy.

small and medium aircraft. Repair schemes developed by the aircraft manufacturer are acceptable, and any other methods of reinforcement will be specifically approved by a representative of the FAA.

(1) **Trailing and Leading Edges and Tip Strips.** Repairs to wing and control surface trailing and leading edges and tip strips should be made by properly executed and reinforced splices. Acceptable methods of trailing edge repairs are shown in figure 2.23.

d. **Repair of Damaged Skin.** In case metal skin is damaged extensively, make repairs replacing an entire sheet panel from one structural member to the next. The repair seams are to lie along stiffening members, bulkheads, etc., and each seam must be made exactly the same in regard to rivet size, splicing, and rivet pattern as the manufactured seams at the edges of the original sheet. If the two manufactured seams are different, the stronger one will be copied. (See figure 2.24 for typical acceptable methods of repairs.)

(1) **Patching of Small Holes.** Small holes in skin panels which do not involve damage to the stiffening members may be patched by covering the hole with a patch plate in the manner shown in figure 2.24.

Flush patches also may be installed in stressed skin-type construction. An acceptable and easy flush patch may be made by trimming out the damaged area and then installing a conventional patch on the underneath side or back of the sheet being repaired. A plug patch plate of the same size as the opening may then be inserted and riveted to the patch plate. Other types of flush patches similar to those used for patching plywood may be used (ref. Chapter 1). The riveting pattern used, however, must follow standard practice to maintain satisfactory strength in the sheet.

In general, patches in metal skin are not restricted as to size or shape; however, those of rectangular, circular, square, oval, and rectangular with round ends usually are more desirable because of appearance and ease of installation.

e. **Splicing of Sheets.** The method of copying the seams at the edges of a sheet may not always be satisfactory; for example, when the sheet has cutouts, or doubler-plates at an edge-seam, or when other members transmit loads into the sheet, the splice must be designed as illustrated in the following examples:

(1) Material: Clad 2024 sheet, 0.032-inch thickness. Width of sheet (i.e., length at splice) = "W" = 10 inches.

(2) Determine rivet size and pattern for a single-lap joint similar to figure 2.18.

(a) Use rivet diameter of approximately three times the sheet thickness, $3 \times 0.032 = 0.096$-inch. Use 1/8-inch 2117 AD rivets (5/32-inch 2117–AD would be satisfactory).

(b) Use the number of rivets required per inch of width "W" from figure 2.29. (Number per inch $4.9 \times .75 = 3.7$ or the total number of rivets required $= 10 \times 3.7$ or 37 rivets.)

(c) Lay out rivet pattern with spacing not less than shown in figure 2.18. Referring to figure 2.18(A), it seems that a double row pattern with the minimum spacing will give a total of 40 rivets. However, as only 37 rivets are required, two rows of 19 rivets each equally spaced over the 10 inches will result in a satisfactory splice.

f. **Straightening of Stringers or Intermediate Frames.** Members which are slightly bent may be straightened cold and examined with a magnifying glass for injury to the material. Reinforce the straightened parts to an extent, depending upon the condition of the material and the magnitude of any remaining kinks or buckles. If any strain cracks are apparent, make complete reinforcement in sound metal beyond the damaged portion.

(1) **Local Heating.** Do not apply local heating to facilitate bending, swaging, flattening, or expanding operations of heat-treated aluminum alloy members, as it is difficult to control the temperatures closely enough to prevent possible damage to the metal, and it may impair its corrosion resistance.

g. **Splicing of Stringers and Flanges.** Make splices in accordance with the manufacturer's

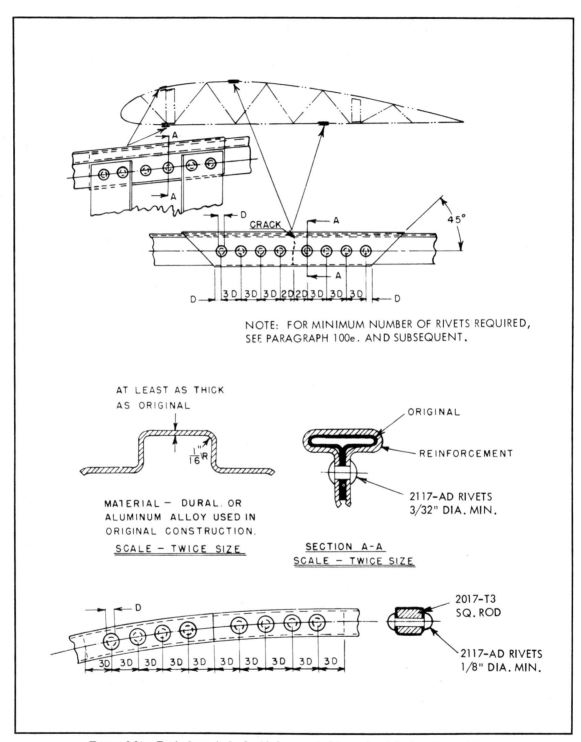

NOTE: FOR MINIMUM NUMBER OF RIVETS REQUIRED, SEE PARAGRAPH 100e. AND SUBSEQUENT.

AT LEAST AS THICK AS ORIGINAL

$\frac{1}{16}"$R

MATERIAL — DURAL. OR ALUMINUM ALLOY USED IN ORIGINAL CONSTRUCTION.

SCALE — TWICE SIZE

ORIGINAL

REINFORCEMENT

2117-AD RIVETS 3/32" DIA. MIN.

SECTION A-A
SCALE — TWICE SIZE

2017-T3 SQ. ROD

2117-AD RIVETS 1/8" DIA. MIN.

FIGURE 2.21.—Typical repair for buckled or cracked formed metal wing rib capstrips.

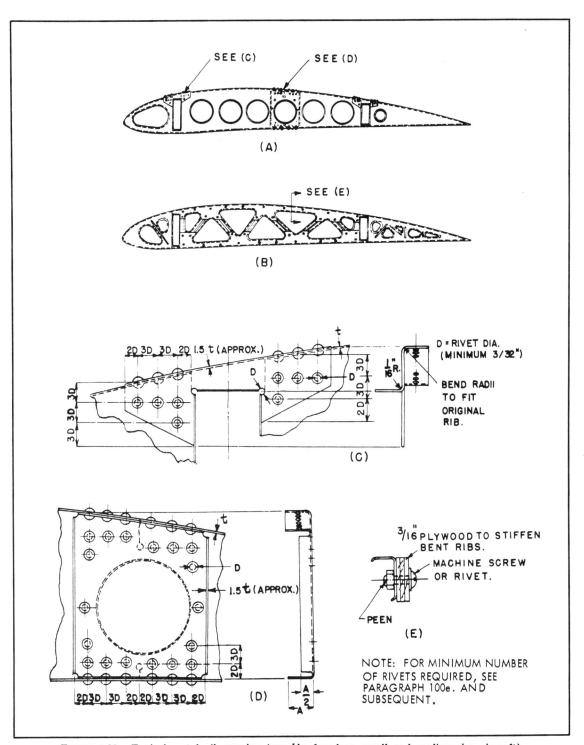

FIGURE 2.22.—Typical metal rib repairs (usually found on small and medium-size aircraft).

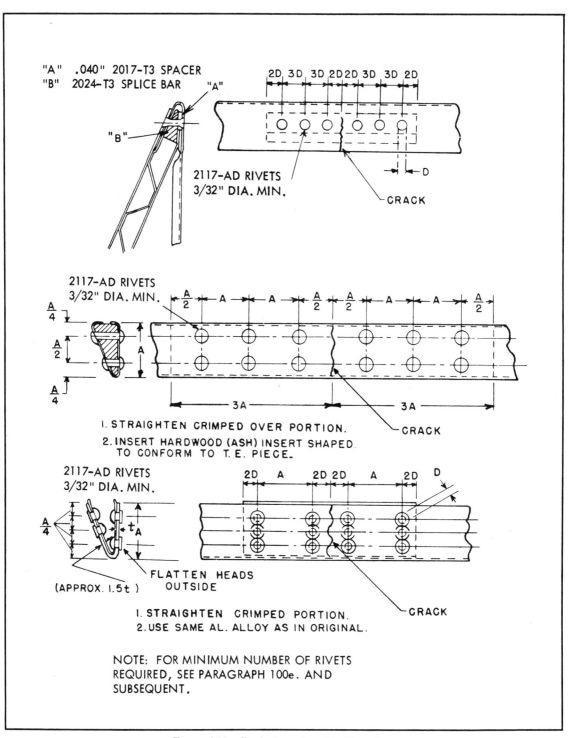

"A" .040" 2017-T3 SPACER
"B" 2024-T3 SPLICE BAR

"A"

"B"

2117-AD RIVETS
3/32" DIA. MIN.

2D 3D 3D 2D 2D 3D 3D 2D

D

CRACK

2117-AD RIVETS
3/32" DIA. MIN.

$\frac{A}{4}$

$\frac{A}{2}$

$\frac{A}{4}$

A

$\frac{A}{2}$ A A $\frac{A}{2}$ $\frac{A}{2}$ A A $\frac{A}{2}$

3A

3A

CRACK

1. STRAIGHTEN CRIMPED OVER PORTION.
2. INSERT HARDWOOD (ASH) INSERT SHAPED
   TO CONFORM TO T. E. PIECE.

2117-AD RIVETS
3/32" DIA. MIN.

$\frac{A}{4}$

t A

2D A 2D 2D A 2D D

(APPROX. 1.5t)

FLATTEN HEADS
OUTSIDE

CRACK

1. STRAIGHTEN CRIMPED PORTION.
2. USE SAME AL. ALLOY AS IN ORIGINAL.

NOTE: FOR MINIMUM NUMBER OF RIVETS
REQUIRED, SEE PARAGRAPH 100e. AND
SUBSEQUENT.

FIGURE 2.23.—Typical repairs of trailing edges.

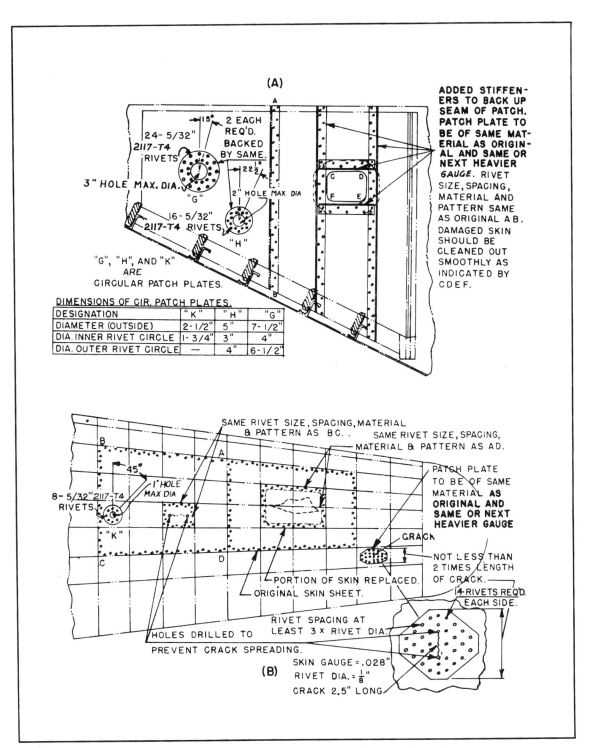

FIGURE 2.24—Typical repairs of stressed sheet metal covering.

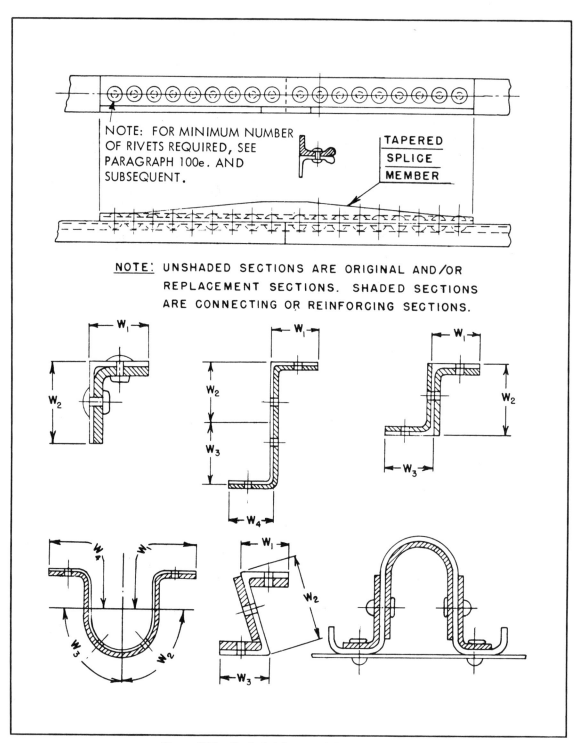

NOTE: FOR MINIMUM NUMBER OF RIVETS REQUIRED, SEE PARAGRAPH 100e. AND SUBSEQUENT.

TAPERED
SPLICE
MEMBER

NOTE: UNSHADED SECTIONS ARE ORIGINAL AND/OR REPLACEMENT SECTIONS. SHADED SECTIONS ARE CONNECTING OR REINFORCING SECTIONS.

FIGURE 2.25.—Typical stringer and flange splices.

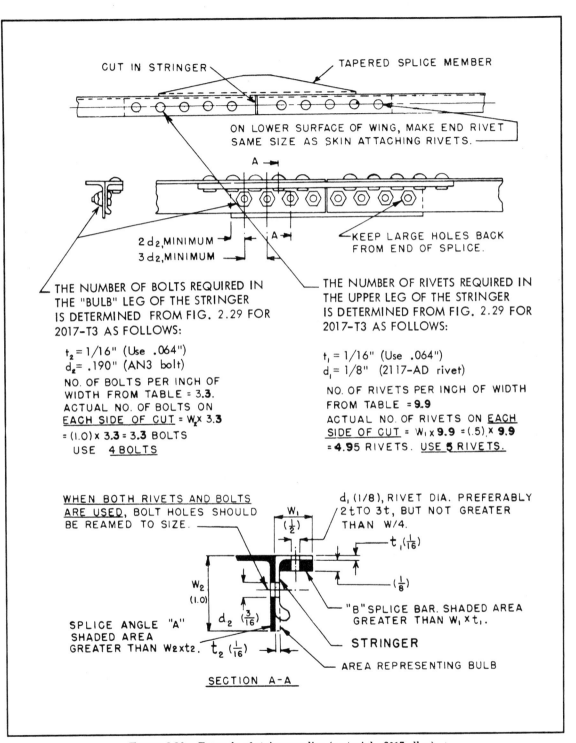

CUT IN STRINGER

TAPERED SPLICE MEMBER

ON LOWER SURFACE OF WING, MAKE END RIVET SAME SIZE AS SKIN ATTACHING RIVETS.

$2 d_2$, MINIMUM

$3 d_2$, MINIMUM

KEEP LARGE HOLES BACK FROM END OF SPLICE.

THE NUMBER OF BOLTS REQUIRED IN THE "BULB" LEG OF THE STRINGER IS DETERMINED FROM FIG. 2.29 FOR 2017-T3 AS FOLLOWS:

$t_2 = 1/16"$ (Use .064")
$d_2 = .190"$ (AN3 bolt)

NO. OF BOLTS PER INCH OF WIDTH FROM TABLE = 3.3. ACTUAL NO. OF BOLTS ON EACH SIDE OF CUT = W_2 x 3.3
= (1.0) x 3.3 = 3.3 BOLTS
USE 4 BOLTS

THE NUMBER OF RIVETS REQUIRED IN THE UPPER LEG OF THE STRINGER IS DETERMINED FROM FIG. 2.29 FOR 2017-T3 AS FOLLOWS:

$t_1 = 1/16"$ (Use .064")
$d_1 = 1/8"$ (2117-AD rivet)

NO. OF RIVETS PER INCH OF WIDTH FROM TABLE = 9.9 ACTUAL NO. OF RIVETS ON EACH SIDE OF CUT = W_1 x 9.9 = (.5) x 9.9
= 4.95 RIVETS. USE 5 RIVETS.

WHEN BOTH RIVETS AND BOLTS ARE USED, BOLT HOLES SHOULD BE REAMED TO SIZE.

d_1 (1/8), RIVET DIA. PREFERABLY 2t TO 3t, BUT NOT GREATER THAN W/4.

W_1 ($\frac{1}{2}$)

t_1 ($\frac{1}{16}$)

($\frac{1}{8}$)

"B" SPLICE BAR. SHADED AREA GREATER THAN W_1 x t_1.

W_2 (1.0)

d_2 ($\frac{3}{16}$)

SPLICE ANGLE "A" SHADED AREA GREATER THAN W_2 x t_2. t_2 ($\frac{1}{16}$)

STRINGER

AREA REPRESENTING BULB

SECTION A-A

FIGURE 2.26.—Example of stringer splice (material—2017 alloy).

recommendations, which are usually contained in a repair manual.

Typical splices for various shapes of sections are shown in figures 2.25 and 2.26. Design splices to carry both tension and compression, and use the splice shown in figure 2.26 as an example illustrating the following principles:

(1) Statement of Principles:

(a) To avoid eccentric loading and consequent buckling in compression, place splicing or reinforcing parts as symmetrically as possible about the centerline of the member, and attach to as many elements as necessary to prevent bending in any direction;

(b) To avoid reducing the strength in tension of the original bulb angle the rivet holes at the ends of the splice are made small (no larger than the original skin attaching rivets), and the second row of holes (those through the bulbed leg) are staggered back from the ends. In general arrange the rivets in the splice so that the design tensile load for the member and spliceplate can be carried into the splice without failing the member at the outermost rivet holes;

(c) To avoid concentration of load on the end rivet and consequent tendency toward progressive rivet failure, the splice is tapered at the ends, in this case, by tapering the backing angle and by making it shorter than the splice bar (ref. figure 2.26); and

(d) The preceding principles are especially important in splicing stringers on the lower surface of stressed skin wings, where high tension stresses may exist. When several adjacent stringers are spliced, stagger the splices if possible.

h. Size of Splicing Members. When the same material is used for the splicing members as for the original member, the next cross-section area (i.e., the shaded areas in figure 2.25) of the splicing member will be greater than the area of the section element which it splices. The area of a section element (e.g., each leg of an angle or channel) is equal to the width multiplied by the thickness. For example, the bar "B" in figure 2.26 is assumed to splice the upper leg of the stringer, and the angle "A" to splice the bulbed leg of the stringer. Since the splice bar "B" is not as wide as the adjacent leg, and since the rivet diameter is also subtracted from the width, the bar is made twice as thick in order to obtain sufficient net area.

i. The Diameter of Rivets in Stringers. The diameter of rivets in stringers might preferably be between 2 and 3 times the thickness "t" of the leg, but must not be more than 1/4 the width "W" of the leg. Thus, 1/8-inch rivets are chosen in the example, figure 2.26. If the splices were in the lower surface of a wing, the end rivets would be made the same size as the skin-attaching rivets or 3/32 inch.

j. The Number of Rivets. The number of rivets required on each side of the cut in a stringer or flange may be determined from standard textbooks on aircraft structures, or may be found in figures 2.28, 2.29, and 2.30. In determining the number of rivets required in the example, figure 2.26, for attaching the splice bar "B" to the upper leg, the thickness "t" of the element of area being spliced is 1/16 inch (use 0.064), the rivet size is 1/8 inch, and figure 2.29 shows that 9.9 rivets are required per inch of width. Since the width "W" is 1/2 inch, the actual number of rivets required to attach the splice-bar to the upper leg on each side of the cut is 9.9 (rivets per inch) × 0.5 (inch width) = 4.95 (use 5 rivets).

For the bulbed leg of the stringer "t" = 1/16 inch (use 0.064); AN–3 bolts are chosen and the number of bolts required per inch of width = 3.3. The width "W" for this leg, however, is 1 inch and the actual number of bolts required on each side of the cut is 1 × 3.3 = 3.3 (use 4 bolts). When both rivets and bolts are used in the same splice, the boltholes must be accurately reamed to size. It is preferable to use only one type of attachment, but in the above example, the dimensions of the legs of the bulb angle indicated rivets for the upper leg and bolts for the bulb leg.

(1) Splicing of Intermediate Frames. The same principles used for stringer-splicing may be applied to intermediate frames, when the following point is considered:

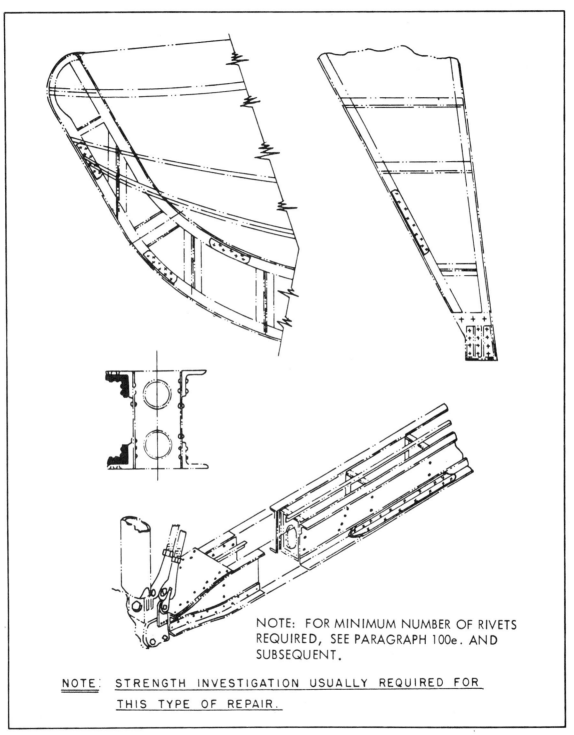

NOTE: FOR MINIMUM NUMBER OF RIVETS
REQUIRED, SEE PARAGRAPH 100e. AND
SUBSEQUENT.

NOTE: STRENGTH INVESTIGATION USUALLY REQUIRED FOR
THIS TYPE OF REPAIR.

FIGURE 2.27.—Application of typical flange splices and reinforcement.

71

FIGURE 2.28.—Number of rivets required for splices (single-lap joint)
in bare 2014–T6, 2024–T3, 2024–T36, and 7075–T6 sheet, clad 2014–T6, 2024–T3, 2024–T36,
and 7075–T6 sheet, 2024–T4, and 7075–T6 plate, bar, rod, tube, and extrusions, 2014–T6 extrusions.

Thickness "t" in inches	No. of 2117–AD protruding head rivets required per inch of width "W"					No. of bolts
	3/32	1/8	5/32	3/16	1/4	AN–3
0.016 ----------	6.5	4.9	----------	----------	----------	----------
.020 ----------	6.9	4.9	3.9	----------	----------	----------
.025 ----------	8.6	4.9	3.9	----------	----------	----------
.032 ----------	11.1	6.2	3.9	3.3	----------	----------
.036 ----------	12.5	7.0	4.5	3.3	2.4	----------
.040 ----------	13.8	7.7	5.0	3.5	2.4	3.3
.051 ----------	----------	9.8	6.4	4.5	2.5	3.3
.064 ----------	----------	12.3	8.1	5.6	3.1	3.3
.081 ----------	----------	----------	10.2	7.1	3.9	3.3
.091 ----------	----------	----------	11.4	7.9	4.4	3.3
.102 ----------	----------	----------	12.8	8.9	4.9	3.4
.128 ----------	----------	----------	----------	11.2	6.2	3.2

NOTES:

a. For stringers in the upper surface of a wing, or in a fuselage, 80 percent of the number of rivets shown in the table may be used.

b. For intermediate frames, 60 percent of the number shown may be used.

c. For single lap sheet joints, 75 percent of the number shown may be used.

ENGINEERING NOTES: *The above table was computed as follows:*

1. The load per inch of width of material was calculated by assuming a strip one inch wide in tension.

2. Number of rivets required was calculated for 2117–AD rivets, based on a rivet allowable shear stress equal to 40 percent of the sheet allowable tensile stress, and a sheet allowable bearing stress equal to 160 percent of the sheet allowable tensile stress, using nominal hole diameters for rivets.

3. Combinations of sheet thickness and rivet size above the heavy line are critical in (i. e., will fail by) bearing on the sheet; those below are critical in shearing of the rivets.

4. The number of AN–3 bolts required below the heavy line was calculated based on a sheet allowable tensile stress of 70,000 p.s.i. and a bolt allowable single shear load of 2,126 pounds.

(a) *Conventional frames of channel or Z section* are relatively deep and thin compared to stringers, and usually fail by twisting or by buckling of the free flange. Reinforce the splice-joint against this type of failure by using a spliceplate heavier than the frame and by splicing the free flange of the frame with a flange of the spliceplate, as illustrated in figure 2.31. Since a frame is likely to be subjected to bending loads, make the length of spliceplate "L" more than twice the width "W₂" and the rivets spread out to cover the plate.

101. REPAIRING CRACKED MEMBERS. Acceptable methods of repairing various types of cracks in structural elements are shown in figures 2.32 to 2.35. The following general procedures apply in repairing such defects:

a. *Drill small holes* 3/32 inch (or 1/8 inch) at the extreme ends of the cracks to minimize the possibility of their spreading further.

b. *Add reinforcement* to carry the stresses across the damaged portion and to stiffen the joints (as shown in figures 2.32 to 2.35).

The condition causing cracks to develop at a particular point is stress concentration at that point in conjunction with repetition of stress, such as produced by vibration of the structure. The stress concentration may be due to the design or to defects such as nicks, scratches, tool marks, and initial stresses or cracks from forming or heat-treating operations. It should be noted, that an increase in sheet thickness alone is usually beneficial, but does not necessarily remedy the conditions leading to cracking.

102. STEEL AND ALUMINUM FITTINGS.

a. Steel Fittings—Inspection for Defects.

(1) **Fittings** are to be free from scratches, vise and nibbler marks, and sharp bends or edges. A careful examination of the fitting with a medium power (at least 10 power) magnifying glass is acceptable as an inspection.

(2) **When repairing aircraft after an accident** or in the course of a major overhaul, inspect all highly stressed main fittings.

(3) **Replace torn, kinked, or cracked fittings.**

(4) **Elongated or worn boltholes** in fittings which were designed without bushings are not to be reamed oversize. Replace such fittings unless the method of repair is approved by a representative of the FAA. Do not fill holes with welding rod. Acceptable methods of repairing elongated or worn boltholes in landing gear, stabilizer, interplane, or cabane-strut ends only, not originally equipped with pin plates, are shown in figure 2.36. (Also see figure 2.11 on longeron repair at fitting.)

b. Aluminum and Aluminum Alloy Fittings.

(1) Replace damaged fittings with new parts, having the same material specifications.

(2) Repairs may be made in accordance with data furnished by the aircraft manufacturer or data substantiating the method of repair may be submitted to the FAA for review.

103. CASTINGS. Damaged castings are to be replaced and not repaired unless the method of

FIGURE 2.29.—Number of rivets required for splices (single-lap joint) in 2017, 2017 ALCLAD, 2024–T36 and 2024– T36 ALCLAD sheet, plate, bar, rod, tube, and extrusions.

Thickness "t" in inches	No. of 2117—AD protruding head rivets required per inch of width "W"					No. of bolts
	3/32	1/8	5/32	3/16	1/4	AN–3
0.016	6.5	4.9				
.020	6.5	4.9	3.9			
.025	6.9	4.9	3.9			
.032	8.9	4.9	3.9	3.3		
.036	10.0	5.6	3.9	3.3	2.4	
.040	11.1	6.2	4.0	3.3	2.4	
.051		7.9	5.1	3.6	2.4	3.3
.064		9.9	6.5	4.5	2.5	3.3
.081		12.5	8.1	5.7	3.1	3.3
.091			9.1	6.3	3.5	3.3
.102			10.3	7.1	3.9	3.3
.128			12.9	8.9	4.9	3.3

NOTES:

a. For stringers in the upper surface of a wing, or in a fuselage, 80 percent of the number of rivets shown in the table may be used.

b. For intermediate frames, 60 percent of the number shown may be used.

c. For single lap sheet joints, 75 percent of the number shown may be used.

ENGINEERING NOTES: *The above table was computed as follows:*

1. The load per width of material was calculated by assuming a strip one inch wide in tension.

2. Number of rivets required was calculated for 2117–AD rivets, based on a rivet allowable shear stress equal to 50 percent of the sheet allowable tensile stress, and a sheet allowable bearing stress equal to 160 percent of the sheet allowable tensile stress, using nominal hole diameters for rivets.

3. Combinations of sheet thickness and rivet size above the heavy line are critical in (i.e., will fail by) bearing on the sheet; those below are critical in shearing of the rivets.

4. The number of AN–3 bolts required below the heavy line was calculated based on a sheet allowable tensile stress of 55,000 p.s.i. and a bolt allowable single shear load of 2,126 pounds.

FIGURE 2.30.—Number of rivets required for splices (single-lap joint) in 5052 (all hardnesses) sheet.

Thickness "t" in inches	No. of 2117–AD protruding head rivets required per inch of width "W"					No. of bolts
	3/32	1/8	5/32	3/16	1/4	AN-3
0.016	6. 3	4. 7				
.020	6. 3	4. 7	3. 8			
.025	6. 3	4. 7	3. 8			
.032	6. 3	4. 7	3. 8	3. 2		
.036	7. 1	4. 7	3. 8	3. 2	2. 4	
.040	7. 9	4. 7	3. 8	3. 2	2. 4	
.051	10. 1	5. 6	3. 8	3. 2	2. 4	
.064	12. 7	7. 0	4. 6	3. 2	2. 4	
.081		8. 9	5. 8	4. 0	2. 4	3. 2
.091		10. 0	6. 5	4. 5	2. 5	3. 2
.102		11. 2	7. 3	5. 1	2. 8	3. 2
.128			9. 2	6. 4	3. 5	3. 2

NOTES:

a. For stringers in the upper surface of a wing, or in a fuselage, 80 percent of the number of rivets shown in the table may be used.

b. For intermediate frames, 60 percent of the number shown may be used.

c. For single lap sheet joints, 75 percent of the number shown may be used.

ENGINEERING NOTES: *The above table was computed as follows:*

1. The load per inch of width of material was calculated by assuming a strip one inch wide in tension.

2. Number of rivets required was calculated for 2117–AD rivets, based on a rivet allowable shear stress equal to 70 percent of the sheet allowable tensile stress, and a sheet allowable bearing stress equal to 165 percent of the sheet allowable tensile stress, using nominal hole diameters for rivets.

3. Combinations of sheet thickness and rivet size above the heavy line are critical in (i.e., will fail by) bearing on the sheet; those below are critical in shearing of the rivets.

repair is specifically approved by the aircraft manufacturer or substantiating data for the repair has been reviewed by the FAA.

104. SELECTIVE PLATING IN AIRCRAFT MAINTENANCE.
Selective plating is a method of depositing metal from an electrolyte to the selected area. The electrolyte is held in an absorbent material attached to an inert anode. Plating contact is made by brushing or swabbing the part (cathode) with the electrolyte-bearing anode.

a. *Selective Plating Uses.* This process can be utilized for any of the following reasons:

(1) To prevent or minimize disassembly, reassembly, or masking costs.

(2) Resizing worn components (plate to size).

(3) Filling in damaged or corroded areas.

(4) To plate small areas of extremely large parts.

(5) To plate electrical contacts.

(6) To plate parts too large for existing baths.

(7) To supplement conventional plating.

(8) To plate components which become contaminated if immersed in a plating bath.

(9) To cadmium-plate ultra high strength steels without hydrogen embrittlement.

(10) On-site plating.

(11) Reverse current applications (e.g., stain removal, deburring, etching, dynamic balancing).

b. *Specifications.* Selective plating (electrodeposition), when properly applied, will meet the following specifications and standards:

THE NUMBER OF RIVETS REQUIRED IN EACH LEG ON EACH SIDE OF THE CUT IS DETERMINED BY THE WIDTH "W", THE THICKNESS OF THE FRAME "t", AND THE RIVET DIAMETER "d" USING FIG. 2.29 IN A MANNER SIMILAR TO THAT FOR STRINGERS IN FIG. 2.26.

NOTE b. IN FIG. 2.29 INDICATES THAT ONLY 60% OF THE NUMBER OF RIVETS SO CALCULATED NEED BE USED IN SPLICES IN INTERMEDIATE FRAMES

EXAMPLE (For 2017-T3 aluminum alloy frame)

FLANGE LEG

t = .040"
d = 1/8" 2117-AD rivet
W_1 & W_3 = .6 inch

NO. OF RIVETS PER INCH OF WIDTH FROM FIG. 2.29 = 6.2

No. of rivets required = W x 6.2 = .6 x 6.2 = 3.72 or 4 rivets. 60% of 4 rivets = 2.4 rivets. USE 3 RIVETS ON EACH SIDE OF THE CUT IN EACH FLANGE LEG.

WEB OF ZEE (OR CHANNEL)

t = .040"
d = 1/8" 2117-AD rivet
W = 2.0 inches

NO. OF RIVETS PER INCH OF WIDTH FROM FIG. 2.29 = 6.2

No. of rivets required = W x 6.2 = 2.0 x 6.2 = 12.4 or 13 rivets. 60% of 13 rivets = 7.8 rivets. USE 8 RIVETS ON EACH SIDE OF CUT IN THE WEB OF ZEE (OR CHANNEL).

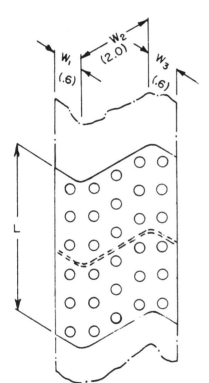

"L" SHOULD BE MORE THAN TWICE W_2
    Thickness of splice plate to be greater than that of the frame to be spliced.

FIGURE 2.31.—Example of splice of intermediate frame (material 2017 AL alloy).

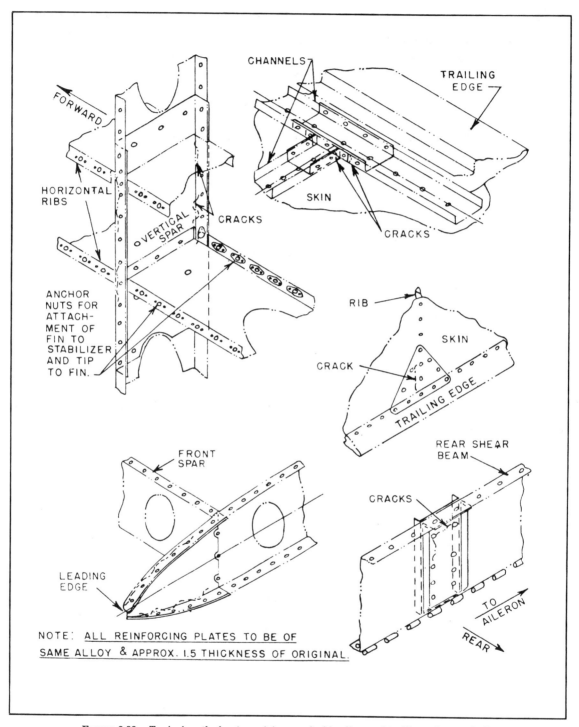

NOTE: ALL REINFORCING PLATES TO BE OF SAME ALLOY & APPROX. 1.5 THICKNESS OF ORIGINAL.

FIGURE 2.32.—Typical methods of repairing cracked leading and trailing edges and rib intersections.

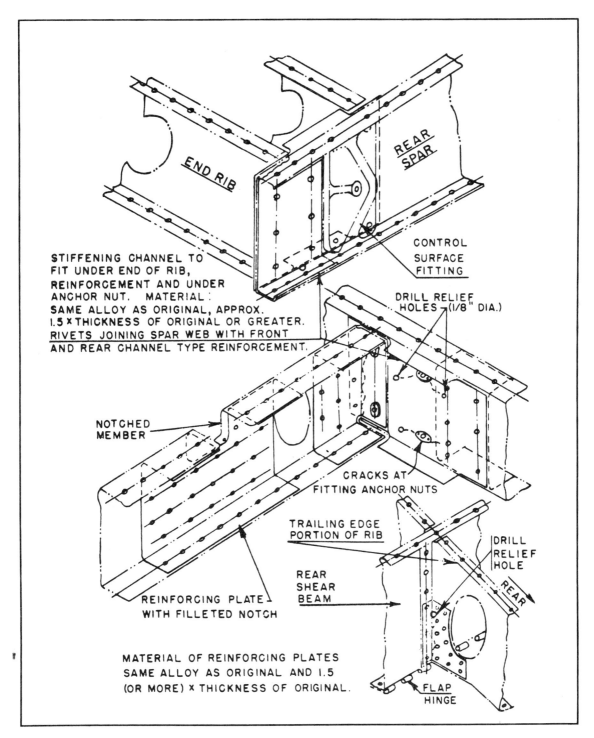

STIFFENING CHANNEL TO
FIT UNDER END OF RIB,
REINFORCEMENT AND UNDER
ANCHOR NUT.   MATERIAL:
SAME ALLOY AS ORIGINAL, APPROX.
1.5 × THICKNESS OF ORIGINAL OR GREATER.
RIVETS JOINING SPAR WEB WITH FRONT
AND REAR CHANNEL TYPE REINFORCEMENT.

END RIB

REAR
SPAR

CONTROL
SURFACE
FITTING

DRILL RELIEF
HOLES (1/8" DIA.)

NOTCHED
MEMBER

CRACKS AT
FITTING ANCHOR NUTS

TRAILING EDGE
PORTION OF RIB

DRILL
RELIEF
HOLE

REAR

REAR
SHEAR
BEAM

REINFORCING PLATE
WITH FILLETED NOTCH

FLAP
HINGE

MATERIAL OF REINFORCING PLATES
SAME ALLOY AS ORIGINAL AND 1.5
(OR MORE) × THICKNESS OF ORIGINAL.

FIGURE 2.33.—Typical methods of replacing cracked members at fittings.

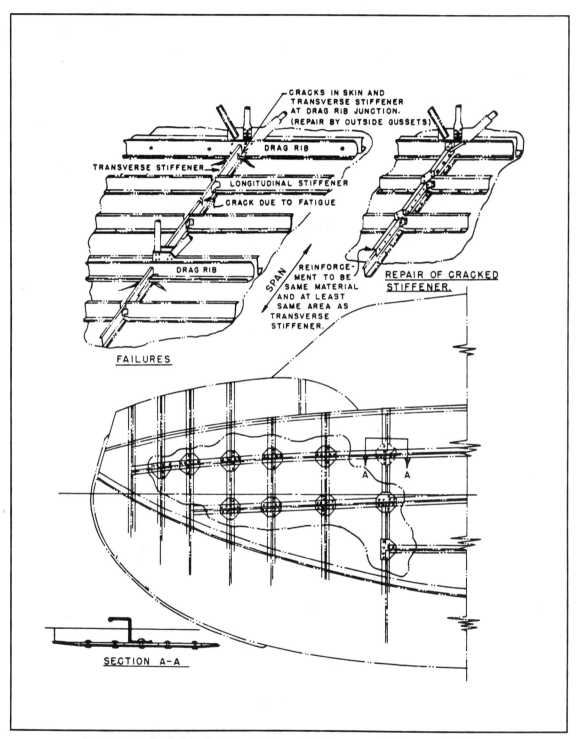

FIGURE 2.34.—Typical methods of repairing cracked frame and stiffener combinations.

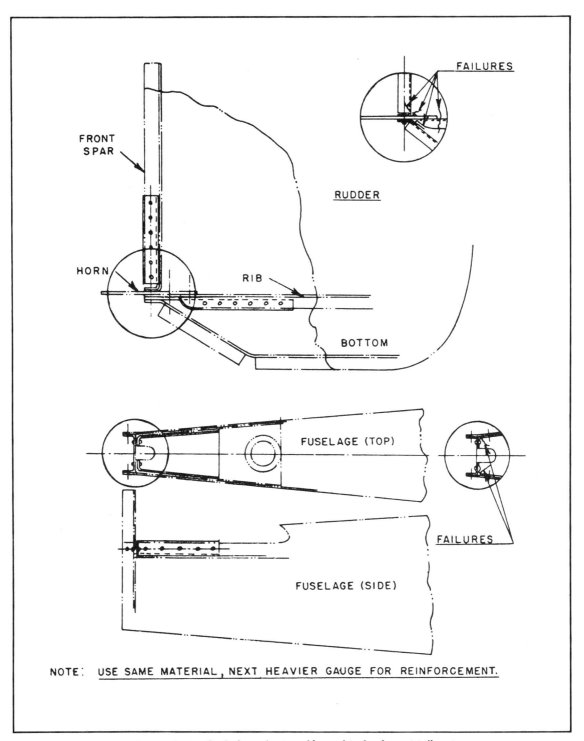

FAILURES

FRONT SPAR

RUDDER

HORN

RIB

BOTTOM

FAILURES

FUSELAGE (TOP)

FUSELAGE (SIDE)

NOTE: USE SAME MATERIAL, NEXT HEAVIER GAUGE FOR REINFORCEMENT.

FIGURE 2.35.—Typical repairs to rudder and to fuselage at tail post.

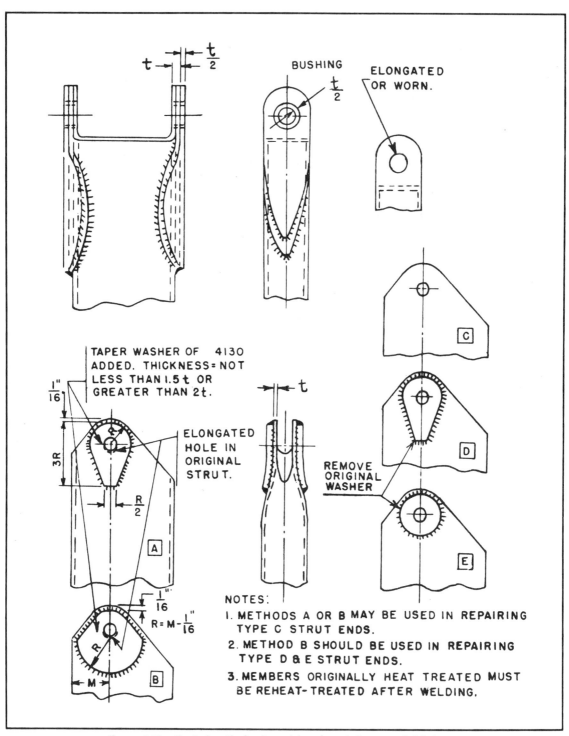

NOTES:
1. METHODS A OR B MAY BE USED IN REPAIRING TYPE C STRUT ENDS.
2. METHOD B SHOULD BE USED IN REPAIRING TYPE D & E STRUT ENDS.
3. MEMBERS ORIGINALLY HEAT TREATED MUST BE REHEAT-TREATED AFTER WELDING.

FIGURE 2.36.—Typical methods of repairing elongated or worn boltholes.

QQ–C–320	Chromium Plating
QQ–N–290	Nickel Plating
QQ–P–416	Plating, Cadmium
QQ–S–365	Silver Plating
QQ–Z–325	Zinc Plating
MIL–T–10727	Tin Plating
MIL–C–14550	Copper Plating
MIL–G–45204	Gold Plating

c. General Requirements.

(1) Areas to be repaired by this process should be limited to reasonably small areas of large parts, although it may be desirable to plate small parts, particularly electrical or electronic parts, in their entirety.

(2) All solutions should be kept clean and free from contamination. Care should be taken to insure that the solutions are not contaminated by used anodes or other plating solutions. Brush plating solutions are not designed to remove large amounts of scale, oil, or grease. Mechanical or chemical methods should be used to remove large amounts of scale or oxide. Use solvents to remove grease or oil.

(3) Brush plating solutions are five to fifty times as concentrated as tank solutions. The current densities used range from 500 to 4,000 amps/feet^2. The voltages listed on the solution bottles have been precalculated to give proper current densities. Too high a current density burns the plating, while too low a current density produces stressed deposits and low efficiencies. Agitation is provided by anode/cathode motion. Too fast a motion results in low efficiencies and stressed deposits; too slow a motion causes burning. A dry tool results in burnt plate, coarse grain structure, and unsound deposits. The tool ✱ ✱ cannot be too wet. Solution temperatures of 110° to 120° F. are reached during operation.

(4) Materials such as stainless steel, aluminum, chromium, and nickel, which have a passive surface, will require an activating operation to remove the passive surface. During the activating process, do not use solutions that have been previously used with reverse current because of solution contamination.

d. Equipment.

The power source should operate on either 110 or 220 volt alternating current (AC), 60 Hertz, single phase input. It should have a capability to produce direct current having smooth characteristics with controlled ripple and be able to output a current of at least 25 amperes at 0 to 25 volts. Minimum instrumentation of the power source should include a voltmeter, ammeter, and ampere-hour meter.

(1) The ammeter should provide a full scale reading equal to the maximum capacity of the power source with an accuracy of ±5 percent of the current being measured.

(2) The voltmeter should have sufficient capacity to provide a full scale reading equal to the maximum capacity of the power source and an accuracy of ±1.0 volt.

(3) An ampere-hour meter should be readable to 0.001 ampere-hour and have an accuracy of ±0.01 ampere-hour.

(4) The stylus should be designed for rapid cooling and to hold anodes of various sizes and configurations. For safety, the anode holder should be insulated.

(5) The containers for holding and catching runoff solutions should be designed to the proper configuration and be inert to the specific solution.

(6) The mechanical cleaning equipment and materials should be designed and selected to prevent contamination of the parts to be cleaned.

e. Materials.

The anodes should be of high-purity dense graphite or platinum-iridium alloys. Do not mix solutions from different suppliers. This could result in contamination.

f. Detail Requirements.

On large parts, no area greater than approximately 10 percent of the total area of the part should be plated by this process. Small parts may be partially or completely plated. Special cases exceeding these limitations should be coordinated with the manufacturer of the plating equipment being used and his recommendations should be followed.

g. Anode Selection.

As a general guide, the contact area of the anode should be approximately one-third the size of the area to be plated. When selecting the anode, the configuration of the part will dictate the shape of the anode.

h. Required Ampere-Hour Calculation.

The selected plating solution has a factor which is equal to the ampere-hours required to deposit 0.0001 inch on one square inch of surface. Determine the thickness of plating desired on a certain area and multiply the solution factor times the plating thickness times the area in square inches to determine the ampere-hours required. This factor may vary because of temperature, current density, etc.

i. *Cleaning.* Remove corrosion, scale, oxide, and unacceptable plating prior to processing. Use a suitable solvent or cleaner to remove grease or oil.

j. *Plating on Aluminum and Aluminum Base Alloys.*

(1) Electroclean the area using forward (direct) current until water does not break on the surface. This electroclean process should be accomplished at 10 to 15 volts, using the appropriate electroclean solution.

(2) Rinse the area in cold clean tap water.

(3) Activate the area with reverse current, 7 to 10 volts, in conjunction with the proper activating solution until a uniform gray to black surface is obtained.

(4) Rinse thoroughly in cold, clean tap water.

(5) Immediately electroplate to color while the area is still wet, using the appropriate nickel solution.

(6) Rinse thoroughly.

(7) Immediately continue plating with any other solution to desired thickness.

(8) Rinse and dry.

k. *Plating on Copper and Copper Base Alloys.*

(1) Electroclean the area using forward (direct) current until water does not break on the surface. The electroclean process should be accomplished at 8 to 12 volts using the appropriate electroclean solution.

* (2) Rinse the area in cold, clean tap water.

(3) Immediately electroplate the area with any of the plating solutions except silver. Silver requires an undercoat.

(4) Rinse and dry.

l. *Plating on 300 and 400 Series Stainless Steels, Nickel Base Alloys, Chrome Base Alloys, High Nickel Ferrous Alloys, Cobalt Base Alloys, Nickel Plate, and Chrome Plate.*

(1) Electroclean the area using forward (direct) current until water does not break on the surface. This electroclean process should be

accomplished at 12 to 20 volts using the appropriate electrocleaning solution.

(2) Rinse the area in cold, clean tap water.

(3) Activate the surface using forward (direct) current for 1 to 2 minutes using the activating solution and accomplish at 6 to 20 volts.

(4) Do not rinse.

(5) Immediately nickel flash the surface to a thickness of 0.00005 to 0.0001 inch using the appropriate nickel solution.

(6) Rinse thoroughly.

(7) Immediately continue plating with any other solution to desired thickness.

(8) Rinse and dry.

m. *Plating on Low-Carbon Steels (Heat Treated to 180,000 psi).*

(1) Electroclean the area using forward (direct) current until water does not break on the surface. This electroclean process should be accomplished at 12 to 20 volts using the appropriate electrocleaning solution.

(2) Rinse the area in cold, clean tap water.

(3) Reverse current etch at 8 to 10 volts, using the appropriate activating solution, until a uniform gray surface is obtained.

(4) Rinse thoroughly.

(5) Immediately electroplate the part using any solutions except copper acid or silver. Both these require undercoats.

(6) Rinse and dry.

n. *Plating on Cast Iron and High-Carbon Steels (Steels Heat Treated to 180,000 psi).*

(1) Electroclean the area using forward (direct) current until water does not break on the surface. This electroclean process should be accomplished at 12 to 20 volts using the appropriate electrocleaning solution.

(2) Rinse the area thoroughly in cold, clean tap water.

(3) Reverse current etch at 8 to 10 volts, using the appropriate etching solution, until a uniform gray is obtained.

(4) Rinse thoroughly.

(5) Remove surface smut with 15 to 25 volts using the appropriate activating solution.

(6) Rinse thoroughly.

(7) Electroplate immediately using any of

the solutions except copper or silver (both these require undercoats).

(8) Rinse and dry.

o. *Plating on Ultra High Strength Steels (Heat Treated Above 180,000 psi).*

(1) Electroclean the area using REVERSE current until water does not break on the surface. This electroclean process should be accomplished at 8 to 12 volts using the appropriate electroclean solution.

(2) Rinse the area thoroughly in cold, clean tap water.

(3) Immediately electroplate the part, using either nickel, chromium, gold, or cadmium. Other metals require an undercoat of one of the above. Plate initially at the highest voltage recommended for the solution so as to develop an initial barrier layer. Then reduce to standard voltage.

(4) Rinse and dry.

(5) Bake the part for 4 hours at 375°±25° F.

NOTE 1: Where the solution vendor provides substantiating data that hydrogen embbrittlement will not result from plating with a particular solution, then a post bake is not required. This substantiating data can be in the form of aircraft industry manufacturers' process specifications, military specifications, or other suitable data.

NOTE 2: Acid etching should be avoided, if possible. Where etching is absolutely necessary, it should always be done with reverse current. Use alkaline solutions for initial deposits.

p. *Dissimilar Metals and Changing Base.* As a general rule, when plating two dissimilar metals, follow the plating procedure for the one with the most steps or activation. If activating
* steps have to be mixed, use reverse current activation steps prior to forward (direct) current activation steps.

q. *Plating Solution Selection.*

(1) Alkaline and neutral solutions are to be used on porous base metals, white metals, high-strength steel, and for improved coating ability. Acid solutions are to be used for rapid buildup

and as a laminating structure material in conjunction with alkaline type solutions.

(2) Chrome brush plating solutions do not yield as hard a deposit as bath plating solutions. The hardness is about 600 Brinell as compared to 1,000 Brinell for hard chrome deposited from a tank.

(3) Silver immersion deposits will form with no current flowing on most base metals from the silver brush plating solutions; such deposits have poor adhesion to the base metal. Consequently, a flash or a more noble metal should be deposited prior to silver plating to develop a good bond.

(4) In general, brush plating gives less hydrogen embrittlement and a lower fatigue strength loss than does equivalent tank deposits. However, all brush-plated, ultra high strength steel parts (heat treated above 180,000 psi) should be baked as mentioned in paragraph 104.o.(5), unless it is specifically known that embrittlement is not a factor.

r. *Qualification Tests.* All brush plated surfaces shall be tested for adhesion of the electrodeposit. Apply a 1-inch wide strip of Minnesota Mining and Manufacturing tape code 250, or an approved equal, with the adhesive side to the freshly plated surface. Apply the tape with heavy hand pressure and remove it with one quick motion perpendicular to the plated surface. Any plating adhering to the tape shall be cause for rejection.

s. *Personnel Training for Quality Control.* Manufacturers of selective plating equipment provide training in application techniques at their facilities. Personnel performing selective plating must have adequate knowledge of the methods, techniques, and practices involved. These personnel should be products of those training programs and certified as qualified operators by the manufacturers of the products used, as well as by local quality control departments.

105.–114. RESERVED.

Comment: Since almost all commercially produced airplanes have been of all-metal construction for many years, most aircraft repair facilities are equipped to

repair them and licensed aircraft mechanics are experienced in such work. However, there are two situations that may involve one who is not a licensed aircraft mechanic in aircraft metalwork, the most common being the construction of an all-metal homebuilt. One may also wish to refurbish an older all-metal production airplane, but we should say right up front that any structural repair to such a machine should be performed by a licensed AP or IA.

Technically, the FARs allow the amateur to repair metal airframes under the direct supervision of a licensed mechanic, but such an arrangement is seldom practical, amounting to on-the-job training that results in little or no savings in cost, while significantly extending the time required to do the work. As a practical matter, the refurbishing of a "store-bought" all-metal airplane that may be accomplished by the amateur is limited to repainting (one can save a bundle on this alone, because 90 percent of the cost of a new paint job, properly done, is charged to labor), reupholstery, installation of side windows (but not the windshield), and some maintenance-type work such as brake and wheel bearing replacement.

All-metal homebuilts are a different story. The good ones are designed for construction with limited equipment by those with limited (or no) metalworking skills. Many of the components may be purchased preformed, while the Pop riveter allows the amateur builder to fasten it all together just like downtown.

The Pop riveter is the simple little tool, along with its special rivets, that has made all-metal homebuilts practical projects for those with no previous metalworking experience. No bucking bars are needed to set the rivets and form "shop heads" on the opposite side of the metal. A Pop rivet has a hollow shank containing a hardened shaft that pulls the end of the softer rivet into a perfect shop head and then breaks off inside the shank (figure 2.37). It is a simple, one-person operation.

Prior to riveting, one must carefully position and drill the rivet holes. The pieces to be joined are then held in place by "Cleco" fasteners until each Cleco is removed and replaced, in turn, by a rivet.

The PRG-400 hand-operated Pop riveter is made by the United Shoe Machinery Corporation, Fastener Division, Shelton, CT. The Pop riveter is also available in powered versions.

SHOP EQUIPMENT

Constructing an all-metal homebuilt will require the same basic power tools as for building a wood airframe: band saw, disc sander, and drill press.

The hand tools needed will include a Pop riveter, Cleco tool with at least two dozen Cleco fasteners; files, electric hand drill, drill bits (twist drills),

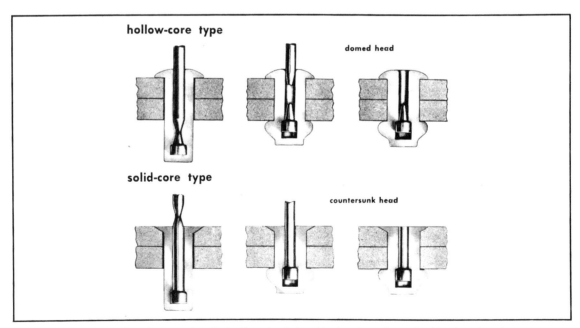

Figure 2.37.—Pop rivets are installed with a simple hand tool and require no bucking bars to set.

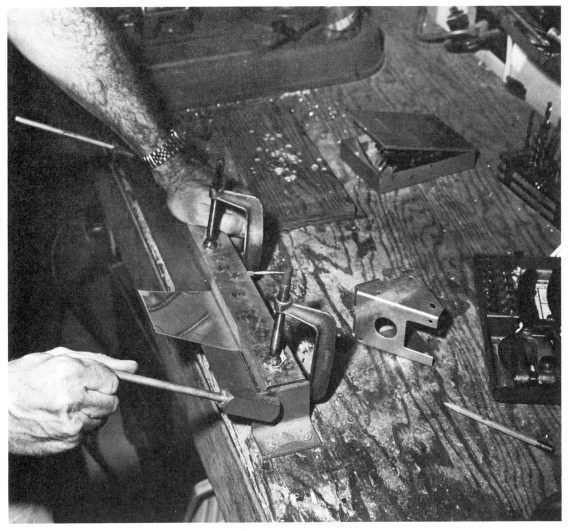

Figure 2.38.—A homemade cornice brake used for the fabrication of metal fittings.

metal shears, bench vise, metal tape measure, square, rawhide mallet, screwdrivers, and pliers (figures 2.38 through 2.40).

The pliers should include the flatnose type that has square, deep jaws, handy for making flanges; roundnose pliers are used for crimping. Diagonals (''dikes'') will be needed for a variety of chores, and the common slip-joint pliers are always useful.

FINISHING/REFINISHING METAL AIRCRAFT

Although 43.13 does not establish standards for painting or repainting metal aircraft (presum-ably because the airplane's paint does not directly affect its structural integrity), it is part of almost every repair job and homebuilt project. It is important that aircraft finishing/refinishing be properly done because it is costly.

Almost all paint jobs look good initially. It's how they look after a year or two that really counts. The owner who pays $1,400 or more to have his single-engine airplane refinished does not expect to find the paint blistering or flaking 18 months later.

Keep in mind that the primary purpose of painting metal airplanes is to protect the airframe from corro-

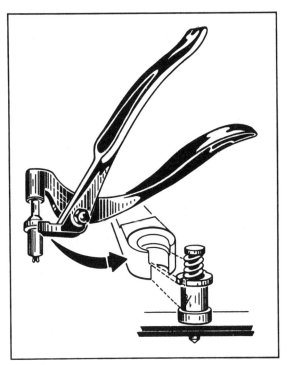

Figure 2.39.—After rivet holes are drilled and the structure is ready for assembly, Celco fasteners hold mating pieces in place until rivets are installed.

sion. To accomplish that most effectively, there are a number of separate operations that must be correctly performed with the proper materials. Do it right and the result is both maximum protection and a finish that will last.

It is easy to choose a paint scheme that detracts, rather than adds to, the overall appearance of an airplane. Stripes that do not blend well into the plane's natural shape are worse than no stripes. If you design an original color combination, it is most helpful to do it on a scale model of the airplane because the end result must be seen in three dimensions in order to know how it will appear from all angles. Side and top views on paper are usually inadequate. If the airplane to be refinished is an older production craft, the safest combination may be a copy of the paint scheme on new airplanes of the same make. During the '50s and early '60s the manufacturers chose some rather uninspired paint schemes, but in recent years have generally selected tasteful combinations.

A new paint job may consist of merely sanding the old paint and spraying a new color finish over it. That is the least costly way to go, providing that the condition of the old finish will allow it. More often, it is necessary to strip the old paint and start over from the bare metal, applying a cleaner, etcher, intermediate primer, and finish coatings. When the entire system is applied—to new metal or to surfaces that have been stripped of previous coatings—what you see is not what you get. Most of the labor and the know-how that result in maximum protection/durability are covered by the shiny final coating.

We will detail a complete paint system, using the best materials available. The best paint and associated products will add little to the overall cost because most of the expense is in the labor.

First, an important rule: Do not mix brands within a given paint system. The enamel, primer, reducer, and thinner should all be of the same brand because the solvents of one brand may not be compatible with those used in another brand.

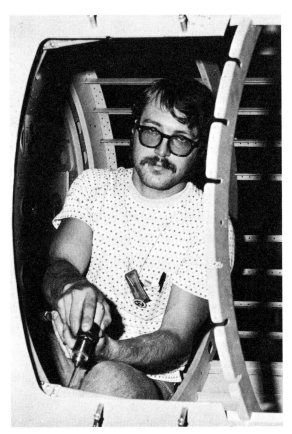

Fig. 2.40.—Learjet craftsman Dennis Heath operators air-driven drill on fuselage assembly. Note Celco fasteners in place.

Figure 2.41.—Paint stripper is washed from this Cessna with high-pressure water.
Steam is advisable only when handled by an experienced aircraft mechanic since it can cause damage if misdirected.

STRIPPING OLD PAINT

The paint stripper will work best if the airframe is first cleaned of grease, oil, dirt, exhaust tracks, etc., with dry cleaning solvent or a cleaner such as Stits C-2200 or Cooper's NAPDA #5.

Paint removers used on metal airplanes are either ammonia or acid type, the latter being the stronger. The acid type should not be used on magnesium or high-strength steels. Cooper Supply Company's NAPDA Stripper #3 is an ammonia-activated paint remover that is safe on all metals. Their NAPDA Stripper #4 is acid-activated and will strip polyurethanes as well as other (perhaps unidentified) finishes. Stits #5 Paint Remover is also an acid type.

You begin by masking off everything the stripper may harm: windshield, windows, window seals (it is best to mask at least ¼ inch onto the metal surrounding the windshield and windows; that narrow strip will be carefully scraped off later by hand), pitot and static system openings, tires, air scoop openings, door seals, etc. Make sure that there are no pinholes or tiny tears in the masking material. The top professional aircraft painters cover the windshield, windows, and seals with at least two layers of heavy paper, including one aluminum-backed.

Apply the stripper generously, according to the directions on the container label, and wash it off with a moderately high-pressure water hose (figure 2.41). Two or even three applications of stripper are usually required. Even so, some bits and chips will always

Figure 2.42.—Two types of
respirators are in common use to protect the craftsman
from paint vapors. The hood type (A) is supplied with pure
equipped with air under pressure. The organic type (B) is
a cartridge that removes vapors by chemical absorption.

remain, often around rivet heads, and these must be patiently removed a piece at a time using fiber scotch pads.

Blow-dry the airframe, remove the control surfaces, then apply a phosphoric acid etch and brightener. This cleans the metal and provides a good bond for the primer.

Any fiberglass components should be sanded and filled next. Then the airframe is completely re-masked and wiped down with a tack cloth to remove any dust, lint, fingerprints, and static-charged particles. This operation is followed by application of a wash primer, a two-part vinyl butyral-phosphoric resin containing corrosion inhibiting pigments that increases primer adhesion, inhibits under-film corrosion in severe environmental conditions, and contributes to a significantly more durable paint job. We recommend Stits #WP-700 Wash Primer. Make sure that the wash primer has totally cured before applying the intermediate primer.

The intermediate primer is a sprayed-on coat of a two-part epoxy (recommended is Stits EP-420 because it has the highest percentage of zinc chromate solids for corrosion control), and it must be applied within 24 hours of wash primer application. The intermediate primer is sanded with Wet-or-dry sandpaper, 360 to 600 grit, depending upon the hardness of this primer. The hardness of this primer is primarily determined by the length of time it is allowed to cure. After scuffing, immediately wipe all surfaces with the reducer used with the system or with Stits C-210 Paint Surface Cleaner. Follow with a final

wipe-down with a tack cloth. Then, if the finish and trim are to be polyurethane in any bright or light color, apply a white base coat of polyurethane. Allow this to dry thoroughly. A white base coat will significantly add to the brightness and reflectivity of the lighter colors most used on aircraft today.

Next, spray three coats of polyurethane color at 15 to 20 minute intervals, allowing only sufficient time between each to avoid runs.

If you have never worked with polyurethane enamel before, you may become a bit apprehensive over what appears to be insufficient coverage, along with a definite lack of gloss. Don't worry; that is just the nature of polyurethane. The color pigments will "crawl" for hours after application and the desired degree of opaqueness will develop, while the high gloss that marks proper cross-linking of the two-part polyurethane enamel will not appear for up to 24 hours after application. Then it will cure to a rock-hard finish with the unique "wet look," and the airplane may be returned to service in about two or three days, although the total curing process usually continues for up to seven or eight days.

We mentioned "cross-linking" above and we will

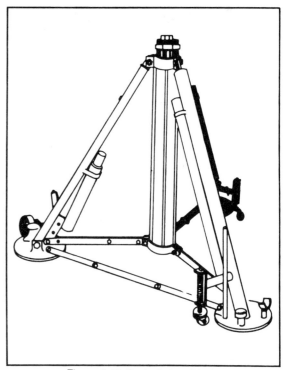

Figure 2-43. Typical aircraft jack.

88

elaborate on that momentarily. Meanwhile, why polyurethane? Because it will substantially outlast the old synthetic enamels and acrylic lacquers, and because it cures to a very shiny, hard finish that is far more resistant to oil, grease, battery acid, and LL100 fuel than other coatings.

All brands of polyurethane enamel are handled in a similar manner. A given amount of catalyst is mixed with the color base material. (The ratios will vary with different brands.) The mixture is thoroughly stirred; 10 to 20 percent reducer is added to obtain a proper viscosity for spraying (additional reducer may be needed on warm days), and the paint is allowed to set for 20 minutes before spraying. A viscosimeter, usually referred to as a "Ford Cup" or "Zahn Cup," is useful in determining proper spraying viscosity. It is a small plastic cup with a hole in the bottom. The cup is filled with paint and the time required, in seconds, for the paint flowing out the bottom to reach its first break is the indicator. (Seventeen to 19 seconds with a #6 cup is optimum for Stits Aluma-Thane.)

Spraying technique of the color finish is simple. Apply a light, wet tack coat over the white base and follow with two medium cross coats at 10 to 20 minute intervals. At first it will appear thin and a bit transparent, but as the catalyst cross-links with the color during the curing process, the color will deepen.

We have mentioned/recommended brand names. As nearly as we have been able to determine, there probably isn't much difference in the quality of the polyurethanes offered by well-known manufacturers. Cessna uses DuPont Imron; Beech uses Dow Chemical's Alumigrip. In the field, the most popular aircraft paint suppliers are Cooper Aviation Supply Company, a regular advertiser in *Trade-A-Plane*; Randolph Products Company (Carlstadt, NJ), and Stits Aircraft Coatings (Riverside, CA). As mentioned, a most important consideration when finishing/refinishing a metal airplane is that the entire operation employ, *exclusively,* the products of a single paint manufacturer to ensure that the solvents and thinners in the several materials are compatible. We lean to Stits products because we regard the Stits two-part epoxy primer as the best available; also because Stits does not skimp on the all-important (and expensive) catalyst in the color mix, and because one of the Stits (father or sons) is always available to take a long-distance phone call and answer any question you may have about a given paint problem.

For the application of polyurethane enamels, we recommend a DeVilbiss spray gun Model MBC-510 or the JGA-502 with a 30 air cap and EX tip and needle operated at 45 to 50 pounds per square inch of pressure.

TIPS AND FACILITIES

Aircraft finishing/refinishing must be done in a facility that is separate from all other activity and shop work. It is extremely important that the airframe surfaces not be contaminated by dust, miniscule droplets of oil, or even fingerprints. Some form of temperature control (no sparks or open flame) and humidity control is necessary for year-round work, and an exhaust fan is needed to carry away fumes and overspray. Wash down the floor—never sweep, because sweeping creates static electricity that can ignite residual solvents and thinners in the paint overspray that appears dry.

An adequate water trap should be installed in the spray gun air line to keep moisture out of the paint. Moisture in the finish results in pinholes and blisters.

Shop towels provided by towel rental services may be contaminated with silicone that will transfer to the aircraft surfaces and cause blemishes in the finish if used to wipe down the airframe.

Use only good quality solvent-resistant masking tape (such as 3M 236) when taping trim lines to avoid solvent penetration through the tapes and seepage of trim colors under the tape edges.

You must wear a respirator for most of the operations attendant to the refinishing of an airplane. The two most suitable types are the hood respirator and the organic vapor types that covers the nose and mouth (figure 2.42). The hood type gives the most protection. It is a covering for the head equipped with a window. An air line supplies pure air under pressure that exhausts through a front opening and keeps out fumes and airborne particles. Hoods are available in paper, cloth, and transparent material. Organic vapor type respirators are equipped with cartridges that remove vapors by chemical absorption. Some are also equipped with pre-filters that remove solid particles from the air before passing it through the cartridge. Dust respirators are useful only when sanding or grinding.

Finally, remember that the FARs require that the reinstallation of control surfaces (it is almost always necessary to remove them in order to properly clean, prepare, and paint hinge areas) must be accomplished by a licensed airframe mechanic, who will also make sure that the static balance of these components has not been altered by excessive or uneven paint coverage.

ALTERNATIVES

In the past, a lot of metal airplanes were painted with acrylic lacquer or synthetic enamel. Both were developed 40 to 50 years ago as automotive and industrial finishes. Acrylic lacquer is not a practical choice for field application because of the carefully controlled conditions, including the narrow time span allowed for its application, under which it must be applied.

A lot of airplanes are still being refinished with synthetic enamel. The most successful such jobs are applied hot, with the material at about 160 degrees F at the spray gun nozzle. Many shops, however, merely apply synthetic enamel at room temperature and allow it to air-dry. A painter experienced with this material can turn out a very nice-looking finish. But even when a properly applied synthetic enamel is kept waxed and the airplane hangared, it will last no more than half as long as polyurethane.

AIRCRAFT JACKING

No one but an experienced aircraft mechanic should jack an entire airplane. The amateur craftsman may safely jack one wheel, but to jack the whole airplane, with all wheels off the surface simultaneously, is to live dangerously unless one knows exactly what he is about.

The AP will begin by consulting the manufacturer's maintenance instructions to determine the location of the jack pads and whether or not a given airplane has removable pads that are fitted into receptacles and bolted into place only when needed. At least three points are provided on all production airplanes for jacking purposes. A fourth point on some aircraft is used to stabilize the machine while it is being jacked. Jacking points will usually be located in relation to the airplane's center of gravity, but there are exceptions. On some airplanes it may be necessary to add weight to the nose or tail to achieve a safe balance. Sandbags are normally used for this purpose.

Before raising an airplane on jacks (figure 2.43), all workstands and other equipment should be removed from under and near the plane. No one should remain in the machine while it is being raised or lowered, unless maintenance manual procedures require such practice for observing leveling instruments in the aircraft.

The airplane must be located in a level position and well protected from the wind. A hangar should be used if possible. Tripod jacks of the appropriate size should be placed under the jack pads and perfectly centered.

Prior to jacking, it should be determined if the aircraft configuration will permit the operation. There may be equipment or fuel that must be off-loaded to avoid structural damage when jacking. If any other work is in progress on the airplane, ascertain if any critical panels have been removed. On some aircraft, the stress panels or plates must be in place when the airplane is jacked to avoid structural damage.

Extend the jacks until they contact the jack pads. A final check for alignment of the jacks should be made before the airplane is raised, since most accidents during jacking are the result of misaligned jacks.

When the aircraft is ready to be raised, a man should be stationed at each jack. The jacks should be operated simultaneously to keep the airplane as level as possible and to avoid overloading of any of the jacks. This is best done with the AP crew leader standing in front of the airplane giving instructions to the three jack operators. Never raise the airplane any higher than is necessary to accomplish the job.

The area around the airplane should be secured while the machine is on the jacks. Climbing on the airplane should be held to an absolute minimum, and no violent movements should be made by persons who are required to go aboard. Any cradles or necessary supports should be placed under the fuselage or wings at the earliest possible time, particularly if the airplane is to remain jacked up for any length of time.

Before releasing jack pressure and lowering the airplane, make certain that all cribbing, workstands, equipment, and people are clear of the airplane, that the landing gear is down and locked, and that all ground locking devices are properly installed.

Fabric Covering

Reprinted from FAA 43.13, Chapter 3)

Section 1. PRACTICES AND PRECAUTIONS

127. TEXTILE MATERIALS. All fabric, surface tape, reinforcing tape, machine thread, lacing cord, etc., used for re-covering or repairing an aircraft structure must be high-grade aircraft textile material of at least as good quality and equivalent strength as those described in subparagraphs a through g.

a. *Aircraft Fabric.* Acceptable fabrics such as cotton and linen for covering wings, control surfaces, and fuselages are listed in figure 3.1. Fabrics conforming to the Aeronautical Material Specifications incorporate a continuous marking showing the specification number to permit identification of the fabric in the field.

b. *Re-covering Aircraft.* Re-cover or repair aircraft with fabric of at least as good quality and equivalent strength as that originally used on the aircraft. However, in re-covering aircraft which were originally covered with low strength or so-called "glider cloth," it is considered more desirable to use Grade A or "intermediate" fabric conforming to AMS 3806 or 3804, as amended, respectively. Certain synthetic and fiberglass fabrics have been developed that are acceptable alternates to AMS 3806 or AMS 3804 fabric, providing the Supplemental Type Certificate (STC) installation instructions furnished with the material are followed. Specification MIL–C–9084, MIL–Y–1140C, and MIL–G–1140 materials in the untreated condition have equivalent strength characteristics to TSO–C15 material specifications.

c. *Reinforcing Tape.* Acceptable reinforcing tape is listed in figure 3.2. Use reinforcing tape of similar quality as the fabric and at least one-half the strength of that conforming to specification MIL–T–5661.

d. *Surface Tape.* Use surface tape (also finishing tape) having approximately the same properties as the fabric used. See figure 3.2.

e. *Lacing Cord.* Use lacing cord having a strength of at least 80 pounds double or 40 pounds single strand. See figure 3.2.

Materials	Specification	Minimum tensile strength new (undoped)	Minimum tearing strength new (undoped)	Minimum tensile strength deteriorated (undoped)	Thread count per inch	Use and remarks
Airplane cloth mercerized cotton (Grade "A").	Society Automotive Engineers AMS 3806 (TSO-C15 references this spec.).	80 pounds per inch warp and fill.	5 pounds warp and fill.	56 pounds per inch.	80 minimum, 84 maximum warp and fill.	For use on all aircraft. Required on aircraft with wing loadings greater than 9 p.s.f. Required on aircraft with placarded never-exceed speed greater than 160 m.p.h.
' '	MIL-C-5646	''	''	''	''	Alternate to AMS 3806.
Airplane cloth cellulose nitrate predoped.	MIL-C-5643	''	''	''	''	Alternate to MIL-C-5646 or AMS 3806 (undoped). Finish with cellulose nitrate dope.
Airplane cloth cellulose acetate butyrate, predoped.	MIL-C-5642	''	''	''	''	Alternate to MIL-C-5646 or AMS 3806 (undoped). Finish with cellulose acetate butyrate dope.
Airplane cloth mercerized cotton.	Society Automotive Engineers AMS 3804 (TSO-C14 references this spec.).	65 pounds per inch warp and fill.	4 pounds warp and fill.	46 pounds per inch.	80 minimum, 94 maximum warp and fill.	For use on aircraft with wing loadings of 9 p.s.f. or less, provided never-exceed speed is 160 m.p.h. or less.
Airplane cloth mercerized cotton.	Society Automotive Engineers AMS 3802.	50 pounds per inch warp and fill.	3 pounds warp and fill.	35 pounds per inch.	110 maximum warp and fill.	For use on gliders with wing loading of 8 p.s.f. or less, provided the placarded never-exceed speed is 135 m.p.h. or less.
Glider fabric cotton.	A. A. F. No. 16128. AMS 3802.	55 pounds per inch warp and fill.	4 pounds warp and fill.	39 pounds per inch.	80 minimum warp and fill.	Alternate to AMS 3802-A.
Aircraft linen___	British 7F1					This material meets the minimum strength requirements of TSO-C15.

FIGURE 3.1.—Textile fabric used in aircraft covering.

f. *Machine Thread.* Use machine thread having a strength of at least 5 pounds single strand (figure 3.2).

g. *Hand-Sewing Thread.* Use hand-sewing thread having a strength of at least 14 pounds single strand (figure 3.2).

128. COVERING PRACTICES. The method of fabric attachment should be identical, as far as strength and reliability are concerned, to the method used by the manufacturer of the airplane to be re-covered or repaired. Fabric may be applied so that either the warp or fill-threads are parallel to the line of flight. Either the envelope method or blanket method of covering is acceptable.

a. *Flutter Precautions.* When re-covering or repairing control surfaces, especially on high performance airplanes, make sure that dynamic and static balances are not adversely affected. Weight distribution and mass balance must be considered to preclude the possibility of induced flutter.

129. PREPARATION OF THE STRUCTURE FOR COVERING. One of the most important items in covering aircraft is proper preparation of the structure. Dopeproofing, covering edges which are likely to wear the fabric, preparation of plywood surfaces, and similar operations, if properly done, will do much toward insuring an attractive and long-lasting job.

a. *Dopeproofing.* Treat all parts of the structure which come in contact with doped fabric with a protective coating such as aluminum foil, dopeproof paint or cellulose tape. Clad aluminum and stainless steel parts need not be dopeproofed.

b. *Chafe Points.* Cover all points of the structure, such as sharp edges, boltheads, etc., which are likely to chafe or wear the covering with doped-on fabric strips or cover with an adhesive tape. After the cover has been installed, reinforce the chafe points of the fabric by doping on fabric patches. Where a stronger reinforcement is required, apply a cotton duck or leather patch sewed to a fabric patch and then dope in place. Reinforce all portions of

the fabric pierced by wires, bolts, or other projections.

c. *Inter-Rib Bracing.* Conventional wing ribs, which do not have permanent inter-rib bracing should be bound in position by means of cotton tape running parallel to the beams. Apply the tape diagonally between the top and bottom capstrips of each successive rib approximately halfway between the front and rear beams. Apply the tape continuously from the butt rib to the tip rib with one turn of tape around each intermediate rib capstrip.

d. *Preparation of Plywood Surfaces for Covering.* Prior to covering plywood surfaces with fabric, prepare the surface by cleaning and applying sealer and dope.

(1) Cleaning. Sand all surface areas which have been smeared with glue in order to expose a clean wood surface. Remove loose deposits such as woodchips and sawdust. Remove oil or grease spots by carefully washing with naphtha.

(2) Application of Sealer and Dope. Apply one brush coat or two dip coats (wiped) of a dopeproof sealer such as that conforming to Specification MIL–V–6894 thinned to 30 percent nonvolatile content and allow to dry 2 to 4 hours. Finally, before covering, apply two brush coats of clear dope allowing the first coat of dope to dry approximately 45 minutes before applying the second coat.

130. FABRIC SEAMS. Seams parallel to the line of flight are preferable; however, spanwise seams are acceptable.

a. *Sewed Seams.*

(1) Machine-sewn seams (parts D, E, and F of figure 3.3) should be of the folded fell or French fell types. Where selvage edges or pinked edges are joined, a plain lap seam is satisfactory.

(2) Begin hand sewing or tacking at the point where machine sewing or uncut fabric is again reached. Lock hand sewing at intervals of 6 inches, and finish the seam with a lock stitch and a knot (figure 3.4). At the point where the hand sewing or permanent tacking is necessary, cut the fabric so that it can be

Materials	Specification	Yarn size	Minimum tensile strength	Yards per pound	Use and remarks
Reinforcing tape, cotton.	MIL-T-5661		150 pounds per one-half-inch width.		Used as reinforcing tape on fabric and under rib lacing cord. Strength of other widths approx. in proportion.
Lacing cord, pre-waxed braided cotton.	MIL-C-5649		80 pounds double.	310 minimum.	Lacing fabric to structures. Unless already waxed, must be lightly waxed before using.
Lacing cord, special cotton.	U.S. Army No. 6-27.	20/3/3/3	85 pounds double.		"
Lacing cord, braided cotton.	MIL-C-5648		80 pounds single.	170 minimum.	"
Lacing cord thread; linen and linen-hemp.	MIL-T-6779	9 ply 11 ply	59 pounds single. 70 pounds single.	620 minimum. 510 minimum.	"
Lacing cord thread; high-tenacity cotton.	MIL-T-5660	Ticket No. 10.	62 pounds single.	450 minimum.	"
Machine thread cotton.	Federal V-T-276b.	20/4 ply	5 pounds single.	5,000 normal.	Use for all machine sewing.
Hand sewing thread cotton.	V-T-276b. Type III B.	8/4 ply	14 pounds single.	1,650 normal.	Use for all hand sewing. Use fully waxed thread.
Surface tape cotton (made from AN-C-121).	MIL-T-5083		80 lbs/in.		Use over seams, leading edges, trailing edges, outer edges and ribs, pinked, scalloped or straight edges.
Surface tape cotton.	Same as fabric used.		Same as fabric used.		Alternate to MIL-T-5083.

FIGURE 3.2.—Miscellaneous textile materials.

doubled under before sewing or permanent tacking is performed (figure 3.3 (C)). After hand sewing has been completed, remove the temporary tacks. In hand sewing, use a minimum of four stitches per inch.

(3) Cover a sewed spanwise seam on a metal- or wood-covered leading edge with pinked-edge surface tape at least 4 inches wide.

(4) Cover a sewed spanwise seam at the trailing edge with pinked-edge surface tape at least 3 inches wide. For aircraft with never-exceed speeds in excess of 200 m.p.h., cut notches at least 1 inch in depth and 1 inch in width in both edges of the surface tape when used to cover spanwise seams on trailing edges, especially the trailing edges of control surfaces. Space notches at intervals not exceeding 18 inches. On tape less than 3 inches wide, the

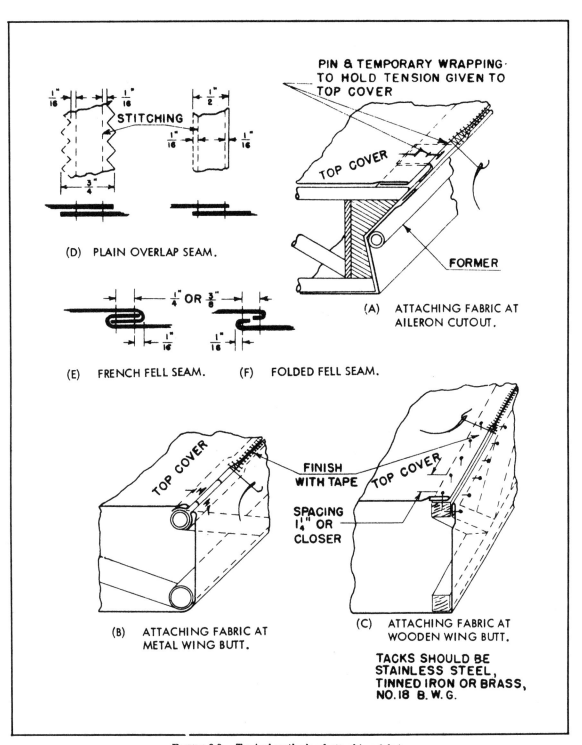

(D) PLAIN OVERLAP SEAM.

(E) FRENCH FELL SEAM. **(F) FOLDED FELL SEAM.**

(A) ATTACHING FABRIC AT AILERON CUTOUT.

(B) ATTACHING FABRIC AT METAL WING BUTT.

(C) ATTACHING FABRIC AT WOODEN WING BUTT.

TACKS SHOULD BE STAINLESS STEEL, TINNED IRON OR BRASS, NO. 18 B. W. G.

FIGURE 3.3.—Typical methods of attaching fabric.

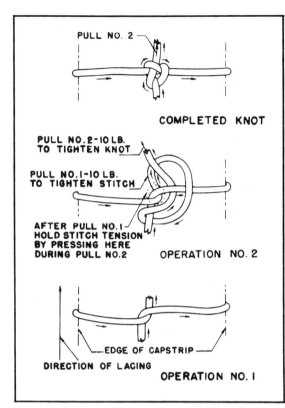

PULL NO. 2

COMPLETED KNOT

PULL NO. 2-10 LB.
TO TIGHTEN KNOT

PULL NO.1-10 LB.
TO TIGHTEN STITCH

AFTER PULL NO.1
HOLD STITCH TENSION
BY PRESSING HERE
DURING PULL NO.2   OPERATION NO. 2

EDGE OF CAPSTRIP

DIRECTION OF LACING

OPERATION NO. 1

FIGURE 3.4.—Standard knot for rib lacing
and terminating a sewed seam (modified seine knot).

notches should be 1/3 the tape width. In the event that the surface tape begins to separate because of poor adhesion or other causes, the tape will tear at a notched section, thus preventing progressive loosening of the entire length of the tape which could seriously affect the controlling of the aircraft.

(5) Cover a double-stitched lap joint with pinked-edge surface tape at least 4 inches wide.

(6) Make sewed spanwise seams on the upper or lower surface in a manner that the amount of protuberance is minimum. Cover the seam with pinked-edge tape at least 3 inches wide.

(7) Sewed seams parallel to the line of flight (chordwise) may be located over ribs; however, place the seam on the rib so that the lacing will not penetrate through the seam.

b. Doped Seams.

(1) For a lapped and doped spanwise seam on a metal- or wood-covered leading edge, lap the fabric at least 4 inches and cover with pinked-edge surface tape at least 4 inches wide.

(2) For a lapped and doped spanwise seam at the trailing edge, lap the fabric at least 4 inches and cover with pinked-edge surface tape at least 3 inches wide.

131. COVERING METHODS.

a. The Envelope Method. The envelope method of covering is accomplished by sewing together widths of fabric cut to specified dimensions and machine sewn to form an envelope which can be drawn over the frame. The trailing and outer edges of the covering should be machine sewn unless the component is not favorably shaped for sewing, in which case, the fabric should be joined by hand sewing.

b. The Blanket Method. The blanket method of covering is accomplished by sewing together widths of fabric of sufficient lengths to form a blanket over the surfaces of the frame. Join the trailing and outer edges of the covering by a plain overthrow or baseball stitch. For airplanes with placard never-exceed speed of 150 miles per hour or less, the blanket may be lapped at least 1 inch and doped to the frame or the blanket, lapped at least 4 inches at the nose of metal- or wood-covered leading edges, doped, and finished with pinked-edge surface tape at least 4 inches wide. When fabricating both the envelope and blanket coverings, cut the fabric in lengths sufficient to pass completely around the frame, starting at the trailing edge and returning to the trailing edge.

132. REINFORCING TAPE. Place reinforcing tape of at least the width of the capstrips under all lacing. In the case of wings with plywood or metal leading edge covering, the reinforcing tape need be brought only to the front spar on the upper and lower surfaces.

a. Use of Antitear Strips. On aircraft with never-exceed speed in excess of 250 miles per hour, antitear strips are recommended under the reinforcing tape on the upper surface of wings, and the bottom surface of that part of the wing in the slipstream. Where the antitear strip is used on both the top and bottom surfaces, pass it continuously up to and around the leading edges and back to the trailing edge. Where the strip is used only on the top surface, carry it up to and around the leading edge and back on the lower surface as far aft as the front beam. For this purpose the slipstream should be considered as being equal to the propeller diameter plus one extra rib space on each side.

Cut antitear strips from the same material as used for covering and wide enough to extend beyond the reinforcing tape on each side so as to engage the lacing cord. Attach the strips by applying dope to that part of the fabric to be covered by the strip, and apply dope freely over the strip.

133. LACING.

a. Securely fasten both surfaces of fabric covering on wings and control surfaces to the ribs by lacing cord or any other method originally approved for the aircraft. Care should be taken to insure that all sharp edges against which the lacing cord may bear are protected by tape in order to prevent abrasion of the cord. Join separate lengths of lacing cord by the splice knot shown in figure 3.5. Do not use the common square knot for this purpose. Exercise the utmost care to assure uniform tension and security of all stitches. For the first or starting stitch use a double loop as illustrated in figure 3.6. Make all subsequent stitches using a single loop tied off with the standard knot for rib lacing (modified seine type shown in figure 3.4). The spacing between the starting stitch and the next stitch should be one-half the normal stitch spacing. Final location of the knot depends upon the original location selected by the manufacturer. If such information is not available, consider positioning the knot where it will have the least effect on the aerodynamics of the airfoil. The seine knot admits a possibility of improper tightening, resulting in a false (slip) form with greatly reduced efficiency and must not be used

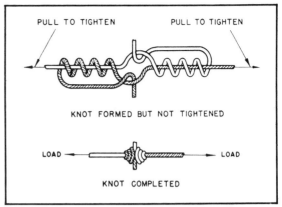

FIGURE 3.5.—Splice knot.

for stitch tie-offs. Lock the tie-off knot for the last stitch by an additional half-hitch. Where stitching ends, as at the rear beam and at the trailing edge, space the last two stitches at one-half normal spacing. Under no circumstances pull tie-off knots back through the lacing holes.

b. *The double-loop lacing* illustrated in figure 3.7 represents a method for obtaining higher strengths than possible with the standard single lacing. When using the double-loop lacing, use the tie-off knot shown in figure 3.8.

c. *Fuselage Lacing.* Fabric lacing is also necessary in the case of deep fuselages, and on fuselages where former strips and ribs shape the fabric to a curvature. In the latter case, lace the fabric at intervals to the formers. Attachment of the fabric to fuselages must be so accomplished as to be at least the equivalent in strength and reliability to that used by the manufacturer of the airplane.

134. STITCH SPACING.

The stitch spacing should not exceed the spacing approved on the original aircraft. In case the spacing cannot be ascertained due to destruction of the covering, acceptable rib-stitch spacing is specified in figure 3.9. Place the lacing holes as near to the capstrip as possible in order to minimize the tendency of the cord to tear the fabric. Lightly wax all lacing cords with beeswax for protection. In case waxed-braided cord is used, this procedure is unnecessary. (See figure 3.2 for acceptable lacing cords.)

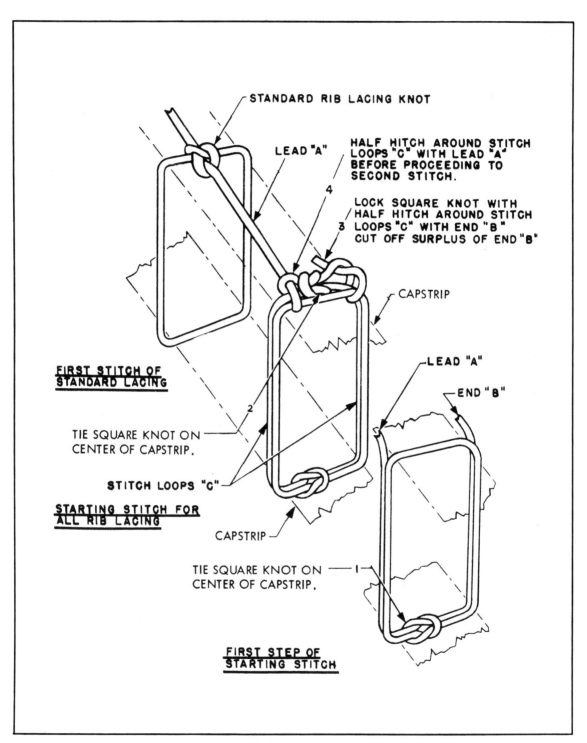

STANDARD RIB LACING KNOT

LEAD "A"

HALF HITCH AROUND STITCH LOOPS "C" WITH LEAD "A" BEFORE PROCEEDING TO SECOND STITCH.

LOCK SQUARE KNOT WITH HALF HITCH AROUND STITCH LOOPS "C" WITH END "B" CUT OFF SURPLUS OF END "B"

CAPSTRIP

FIRST STITCH OF STANDARD LACING

LEAD "A"

END "B"

TIE SQUARE KNOT ON CENTER OF CAPSTRIP.

STITCH LOOPS "C"

STARTING STITCH FOR ALL RIB LACING

CAPSTRIP

TIE SQUARE KNOT ON CENTER OF CAPSTRIP.

FIRST STEP OF STARTING STITCH

FIGURE 3.6.—Starting stitch for rib stitching.

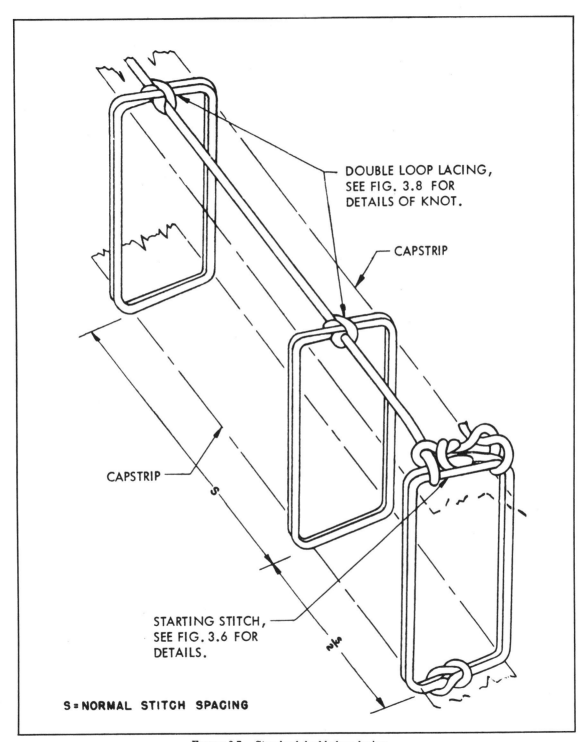

DOUBLE LOOP LACING,
SEE FIG. 3.8 FOR
DETAILS OF KNOT.

CAPSTRIP

CAPSTRIP

STARTING STITCH,
SEE FIG. 3.6 FOR
DETAILS.

S = NORMAL STITCH SPACING

FIGURE 3.7.—Standard double loop lacing.

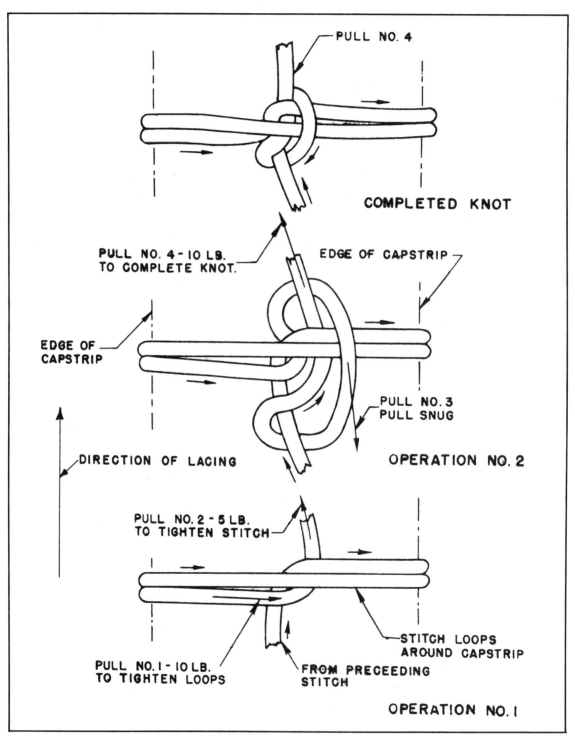

PULL NO. 4

COMPLETED KNOT

PULL NO. 4 - 10 LB.
TO COMPLETE KNOT.

EDGE OF CAPSTRIP

EDGE OF
CAPSTRIP

PULL NO. 3
PULL SNUG

DIRECTION OF LACING

OPERATION NO. 2

PULL NO. 2 - 5 LB.
TO TIGHTEN STITCH

STITCH LOOPS
AROUND CAPSTRIP

PULL NO. 1 - 10 LB.
TO TIGHTEN LOOPS

FROM PRECEEDING
STITCH

OPERATION NO. 1

FIGURE 3.8.—Standard knot for double loop lacing.

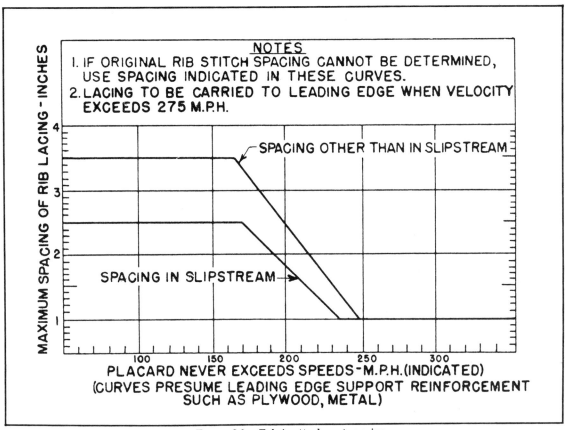

Inside the figure:

NOTES
1. IF ORIGINAL RIB STITCH SPACING CANNOT BE DETERMINED, USE SPACING INDICATED IN THESE CURVES.
2. LACING TO BE CARRIED TO LEADING EDGE WHEN VELOCITY EXCEEDS 275 M.P.H.

MAXIMUM SPACING OF RIB LACING - INCHES

SPACING OTHER THAN IN SLIPSTREAM

SPACING IN SLIPSTREAM →

PLACARD NEVER EXCEEDS SPEEDS - M.P.H. (INDICATED)
(CURVES PRESUME LEADING EDGE SUPPORT REINFORCEMENT SUCH AS PLYWOOD, METAL)

FIGURE 3.9.—Fabric attachment spacing.

135. SURFACE TAPE (FINISHING TAPE). Cover all lacing with tape of at least the quality and width used on the original airplane. This tape should not be applied until the first coat of dope has dried. Replace all inspection openings in the covering, and reinforce the fabric around them and along leading edges with tape. Wear or friction, induced by moving parts or fittings, can be repaired by sewing a leather patch on a fabric patch and doping in place. Pinked surface tape is sometimes applied over the trailing edges of control surfaces and airfoils. For sure application, the tape must be at least 3 inches in width, and if the aircraft never-exceed speed is greater than 200 miles per hour, notch the tape at intervals not exceeding 18 inches. If separation of the tape from the trailing edge begins, it will tear at a notched section and thereby prevent loosening of the entire strip which could seriously affect the controllability of the aircraft.

136. SPECIAL FASTENERS. When repairs are made to fabric surfaces attached by special mechanical methods, duplicate the original type of fastener. When self-tapping screws are used for the attachment of fabric to the rib structure, observe the following procedure:

a. Redrill the holes where necessary due to wear, distortion, etc., and in such cases, use a screw one size larger as a replacement.

b. Extend the length of the screw beyond the rib capstrip at least two threads of the grip (threaded part).

c. Install a thin washer, preferably celluloid, under the heads of screws and dope pinked-edge tape over each screw head.

137.-147. RESERVED.

Section 2. DOPING

148. APPLICATION OF AIRCRAFT DOPE, EPOXY, AND RESINS. Determine that dope and fabric materials are compatible by consulting the product manufacturer's instructions before applying finish to aircraft surfaces. Compatibility of products may also be determined by wetting samples of the fabric with the impregnating materials and thorough examination of the material after it has dried. The following military specifications, or later revisions thereof, apply to aircraft dope, epoxy, and polyester resins:

MIL–D–5549A–1 .. Clear dope, cellulose-acetate butyrate.

MIL–D–7850 ...... Fungicidal dope, first coat, cellulose-acetate, butyrate.

MIL–D–5550A–1 ... Pigmented dope, cellulose-acetate, butyrate.

MIL–D–5551A–2 ... Pigmented dope, gloss, cellulose-acetate butyrate.

MIL–D–5553A–2 ... Clear dope, nitrate.

MIL–D–5552A–1 ... Clear dope, gloss, cellulose nitrate.

MIL–D–5554A–1 ... Gloss dope, cellulose nitrate.

MIL–D–5555–1 .... Pigmented dope, cellulose nitrate.

MIL–R–9300A ..... Resin, epoxy, low pressure laminating.

MIL–R–25042A .... Resin, polyester, low pressure laminating.

MIL–R–7575B ..... Resin, polyester, low pressure laminating.

a. Thinning. Finishing materials are generally supplied at a consistency ready for brush application. For spraying operations, practically all aircraft dope, epoxy, or resin requires thinning. Thinning instructions are usually listed on the container label. Avoid use of thinning agents other than those specified by the product manufacturer. To do so may result in adverse chemical action. The amount of thinner to be used will depend on the material, atmospheric conditions, spraying equipment, the spraying technique of the operator, and the type of thinning agent employed. Thinning influences the drying time and the tautening properties of the finish, and it is necessary that it be done properly. Since local atmospheric conditions affect the doping process, determine the amount of thinner necessary at the time the finishing material is to be applied by first using it on experimental panels.

149. BLUSHING AND USE OF BLUSH-RETARDING THINNER. Blushing of dopes is very common when doping is accomplished under humid conditions. The condition is caused by the rapid evaporation of thinners and solvents, which lowers the temperature on the surface, causing condensation of moisture and producing the white appearance known as "blush." Blushing tendencies are also increased, if strong currents of air flow over the surface when applying dope or immediately thereafter.

A blushed finish has very little protective or tautening value. When the relative humidity is such that only a small amount of blushing is encountered, the condition may be eliminated by thinning the dope with a blush-retarding thinner and slightly increasing the room temperature. If it is not possible to correct humidity conditions in the dope room, suspend doping operations until more favorable atmospheric conditions prevail. The use of large amounts of blush-retarding thinner is not advisable because of the undesirable drying properties accompanying the use of this material.

150. NUMBER OF COATS. Apply as many coats of dope as are necessary to result in a taut and well-filled finish job. A guide for finishing fabric-covered aircraft follows:

a. Two coats of clear dope, brushed on and sanded after the second coat.

b. One coat of clear dope, either brushed or sprayed, and sanded.

c. Two coats of aluminum pigmented dope, sanded after each coat.

d. Three coats of pigmented dope (the color desired), sanded and rubbed to give a smooth glossy finish when completed.

e. Care should be taken not to sand heavily over the center portion of pinked tape and over spars in order not to damage the rib-stitching cord and fabric.

151. TECHNIQUE. Use a brush to spread the first two coats of dope uniformly on the surface. Work the dope into the fabric thoroughly, exercising care not to form an excessive film on the reverse side. The first coat should produce a thorough and uniform wetting of the fabric. To do so, work the dope with the warp and the filler threads for three or four brush strokes and stroke away any excess material to avoid piling up or dripping. Apply succeeding brush or spray coats with only sufficient brushing to spread the dope smoothly and evenly.

When doping fabric over plywood or metal-covered leading edges, make sure that an adequate bond is obtained between the fabric and the leading edge. Also, when using pre-doped fabric, use a thinned dope in order to obtain a good bond between the fabric and the leading edge.

a. Surface Tape and Reinforcement Patches. Apply surface tape and reinforcement patches with the second coat of dope. Apply surface tape over all rib lacing and over all sewed seams as well as at all other points of the structure where tape reinforcements are indicated.

b. Installation of Drain Grommets. With the second coat of dope, install drain grommets on the underside of airfoils, at the center of the underside in each fuselage bay, located so that the best possible drainage is effected. On seaplanes, installation of special shielded or marine grommets is recommended to prevent the entry of spray. Also, use this type of grommet on landplanes in that part of the structure which is subject to splash from the landing gear when operating from wet and muddy fields. Dope plastic-type grommets directly to the covering. When brass grommets are used, mount them on fabric patches and then dope them to the covering. After the dope scheme is completed, open the drainholes by cutting out the fabric with a small-bladed knife. Do not open drain-grommets by punching.

c. Use of Fungicidal Dope. Fungicidal dope is normally used as the first coat for fabrics to prevent rotting. While it may be more advisable to purchase dope in which the fungicide has already been incorporated, it is feasible to mix the fungicide with the dope.

Specification MIL–D–7850 specifies that the requirements for cellulose acetate butyrate dope incorporate a fungicide for first coat use on aircraft. The fungicide specified in this specification is zinc dimethyldithiocarbonate which forms a suspension with the dope. This material is a fine powder, and if it is mixed with the dope, it should be made into a paste using dope and then diluted to the proper consistency according to the manufacturer's instructions. It is not practicable to mix the powder with a large quantity of dope.

Copper napthonate is also used as a fungicide and forms a solution with dope. However, this substance has a tendency to "bleed out," especially on light-colored fabric. It is considered satisfactory from a fungicidal standpoint.

Apply the first coat of fungicidal dope extremely thin so that the dope can thoroughly saturate both sides of the fabric. Once the fabric is thoroughly saturated, subsequent coats can be applied at any satisfactory working consistency.

152. REJUVENATION OF FABRIC. Before using fabric rejuvenator products to improve the appearance or condition of doped surfaces, care should be exercised to establish that the fabric strength has not deteriorated beyond safe limits. Experience has indicated that rejuvenation may at times cause fabric-sag rather than tautening. When the surface to be rejuvenated has been thoroughly cleaned and the rejuvenator applied according to the manufacturer's directions, the old dope should soften through to the fabric. Cracks may then be sealed and the surface allowed to set. Finishing coats of clear and pigmented dopes can then be applied in the normal manner.

153. COMMON DOPE TROUBLES.

a. In cold weather, dopes become quite viscous. Cold dopes pull and rope under the brush, and if thinned sufficiently to spray, lack body when dry. Prior to use, allow dopes to come to a temperature approximately that of the dope room, 24° C. (75° F.).

b. Orange peel and pebble effect result from insufficiently thinned dope or when the spray gun is held too far from the surface being sprayed.

c. Runs, sags, laps, streaks, high and low spots are caused by improperly adjusted spraying equipment or improper spraying technique.

d. Blisters may be caused by water or oil entering the spray gun. Drain air compressors, air regulators, and air lines daily.

e. Pinholes may be caused by not allowing sufficient time for drying between coats or after water sanding, or they may be due to insufficiently reduced dope.

f. Wet areas on a doped surface indicate that oil, grease, soap, etc., had not been properly removed before doping.

154.–164. RESERVED.

Section 3. REPAIRS TO FABRIC COVERING

165. GENERAL. Make repairs to fabric-covered surfaces in a manner that will return the original strength and tautness to the fabric. Sewed repairs and unsewed (doped-on patches or panels) may be made. Do not dope fabric or tape onto a surface which contains aluminum or other color coats. Whenever it is necessary to add fabric reinforcement, remove the old dope either by softening and scraping or by sanding down to the point where the base coat or clear coat is exposed. Use clear dope in doping the fabric to the surface. After reinforcement is made, normal finishing procedures may be followed.

166. REPAIR OF TEARS IN FABRIC. Repair tears as shown in figure 3.10 by sewing the torn edges together using a baseball stitch and doping a piece of pinked-edge fabric over the tear. If the tear is a straight rip, the sewing is started at one end so that, as the seam is made, the edges will be drawn tightly together throughout its entire length. If the openings are cut in wings to inspect the internal structure, start the sewing at the corner or point so that the edges of the cover will be held in place while the seams are being made. The sewing is done with a curved needle and well-waxed thread. Clean the surface to be covered by the patch by rubbing the surface with a rag dipped in dope, wiping dry with a clean rag, or by scraping the surface with a putty knife after it has been softened with fresh dope. Dope solvent or acetone may be used for the same purpose, but care should be taken that it does not drop through on the inside of the opposite surface, causing the dope to blister. Cut a patch of sufficient size from airplane cloth to cover the tear and extend at least 1 1/2 inches beyond the tear in all directions. The edges of the patch should either be pinked similar to surface tape or frayed out about 1/4 inch on all edges.

167. SEWED PATCH REPAIR. When the damage is such that it will not permit sewing the edges together, a sewed-in repair patch may be used if the damage is not longer than 16 inches in any one direction (see figure 3.10). Cut out the damaged section, making a round or oval-shaped opening trimmed to a smooth contour. Clean the area of the old fabric to be doped as indicated in paragraph 166. Turn the edges of the patch 1/2 inch and sew to the edges of the opening. Before sewing, fasten the patch at several points with a few temporary stitches to facilitate sewing the seams. After the sewing is completed, clean the area of the old fabric to be doped as indicated for small repairs and then dope the patch in the regular manner. Apply surface tape over the seam with the second coat of dope. If the opening extends over or closer than 1 inch to a rib or other laced member, extend the patch 3 inches beyond the member. After sewing has been completed, rib lace the patch to the rib over a new section of reinforcing tape, using the method explained in paragraph 133. Do not remove the old rib lacing and reinforcing tape.

168. UNSEWED (DOPED-ON) REPAIRS. Unsewed (doped-on) repairs may be made on all aircraft

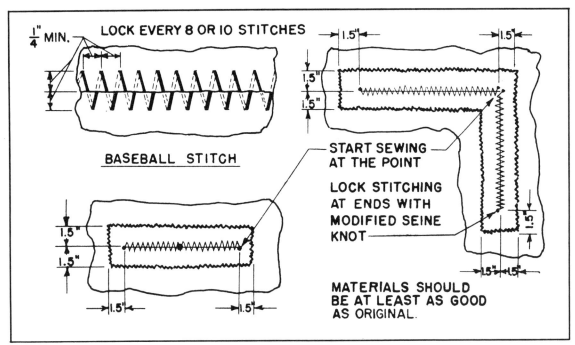

LOCK EVERY 8 OR 10 STITCHES

1/4" MIN.

BASEBALL STITCH

START SEWING AT THE POINT

LOCK STITCHING AT ENDS WITH MODIFIED SEINE KNOT

MATERIALS SHOULD BE AT LEAST AS GOOD AS ORIGINAL.

FIGURE 3.10.—Repair of tears in fabric.

fabric-covered surfaces provided the never-exceed speed is not greater than 150 miles per hour. A doped patch repair may be used if the damage does not exceed 16 inches in any direction. Cut out the damaged section making a round or oval shaped opening, trimmed to a smooth contour. Clean the edges of the opening which are to be covered by the patch with a grease solvent. Sand or wash off the dope from the area around the patch with dope thinner. Support the fabric from underneath while sanding.

For holes up to 8 inches in size, make the fabric patch of sufficient size to provide a lap of at least 2 inches around the hole. On holes over 8 inches in size, make the overlap of the fabric around the hole at least 1/4 the hole diameter with a maximum limit of lap of 4 inches. If the hole extends over a rib or closer than the required overlap to a rib or other laced member, extend the patch at least 3 inches beyond the rib. In this case, after the edges of the patch have been doped in place and the dope has dried, lace the patch to the rib over a new section of reinforcing tape in the usual manner. Do not remove the old rib lacing and reinforcing tape. All patches should have pinked edges or, if smooth, should be finished with pinked-edge surface tape.

169. REPAIR BY A DOPED-IN PANEL. When the damage exceeds 16 inches in any direction, make the repair by doping in a new panel. This type of repair may be extended to cover both the upper and lower surfaces and to cover several rib bays if necessary. Lace the panel to all the ribs covered, and dope or sew as in the blanket method.

a. Remove the surface tape from the ribs adjacent to the damaged area and from the trailing and leading edges of the section being repaired. Leave the old reinforcing tape and lacing in place. Next, cut the fabric along a line approximately 1 inch from the ribs on the sides nearest the injury and continue the cuts to completely remove the damaged section. Do not remove the old fabric from the leading and trailing edges, unless both upper and lower surfaces are being re-covered.

105

b. Cut a patch to run around the trailing edge 1 inch and to extend from the trailing edge up to and around the leading edge and back approximately to the front beam. Extend the patch approximately 3 inches beyond the ribs adjacent to the damage.

As an alternative attachment on metal- or wood-covered leading edges, the patch may be lapped over the old fabric at least 4 inches at the nose of the leading edge, doped, and finished with at least 4 inches of pinked-edge surface tape.

c. Clean the area of the old fabric that is to be covered by the patch and apply a generous coat of dope to this area. Put the new panel in place, pull as taut as possible, and apply a coat of dope to that portion of the panel which overlaps the old fabric. After this coat has dried, apply a second coat of dope to the overlapped area and let dry.

d. Place reinforcing tape over the ribs under moderate tension and lace down in the approved manner.

e. Give the panel a coat of clear dope and allow to dry. Install surface tape with the second coat of dope over the reinforcing tape and over the edges of the panel. Finish the dope scheme, using the regular doping procedure.

170.–180. RESERVED.

Section 4. FABRIC TESTING

181. TESTING OF FABRIC COVERING. Field test instruments that are commonly used to test the tensile strength of aircraft fabric covering give only approximate indications of the fabric condition. Since the accuracy of field test instruments is affected by climatic and environmental conditions, a laboratory test is recommended when aircraft fabric covering is found to be marginal by field test methods. Laboratory test procedures are set forth in Federal Specification CCC–T–191B, methods 5122, 5132, 5134, or 5136; American Society of Testing Materials (ASTM) Method D39–61 or D39–49, and others. In all cases, test fabric specimens in the undoped condition. Use acetone, dope thinner, or other appropriate thinning agents for the removal of finishing materials.

a. Strength Criteria for Aircraft Fabric.

(1) Present minimum strength values for new aircraft fabric covering are contained in figure 3.1.

(2) The maximum permissible deterioration for used aircraft fabric based on a large number of tests in 30 percent. Fabric which has less than 70 percent of the original required tensile strength would not be considered airworthy. Figure 3.1 contains the minimum tensile strength values for deteriorated fabric as tested in the undoped condition.

(3) Grade A fabric may be used where only intermediate fabric is required. When testing for deteriorated condition, 46 pounds (70 percent of original requirements for intermediate fabric) is considered airworthy.

(4) Failures may occur in fiberglass covering where rib stitching has worn through the reinforcing tape and covering material without being detected through visual inspection. Such failures can be located by using a suitable suction cup and lifting the fabric in the rib stitched area. If the fabric pulls away from the ribs, new stitching will need to be applied using additional reinforcing tape and doubling the number of stitches throughout the affected area. Five particular attention to the areas within the propeller slipstream area.

182.–192. RESERVED.

Comment: There are two types of cloth used for the covering of airframes, organic and synthetic. The organic may be cotton or linen; the synthetics are Dacron and fiberglass. Whatever is used must be FAA-approved and must meet or exceed the standards listed in 43.13, figure 3.1

Figure 3.11.—The blanket of attaching fabric to an airframe allows the fuselage to be covered with four pieces of cloth — Top, bottom, and two sides —cemented to the main longerons. (courtesy Razorback)

You will note that the synthetics are not mentioned in figure 3.1, probably because the synthetics greatly exceed these standards, and because the FAA avoids mention of brand names, listing instead Military Specifications or Aeronautical Material Specifications. Commercial products that meet or exceed such specs are usually so labeled. However, item 127, paragraph 6, in the foregoing Section of 43.13 makes provision for the synthetics and specifically states that only the synthetic aircraft cloths possessing a Supplemental Type Certificate (STC) are acceptable. There are four of them: Ceconite, Stits Poly-Fiber, Eonnex, and Razorback Fiberglass.

We should note that "Dacron-type" cloth with no brand name is available from aircraft supply houses at about half the price of STC Dacrons. It is legal only on aircraft licensed in the experimental and restricted categories, and the only measure of its quality (tensile strength, threads per sq/inch in each direction, etc.) is the seller's claims for it.

In recent years, aircraft-grade cotton fabric has become significantly more expensive than STC Dacron; and the price of Irish linen for aircraft covering places it beyond practical consideration. A steadily declining demand for the organic airplane cloths has probably contributed to this rather unreal situation—unreal because Dacron will last at least twice as long as cotton or linen on an airframe.

The older aircraft mechanics, experienced in covering airplanes with cotton or linen and finishing them with nitrate and butyrate dopes, were slow to accept the Dacron systems, partly because the old hands could turn out such beautiful finishes on the organic materials, and also because some time was required to discover the proper finishing materials for Dacron. The almost universally used butyrate dope did not adhere well to it. Even today one cannot get the glassy-smooth finish on Dacron that is possible on cotton or linen.

Nevertheless, the greater strength of Dacron and its much longer life—15 to 20 years when properly finished and reasonably cared for—along with owner preference for the synthetics, have all but eliminated the organic coverings. All commercially produced fabric-covered planes are leaving the factories wearing Dacron, except for the Maule which has a fiberglass cover on its fuselage (metal wings). The last U.S. production airplane to be covered with cotton was the Great Lakes sport biplane built in Enid, OK, during the late '70s.

The secret of a successful Dacron cover on an airframe is good adhesion of the protective finish. Ceconite achieves this by employing old-fashioned nitrate dope as a primer and base for the butyrate dope that follows. Stits has developed resin compounds specifically for use on Dacron, and the pre-coated Eonnex cloth is finished with water-based emulsion paints. Ceconite's system is the most popular; Stits' is probably the best, and Eonnex's the fastest, lowest in cost, and a weight-saver.

Razorback's fiberglass is a flight into different weather. The cloth itself does, literally, last a lifetime. It will not burn and it does not deteriorate. The FAA requires no strength test of Razorback, not ever. It is pre-treated with a butyrate formula to aid adhesion of its finish materials, which must be cellulose acetate butyrate dopes *only*. Since fiberglass cloth filaments do not shrink, the only tautening takes place when the butyrate dope pulls the weave together with about the fourth or fifth coating. There is seldom if ever any problem with the cloth itself, only with its finish, or perhaps installations that are either too loose or too snug.

The final finish coats on Razorback are "nontautening" butyrate that contains additional amounts of plasticizers (triphenyl phosphate and tricresyl phosphate), but these plasticizers degrade after a few years in the sun and, eventually, that may result in a slight amount of additional fabric tautness. Fabric that is over-taut can distort light airframe components.

Ceconite is available in three weights:

□ Style 101—3.7 oz sq/yd; average strength, 130 lbs per inch width. Thread count, 49 × 58.

□ Style 102—2.8 oz sq/yd; a fine weave with a tensile strength slightly greater than aircraft grade cotton.

□ Style 103—1.7 oz sq/yd; a fine weave for use over plywood.

Stits Poly-Fiber is also sold in three weights:

□ Style D-101A—3.7 oz sq/yd; average strength, 130 lbs per inch width. Thread count, 53 × 53.

□ Style D-103—2.7 oz sq/yd; average strength, 95 lbs per inch width. A fine weave, 15 lbs stronger than aircraft grade cotton.

□ Style D-104—1.7 oz sq/yd; average strength, 60 lbs per inch width. A fine weave for use over plywood surfaces.

Eonnex (now available from Ceconite) is offered as:

□ Style 7605—4 oz sq/yd (pre-coated); average strength, 150 lbs per inch width.

□ Style 7606—weight not announced; average strength, 115 lbs per inch width.

Razorback Fiberglass is marketed in only one weight, 3.92 oz sq/yd (pre-coated), and has a tensile strength of 160 lbs in one direction, 150 lbs per inch width in the other.

All four of the approved synthetics sell for about $5.00 per yard in 66 to 72-inch widths. Approximately 42 yards are needed to cover a Super Cub, T-Craft, or Aeronca Champ. The total cost of all materials for such an airplane will be somewhere between $450 and $600. Shop prices for such a job in the early '80s start at about $4,000.

AIRFRAME PREPARATION

Remove the old fabric carefully and save it for reference. Remember, the airplane was certificated with that cover and Item 128 in the foregoing Chapter 3 of 43.13 specifically states that the "... method of fabric attachment should be identical ... to the method used by the manufacturer." The only legal deviation from the original that is allowed is provided in paragraph "b" of Item 127 which says that the "acceptable alternates" (employing synthetics) are those that are indicated in "installation instructions furnished with the material." This obviously assumes that the material is one of the four synthetic STC covering/finishing systems.

One thing that is permissible that doesn't nec-essarily conform with the original installation is additional drain grommets if you find areas of trapped moisture that have promoted rust or deterioration of wood. If you feel that an additional inspection opening or two should be cut in the new cover to provide periodic visual checks of an area or operating system, mention it to the GADO examiner, who will undoubtedly agree. There's room for common sense in the FARs.

While on the subject of drain grommets, we recommend that regular grommets be replaced with seaplane grommets at points where the landing gear and/or spiraling propeller wash can splash or blow water directly against these openings. The hooded seaplane grommets not only prevent water from being forced inside, but each creates a tiny suction in its wake while the airplane is in flight, which aids in the internal ventilation of the airframe.

Once the old cover is off you can make a detailed inspection of the airframe. Start by thoroughly cleaning the airframe. Stoddard dry cleaning solvent is an effective cleaning agent on dirt and grease; rust on 4130 chrome moly steel tubing may be removed with the aid of aluminum oxide abrasive paper, 300 grit or finer. Use a magnifying glass to inspect all welds and the areas directly adjacent to welds where the tubing tends to be more brittle due to the welding process.

The fuselage tubing is also subject to interior rust. The airplane manufacturers guarded against internal tubing rust by making the welded structure airtight or, more commonly, forced hot linseed oil or paralketone through it. A means of checking for this insidious danger is to drill several small holes in the bottoms of the lower longerons at the low points of the airframe when it is in its normal at-rest attitude. If any water drains from these holes, it is necessary to determine the extent of the damage. That means probing the area with an ice pick, tapping with a hammer, or cutting out limited sections of the tubing. Drilled holes may be sealed with cad-plated self-tapping screws or welded. After treating the interior and resealing, the thoroughly cleaned exterior of the fuselage tubing should be sprayed with a primer that is high in zinc chromate solids. A two-part epoxy such as Stits EP-420 is best.

All steel fittings should be cleaned and carefully inspected for cracks. Rust will destroy flat steel fittings rather quickly once it starts. If the fittings are sound, treat them with a chromic acid etch and then spray with a good two-part epoxy primer.

Aluminum parts are treated in much the same

way. Thoroughly clean, inspect, and apply a phosphoric acid etch, followed by a primer containing a high percentage of zinc chromate solids. Zinc chromate is the best corrosion fighter available. Many primers are offered in the aviation market, but most were originally developed and still used for automotive and industrial applications. The fact that some of these are also marketed bearing "aircraft primer" labels should not mislead you.

The problem with zinc chromate is that it does not bond well to aircraft aluminum alloy. That is why such surfaces are first treated with an acid etch. That is also why the other primers contain little or no zinc chromate.

Do not use steel wool, emery cloth, or steel brushes to clean surface corrosion from aluminum alloy, because tiny particles from these abrasive aids will remain embedded in the aluminum and promote corrosion *beneath* the new primer.

If you are not a licensed AP, consult an experienced aircraft mechanic when in doubt about the serviceability of a component damaged by rust or corrosion. It doesn't take much rust to significantly weaken a steel fitting, and all but light surface corrosion on aluminum alloy should be highly suspect by anyone who is not experienced in assessing such damage.

Examine the control system, looking for rusted or frayed cables, and check the bellcranks for cracks, proper alignment, and security of attachment. Rotate the pulleys to check for flat spots and to determine that they are accurately aligned with the cables. Worn or rusted cables should be replaced even if they contain no broken strands.

Inspect the hydraulic lines and fittings, and check the electrical wiring. Look at the wires' grommets and connectors. Make sure that soldered connections are not corroded and that terminals are not dirty or misaligned. Separate wiring from hydraulic and fuel lines; gasoline and hydraulic oil will deteriorate insulation on electrical wires, and an arcing fault in an electric line can puncture a fuel or hydraulic line and result in fire. Use only plastic electrical tape that carries the Fire Underwriter's Laboratory (UL) approval as flame-resistant.

The primer to be applied to the fuselage tubing prior to re-cover should be brushed or sprayed on the same day that the tubing is cleaned. If Stits epoxy primer is used, no dope-proofing is necessary because this primer will not "lift" in contact with fabric finishing materials. If you are covering the airplane

with cotton, Ceconite, or Eonnex, you may prime the tubing with the recommended primer and then treat all parts of the structure that will come in contact with the doped fabric with dope-proof paint or cellulose tape.

Cover all points of the structure, such as sharp edges, boltheads, etc., that are likely to chafe or wear the covering with fabric strips, either cemented or doped on. After the fabric has been installed, reinforce the chafe points (the old cover will reveal these for you) with fabric patches.

If the wings are metal-framed, they will be cleaned as was the fuselage and checked for corrosion and cracks. Inspect all metal fittings with a magnifying glass. Check the fuel tanks for security of mounting and any sign of leakage. Also inspect the overflow and drain lines for kinks and proper routing to the outside air. The metal-framed wings will be chemically treated and primed if new metal, thoroughly cleaned and given a new coating of primer if being refurbished.

Wooden wings can present problems, especially the plywood-covered wings such as those found on the Bellancas and early Mooneys. They are hard to thoroughly inspect internally, and while it is true that aircraft grade spruce is equal to or superior to metal in many ways, it must be kept free of moisture, including oil, grease, hydraulic fluid, and gasoline. This means good ventilation and drainage, along with a protective coating of varnish or epoxy. If any internal wood deterioration is suspected, the plywood skin will have to come off. In any wing with wood spars that has seen years of service, moisture can be present under metal fittings; wood can shrink leaving loose bolts, and the film of protective varnish may have deteriorated. The only way that you can be absolutely sure that a wood-framed wing is sound is to be able to inspect every inch of it.

Always check both sides of the spars; look for cracks, checks, and compression damage. Check the butt ends of the spars at the fuselage or center section attach points. These spots are especially susceptible to moisture damage. All bolts should be removed for cleaning and inspection under a 10-power magnifying glass. If bolt holes have become elongated, it is best to redrill the hole and install a slightly larger size bolt. Be careful not to crush the wood by over-tightening when replacing the bolts.

Test glued joints by probing with a thin-blade blunt-end knife. While the old casein glue, which deteriorated with age, hasn't been used for years, the modern adhesives can be improperly handled and therefore glued joints should be checked.

If compression members, drag and anti-drag wires are replaced, or if you have merely removed them to check beneath their fittings, it will be necessary to trammel the wing. Mark exact center points at the centerline of each spar where the centerlines of compression members line up. The spars must remain exactly parallel to each other. If any shrinkage of the wood has occurred, it may be necessary to shim one end of one or more of the compression members. Do not over-tighten the drag and anti-drag wires. All that is necessary is to have each bay perfectly square and all the wires as nearly the same tension as possible.

The interior of the wood-framed wing should receive two fresh coats of spar varnish. These are allowed to thoroughly dry before the new cover goes on.

Plywood-covered surfaces should be cleaned, then apply one brush coat of a dope-proof sealer that conforms to Mil Spec V-6894, or Stits Poly-Brush, and allowed to dry. If the cloth covering is to be finished in butyrate dope, then give the plywood surface two clear coats, allowing the first about 45 minutes to dry before applying the second. If the Stits system is being used, the two coats of clear dope are not needed, because the Poly-Brush sealer provides both protection for the wood and a good adhesive base for the Poly-Fiber cloth.

Airframe preparation usually means a lot of work before the new fabric is installed and you may be tempted to cut a corner or two. Remind yourself that, covering and finishing with modern materials, it will be 15 years or more before this airplane is again uncovered for a thorough inspection and refurbishing, so it is prudent and profitable to have the internal structure and the operating systems in top condition and well-protected before installation of the new fabric. This is equally important whether you intend to keep the machine that long or expect to sell or trade in a couple of years. The condition of the fabric and finish—and the bones beneath—make a difference of thousands of dollars when such craft are offered in the used market.

That is also why the synthetics are so desirable. The FARs require that fabric must be replaced when it tests below 56 lbs tensile strength. Aircraft grade cotton, which is produced to meet the FAR requirement that it test 80 lbs per inch width when new, will seldom give more than eight or nine years' service with the best of care, much less if the airplane is not hangared. During that time, the cotton fabric is steadily deteriorating and will test somewhere between 56 and 80 lbs. Meanwhile, eight or nine year-old Dacron—properly finished and cared for—will usually test well above 80 lbs tensile strength per inch width.

Sun is fabric's worst enemy. That is why cotton, linen, and Dacron coverings must receive several undercoats of silver. Stits conducted comparison tests and their results showed that ". . . bare dacron test panels deteriorate in eight months from exposure to the sun in Southern California. Bare cotton and linen deteriorate in three to four months."

ATTACHING THE FABRIC

The mechanics of attaching fabric to an airframe have changed very little over the years. The foregoing standards in 43.13 are practically the same as those contained in the old CAA *Manual 18* which was written before WWII, and those procedures are used today, whatever the type of fabric being installed. Perhaps the most significant advance (besides superior fabrics) has been greatly improved adhesives, such as Stits Poly-Tac which permits the cementing, rather than stitching, of seams. The fabric on either side of such seams will fail before Poly-Tac seams will part. This is a time and labor saver.

Another time (and therefore money) saver is the availability of pre-sewn "envelopes" for most production airplanes. These pieces slip over the airframe components with just one open end to be closed by hand stitching. The envelopes not only save labor and eliminate waste, but cost very little more than uncut cloth. After selecting a fabric system, determine whether or not pre-sewn envelopes (or "slip covers," as they are sometimes called) are offered for the airplane being re-covered.

THE STITS SYSTEM

Stits Poly-Fiber fabric may be attached to the airframe in the identical manner as the original covering, employing the blanket or sewn-sleeve method, if you are working with uncut cloth. Overlapping cement seams may be made directly on the airframe using Poly-Tac cement, or any combination of machine-sewn seams, hand-sewn seams, and cemented seams are permitted.

All cemented seams are to be located only over supporting airframe structures conforming to the final contour of the taut fabric cover. Cement seams are to be made by cementing the full seam width directly on the airframe (not a flat surface, then transferred to the airframe). No cement seams are to be located in open bay areas except when making repairs to previously finished surfaces.

Employing the blanket method, you may cover the fuselage with four large pieces of cloth, installing the sides first, then the bottom, and then the top. It is best to temporarily attach cloth of sufficient length to each side with spring-type clothespins or other suitable clamps so that each piece may be accurately cut, leaving overlap of sufficient width to wrap around the inside surfaces of the longerons (figure 3.11).

Cement the cloth to the inside surfaces of each longeron. Then, when it comes time to tauten the cloth, it will tauten more evenly. The bottom and top pieces will be cemented to the side pieces with a one-inch overlap.

An alternate method is to sew two lengths of fabric side-by-side with sufficient length to reach the full length of the fuselage section that is to be covered with cloth. The sewn seam will discontinue at the start of the vertical stabilizer. Position the blanket on top of the fuselage with the seam down the center.

Cut and fit two pieces of fabric for the sides of the vertical stabilizer; fasten them to the blanket with pins, and to each other up the leading edge of the vertical stabilizer.

Remove this fabric assembly and machine-sew the vertical stabilizer panels to the blanket, and sew the seam at the leading edge of the stabilizer. Most types of household sewing machines can be adjusted to sew Dacron. However, upholstery machines are usually used.

Sew together two wedge-shaped pieces to fit the bottom of the fuselage, leaving a one inch overlap that is attached to the lower longerons' inside surfaces with Poly-Tac cement.

Reinstall the blanket on the top of the fuselage and overlap the bottom edges a minimum of one inch on each side. Cement the fabric to the fuselage structure with Poly-Tac cement. Partially heat-shrink, then cover all cemented seams with two inch finishing tape and Stits Poly-Brush. After sufficient drying—about one hour at 70 degrees F—complete the heat-shrinking process to the tautness desired.

The fabric is initially installed snug or with only a few minor wrinkles, since unfinished Dacron will shrink about 10 percent (figure 3.12). Keep in mind that a blanket stretched in one direction but very loose in the other direction will heat taut in the same proportion.

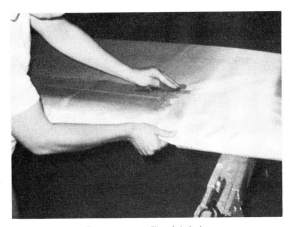

Figure 3.12.—The fabric is installed snug or with only a few wrinkles; application of heat will shrink Dacron about 10 percent.

Shrinking the Fabric

When the Poly-Fiber has been attached to the airframe, heat is applied with a household electric iron to tauten the cloth. This should be done in several increments of heat increase. The first application is made with a setting of 225 to 250 degrees F, or with the indicator set on "Rayon" or slightly above. After the entire surface has been pulled snug with all the wrinkles removed, increase the temperature to about 350 degrees F or the setting for "Wool," and go over the surface again. Keep the iron moving at a rate of about four to seven inches per second. A slower iron movement may be necessary over structural members where a heat sink is caused by the proximity of the cloth to the structure. Do not overheat; the Dacron will begin to deteriorate above 400 degrees F.

When the fabric is attached with Poly-Tac rather than sewn seams, it is best to partially tauten and cover all seams with two inch tape after giving each seam a coat of Poly-Brush for good tape adhesion. After the cement and Poly-Brush, have dried, the tautening procedure is completed.

There are no specifications for determining the correct tension for aircraft fabric. The fabric should be sufficiently taut to be stable in the slipstream, but not tight enough to distort the structure. If it is tight enough to bounce a twenty-five cent piece, it is satisfactory. Since Poly-Dope is a non-tautening formula, it will not tighten the fabric after application.

Stits Coatings

After the fabric has been shrunk, brush or spray

one coat of Poly-Brush, obtaining good penetration. The brushing technique is the same as with nitrate or butyrate dope, but spraying is preferred because it eliminates the possibility of brush marks. For spray gun application, Poly-Brush should be reduced with Poly-Dope Reducer (RR-8500) at a ratio of three parts Poly-Brush to one part reducer.

The first spray coat should be applied working small areas with several cross-coats, applied one immediately after the other, until the fabric is saturated and the dope no longer sinks into the fabric weave but leaves a gloss on the surface. This will take two to four passes with the spray gun and will be equivalent to the first brush coat. The Poly-Brush sprayed coat will dry in about one hour at 70 degrees F. Drying time for brushed Poly-Brush will be about 45 minutes.

The drain grommets and inspection rings should be installed before application of the second coat of Poly-Brush. Since the chemical composition of these pieces won't be known, don't use Poly-Tac; it might dissolve them. Use Goodyear Pliobond or good all-purpose cement. There is no need to cut out the fabric inside the inspection rings at this time; wait until the first scheduled inspection of the airplane. *Do* open the holes inside the drain grommets with a heated rod.

The second coat of Poly-Brush should be applied only after the first coat has dried. Premature application of the second coat may trap solvents, resulting in blisters. Any attempt at fast drying with heat lamps will have a similar effect. If working with a brush, spread evenly and allow to dry. Do not go back over the wet coating with the brush. If all Poly-Brush is applied with a spray gun, a third spray coat is recommended. Three spray coats or two brush coats of Poly-Brush are equal to about six coats of nitrate or butyrate dope.

After sealing the fabric with Poly-Brush, next apply a coat of Poly-Spray. This must be done with a spray gun for satisfactory results, and if it tends to dry too fast for a "wet" coat application, the drying time may be slowed with addition of Poly-Dope Retarder (RR-8500). The first cross-coat of Poly-Spray is applied wet in wide, overlapping passes, working the normal three to four-foot strokes. A cross-coat is one coat applied with overlapping passes in one direction, followed by another coat with the strokes 90-degrees to the first.

After the first coat of Poly-Spray has dried, sand with 280 grit Wet-or-dry sandpaper. A minimum of three coats of Poly-Spray is required; four to six coats

are usual. The amount of sanding between each coat will depend upon the quality of the finish you are trying to obtain. After each sanding operation, the sanding residue should be washed from the surfaces. Use only clean rags.

When the final coat of Poly-Spray has dried a minimum of two hours, the finish (color), Stits Poly-Tone, is applied. Three to five coats are sprayed, wet-sanding each coat (except the last) with 400 grit paper after each has dried sufficiently to produce a suitable sanding residue. Wash away the residue, dry with clean cloths, and wipe with a tack cloth just before applying the next coat.

Spraying equipment that is rated for the use of lacquer, nitrate or butyrate dope, synthetic enamel, and shellac may be used to apply the Stits finishes.

THE CECONITE SYSTEM

The attachment of Ceconite and Poly-Fiber to the airframe is essentially the same, the only difference being that the Dacron cloth probably should be installed slightly looser when using the Ceconite system because the butyrate finish will further shrink the fabric following the normal heat-tautening process. Ceconite calls for the use of non-tautening butyrate, but the non-tautening formula may, after a few years' service, also shrink a little because it is simply butyrate with a higher percentage of plasticizers (triphenyl phosphate and tricresyl phosphate), and these tend to lose their effectiveness after a few years in the sun. Also, the Ceconite system employs three coats of nitrate dope as a base for the butyrate, since butyrate does not adhere well to raw Dacron, and the nitrate dope does cause some shrinkage.

Craftsmen experienced in aircraft fabric work often feel more comfortable with the Ceconite system because they have extensive experience with cellulose acetate butyrate (CAB), usually going back to the years when they were covering airplanes with cotton fabric. The switch to Ceconite Dacron is therefore not much of a transition, the only significant differences being in the method of tautening the fabric prior to applying the finish (cotton cloth is tautened with distilled water), plus the fact that Ceconite is applied slightly looser than cotton (or Poly-Fiber).

If you are not using pre-sewn envelopes and opt for the blanket method of covering the airframe, you may employ Ceconite "Super Seam" cement in the same way Poly-Tac is used in the Stits system.

In the cementing method of covering the wings,

the fabric may be run spanwise on one surface and cemented with Super Seam to the leading and trailing edges as well as to root ribs and wingtips. The opposite surface is then attached using Super Seam with at least a four-inch overlap at the leading edge, a three-inch overlap at the trailing edge, and at least a one-inch overlap at the tips. Surface tape of six-inch width should be cemented over the leading edge overlap, and at least three-inch width tape cemented over the trailing edge and wingtip overlaps.

If the wing chord is too great to allow sufficient overlap at the leading and trailing edges with a single length of fabric, you can run the fabric chordwise and gain the needed spanwise length by machine-sewing together as many widths of cloth as necessary. This will result in a much better appearance than a spanwise seam.

After the Ceconite cover has been heat-tautened, apply three brush coats of nitrate dope, with the first coat thinned about 30 percent with nitrate thinner, and the other coats thinned to a good brushing consistency. A quart of Super Seam added to each gallon of dope improves adhesion. It is important that the first coat of nitrate dope be thoroughly worked into the fabric weave, but do not oversaturate and allow drips inside the structure because this will make blemishes in the finish of the opposite surface. Allow each coat of nitrate to dry thoroughly before applying the next.

With the nitrate base coats on the fabric, install grommets and inspection rings, lay the reinforcing tapes, and accomplish the wing rib stitching. This is done with nitrate dope to which a quart of Super Seam has been added per gallon of dope. Ceconite offers a pre-doped tape that goes down well and stays in place. The rib lacing cord must be Ceconite D-693.

For the buildup coats, spray or brush three coats of clear butyrate followed by at least two coats (three are better) of silver butyrate. Use three to four ounces of aluminum powder per gallon of clear dope before thinning. Use of more aluminum powder will result in peeling. Aluminum paste is also available, as is pre-mixed aluminum butyrate dope. If these coats are brushed on, apply each at right angles to the preceding one. In general, more coats of thinned dope will give a more durable finish than fewer coats of heavy or unthinned dope. Little or no sanding is required on Dacron. If any sanding is indicated, use 320 grit Wet-or-dry sandpaper.

Three color coats are recommended, and gloss will be enhanced by the addition of 30 percent buty-

rate dope retarder to the final color coat.

We should note that enamel has often been used on fabric as a final color coat—sometimes to hide a deteriorating dope finish with marginal fabric beneath while an unsuspecting buyer is sought for the airplane. Enamel is not exactly the ideal finish on fabric. It cannot be rejuvenated and is difficult to repair. Enamel cannot be removed without damaging the underlying protective coatings of dope, and probably the fabric itself. It is more subject to cracks since it is less flexible than dope or the Stit epoxy finishes—and cracks in an enamel finish are very difficult to repair on fabric.

THE RAZORBACK FIBERGLASS SYSTEM

Razorback fiberglass cloth is attached to an airframe by the blanket method, with overlapping cemented seams in the same manner as Ceconite and Poly-Fiber. Super Seam or clear butyrate dope may be used as an adhesive.

Razorback cloth is pretreated and *must* be finished with cellulose acetate butyrate dope. Other coatings are not chemically compatible with the pretreatment formula. Do not under any circumstances apply the first coats of dope with a brush or roller. Use pressure pot equipment if possible, with 18 lbs sq/in pot pressure; 60 lbs sq/in at the spray gun. A suction-type gun may be used, but requires more thinner, more coats, and more drying time between coats.

This first coat of clear butyrate is very important to the entire finishing system. Do not—repeat, *not*—blow or run dope through the weave of the cloth. However, do not spray so lightly that the dope is dry on contact with the surface.

The second coat may be sprayed a little heavier than the first, and each succeeding coat a little heavier than the previous one. At first, the cloth will become looser. Depending upon humidity and temperature, the tautening action will occur between the second and fifth coats. Do not apply more than two or three coats in a one-day period.

When the weave is completely sealed and the fabric taut, apply inspection rings, drain grommets, Razorback reinforcing tapes, and rib-stitch the wings.

Installation of the finishing tapes over the wing ribs following rib-stitching has caused problems for some craftsmen because Razorback says that one should not apply dope to the finishing tapes at this time. Two people are needed, one working from the trailing edge and one from the leading edge of the

Figure 3.13.—Cementing
fabric on leading edge of wing with a generous overlap.

wing. A strip of dope slightly wider than the finishing tape is brushed the length of the rib. Then each worker positions the tape over the rib, pulls it taut and, working from the center, smooths the tape, leaving a sufficient amount hanging from both trailing and leading edge to cover the rib beneath the wing with a one-inch overlap at the center (figures 3.13, 3.14).

After all tapes are on and the dope is thoroughly dry, one must build up clear dope over the tapes to match the coatings already on the fabric.

From this point, Razorback recommends that you switch to non-tautening butyrate and spray two

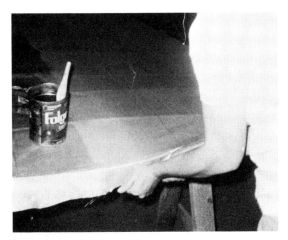

Figure 3.14.—Razorback fiberglass cloth being cemented to wingtip bow. Razorback fabric is tautened by application of cellulose acetate butyrate dope. (courtesy Razorback)

additional coats of clear dope on all surfaces. This is followed by two coats of silver, thoroughly sanding the first coat of silver with 280 grit Wet-or-dry. Two coats of color complete the finish.

THE EONNEX SYSTEM

The Eonnex pretreated cloth may be installed either as envelopes or by the blanket method. It should be attached to the airframe slightly looser than cotton. Cement laps around the structural members employ Eonnex #204 cement or #7602 cement mixed with #7603 activator. Machine-stitched seams must be made in accordance with the standards listed in 43.13. In short, the Eonnex fabric is attached and tautened very much like Poly-Fiber and Ceconite. The big difference is in the finishing process.

This system offers wing rib reinforcing tapes that are self-adhering and need no dope or cement for installation. Cement the drain grommets and inspection rings, perform rib-stitching, and apply finishing tapes with #7603 activator after tautening but before applying the filler.

The Eonnex finishing system is unique. These materials are water-based emulsions and they do not tauten the fabric—not upon application, not ever. Therefore, make sure that the fabric is properly tautened and all wrinkles have disappeared through heat application before applying the finish.

The entire finishing process may consist of as few as three coats (two filler and one color coat), but for best results a total of five coats should be applied: two filler, two color, and one of clear urethane enamel.

The Eonnex filler/primer is black, applied with a pad, and the second coat, applied after the first has thoroughly dried, goes on at right angles to the initial coat. This may be dry sanded if necessary using 150-C No-Fill Durite paper, followed by a light sanding with Wet-or-dry up to 400 grit. Then wash and dry all surfaces. Use no solvents. A third filler/primer coat is usually not needed.

Spray two color coats of #7640 pigmented emulsion paint, and complete the job with a spray coat of #7630 urethane, which seals and adds gloss. Masking for other colors (prior to applying the clear urethane) may be done as soon as the paint is dry, which ranges from five minutes to one hour depending upon temperature and humidity. Sags or overspray can be washed off at once with a wet cloth. The 7640 paint is thinned with water, but it is *not* water-soluble once it has dried. Overspray does not carry great distances, so less masking is required. The fire hazard is zero, and there are no toxic fumes.

It is best to test masking tape with 7640 before use. Emulsion type paints may bleed under or soften conventional crepe back tapes. Film back and flat back waterproof masking tapes are superior.

Chapter 4

Control Cables and Terminals

(Reprinted from FAA 443.13, Chapter 4)

Section 1. INSPECTION AND REPAIR

193. GENERAL. Aircraft control cables are generally fabricated from carbon steel or corrosion-resistant steel wire and may consist of either flexible or nonflexible type construction.

Contents of this section may be used for control cable installations pertaining to both primary and secondary system applications.

a. Cable Definitions. Construction features of various cables are shown in figure 4.1. The following terms define components used in aircraft control cables.

(1) Wire—Each individual cylindrical steel rod or thread.

(2) Strand—Each group of wires helically twisted or laid.

(3) Core Strand—The central strand about which the remaining strands of the cable are helically laid.

(4) Cable—A group of strands helically twisted or laid about a central core.

(5) Preformed Cable—Cable in which the wires and strands are shaped prior to fabrication of the cable.

(6) Diameter—The diameter of cable is the diameter of the circumscribed circle.

(7) Lay or Twist—The helical form taken by the wires and strands in a cable. A cable is said to have a right-hand lay if the wires and strands twist in the same direction as the thread on a right-hand screw.

(8) Pitch—The distance in which a strand or wire makes one complete revolution about the axis of the cable or strand respectively.

194. CABLE SPECIFICATIONS. Cable size and strength data are given in figure 4.2. These values are acceptable for repair and modification of civil aircraft.

a. Cable Proof Loads. Cable terminals and splices should be tested for proper strength prior to installation. Gradually apply a test load equal to 60 percent of the cable breaking strengths given in figure 4.2 for a period of 3 minutes. Place a suitable guard over the cable during the test to prevent injury to personnel in the event of cable failure.

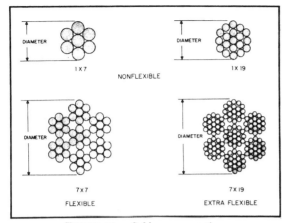

FIGURE 4.1.—Cable cross section.

195. REPLACEMENT OF CABLES. Replace control cables when they become worn, distorted, corroded, or otherwise injured. If spare cables are not available, prepare exact duplicates of the damaged cable. Use materials of the same size and quality as the original. Standard swaged cable terminals develop the full cable strength and may be substituted for the original terminals wherever practical. However, if facilities and supplies are limited and immediate corrective action is necessary, repairs may be made by using cable bushings, eye splices, and the proper combination of turnbuckles in place of the original installation. (See figure 4.6c.)

a. Location of Splices. Locate splices so that no portion of the splice comes closer than two inches to any fair-lead or pulley. Locate connections at points where jamming cannot occur during any portion of the travel of either the loaded cable or the slack cable in the deflected position.

b. Cutting and Heating. Cut cables to length by mechanical means. The use of a torch in any manner is not permitted. Do not subject wires and cables to excessive temperature. Soldering bonding braid to control cable will not be considered satisfactory.

c. Ball-and-Socket Type Terminals. Do not use ball-and-socket type terminals or other types

Diameter (inch)	1×7 and 1×19				7×7, 7×19, and 6×19 (1WRC)			
	Nonflexible, carbon		Corrosion resisting		Flexible, carbon		Flexible, corrosion resisting	
	MIL–W–6940		MIL–C–5693		MIL–W–1511		MIL–C–5424	
	Weight, pounds per 100 feet	Breaking strength, pounds	Weight, pounds per 100 feet	Breaking strength, pounds	Weight, pounds per 100 feet	Breaking strength, pounds	Weight, pounds per 100 feet	Breaking strength, pounds
1/32	0. 25	185	0. 25	150	---------	---------	---------	---------
3/64	. 55	375	. 55	375	---------	---------	---------	---------
1/16	. 85	500	. 85	500	0. 75	480	0. 75	480
5/64	1. 40	800	1. 40	800	---------	---------	---------	---------
3/32	2. 00	1, 200	2. 00	1, 200	1. 60	920	1. 60	920
7/64	2. 70	1, 600	2. 70	1, 600	---------	---------	---------	---------
1/8	3. 50	2, 100	3. 50	2, 100	2. 90	2, 000	2. 90	1, 760
5/32	5. 50	3, 300	5. 50	3, 300	4. 50	2, 800	4. 50	2, 400
3/16	7. 70	4, 700	7. 70	4, 700	6. 50	4, 200	6. 50	3, 700
7/32	10. 20	6, 300	10. 20	6, 300	8. 60	5, 600	8. 60	5, 000
1/4	13. 50	8, 200	13. 50	8, 200	11. 00	7, 000	11. 00	6, 400
9/32	---------	---------	---------	---------	13. 90	8, 000	13. 90	7, 800
5/16	21. 00	12, 500	21. 00	12, 500	17. 30	9, 800	17. 30	9, 000
11/32	---------	---------	---------	---------	20. 70	12, 500	---------	---------
3/8	---------	---------	---------	---------	24. 30	14, 400	24. 30	12, 000
7/16	---------	---------	---------	---------	35. 60	17, 600	35. 60	16, 300
1/2	---------	---------	---------	---------	45. 80	22, 800	45. 80	22, 800

*The strength values listed were obtained from straight tension tests and do not include the effects of wrapped ends.

FIGURE 4.2.—Strength of steel cable.

for general replacement that do not positively prevent cable untwisting, except where they were utilized on the original installation by the aircraft manufacturer.

d. Substitution of Cable. Substitution of cable for hard or streamlined wires will not be acceptable unless specifically approved by a representative of the Federal Aviation Administration.

196. MECHANICALLY FABRICATED CABLE ASSEMBLIES.

a. Swage Type Terminals. Swage type terminals, manufactured in accordance with Air Force-Navy Aeronautical Standard Specifications, are suitable for use in civil aircraft up to and including maximum cable loads. When swaging tools are used, it is important that all the manufacturers' instructions, including "go and no-go" dimensions, be followed in detail to avoid defective and inferior swaging. Observance of all instructions should result in a terminal developing the full rated strength of the cable. Critical dimensions, both before and after swaging, are shown in figure 4.3.

(1) Terminals. When swaging terminals onto cable ends, observe the following procedure:

(a) Cut the cable to the proper length, allowing for growth during swaging. Apply a preservative compound to the cable ends before insertion into the terminal barrel.

NOTE: Never solder cable ends to prevent fraying since the presence of the solder will greatly increase the tendency of the cable to pull out of the terminal.

(b) Insert the cable into the terminal approximately one inch, and bend toward the terminal; straighten the cable back to normal position and then push the cable end entirely into the terminal barrel. The bending action puts a kink or bend in the cable end and provides enough friction to hold the terminal in place until the swaging operation can be performed. Bending also tends to separate the strands inside the barrel, thereby reducing the strain on them.

NOTE: If the terminal is drilled completely through, push the cable into the terminal until it reaches the approximate position shown in figure 4.4. If the hole is not drilled through, insert the cable until the end rests against the bottom of the hole.

(c) Accomplish the swaging operation in accordance with the instructions furnished by the manufacturer of the swaging equipment.

(d) Inspect the terminal after swaging to determine that it is free from die marks and splits, and is not out-of-round. Check for cable slippage in the terminal and for cut or broken wire strands.

(e) Using a "go no-go" gauge or a mi-

Cable size (inches)	Wire strands	Before swaging				After swaging	
		Outside diameter	Bore diameter	Bore length	Swaging length	Minimum breaking strength (pounds)	Shank diameter*
1/16	7×7	0. 160	0. 078	1. 042	0. 969	480	0. 138
3/32	7×7	. 218	. 109	1. 261	1. 188	920	. 190
1/8	7×19	. 250	. 141	1. 511	1. 438	2,000	. 219
5/32	7×19	. 297	. 172	1. 761	1. 688	2,800	. 250
3/16	7×19	. 359	. 203	2. 011	1. 938	4,200	. 313
7/32	7×19	. 427	. 234	2. 261	2. 188	5,600	. 375
1/4	7×19	. 494	. 265	2. 511	2. 438	7,000	. 438
9/32	7×19	. 563	. 297	2. 761	2. 688	8,000	. 500
5/16	7×19	. 635	. 328	3. 011	2. 938	9,800	. 563
3/8	7×19	. 703	. 390	3. 510	3. 438	14,400	. 625

*Use gages in kit for checking diameters.

FIGURE 4.3.—Straight-shank terminal dimensions (AN-666, 667, 668, and 669).

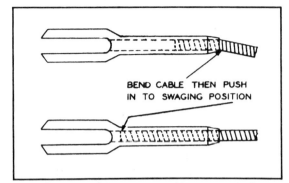

FIGURE 4.4.—Insertion of cable into terminal.

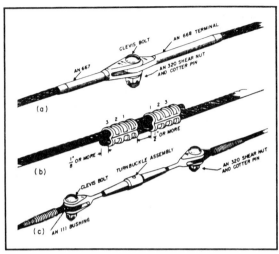

FIGURE 4.6.—Typical cable splices.

crometer, check the terminal barrel diameter as shown in figure 4.5.

(f) Test the cable by proof-loading it to 60 percent of its rated breaking strength.

(2) **Splicing.** Completely severed cables, or those badly damaged in a localized area, may be repaired by the use of an eye terminal bolted to a clevis terminal. (See figure 4.6a.) However, this type of splice can only be used in free lengths of cable which do not pass over pulleys or through fair-leads.

(3) **Swaged Ball Terminals.** On some aircraft cables, swaged ball terminals are used for attaching cables to quadrants and special connections where space is limited. Single shank terminals are generally used at the cable ends, and double shank fittings may be used at either the end or in the center of the cable. Dies are supplied with the swaging machines for attaching these terminals to cables in the following manner:

(a) The steel balls and shanks have a hole through the center, and are slipped over the cable and positioned in the desired location.

(b) Perform the swaging operation in accordance with the instructions furnished by the manufacturer of the swaging equipment.

(c) Check the swaged fitting with a "go no-go" gauge to see that the fitting is properly compressed. (See figure 4.7.) Also inspect the physical condition of the finished terminal.

(4) **Cable Slippage in Terminal.** Ensure that the cable is properly inserted in the terminal after the swaging operation is completed. Instances have been noted wherein only 1/4 inch of the cable was swaged in the terminal. Ob-

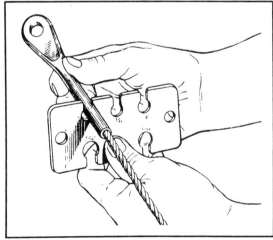

FIGURE 4.5.—Gauging terminal shank after swaging.

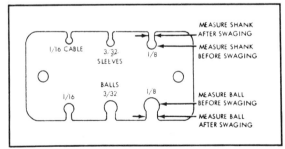

FIGURE 4.7.—Typical terminal gauge.

servance of the following precautions should minimize this possibility:

(a) Measure the length of the terminal end of the fitting to determine the proper length of cable to be inserted into the barrel of the fitting.

(b) Lay off this length at the end of the cable and mark with masking tape. Since the tape will not slip, it will provide a positive marking during the swaging process.

(c) After swaging, check the tape marker to make certain that the cable did not slip during the swaging operation.

(d) Remove the tape and, using red paint, paint the junction of the swaged fitting and cable.

(e) At all subsequent service inspections of the swaged fittings, check for a gap in the painted section to see if cable slippage has occurred.

b. *Nicopress Process.* A patented process using copper sleeves may be used up to the full rated strength of the cable when the cable is looped around a thimble. This process may also be used in place of the five-tuck splice on cables up to and including 3/8-inch diameter. The use of sleeves that are fabricated of materials other than copper will require engineering approval of the specific application by a representative of the Federal Aviation Administration.

Before undertaking a nicopress splice, determine the proper tool and sleeve for the cable to be used. Refer to figures 4.8 and 4.10 for details on sleeves, tools, and the number of presses required for the various sizes of aircraft cable. The tool must be in good working condition and properly adjusted to assure a satisfactory splice.

To compress a sleeve, have it well centered in the tool groove with the major axis of the sleeve at right angles to the tool. If the sleeve appears to be out of line after the press is started, open the tool, re-center the sleeve, and complete the press.

(1) **Thimble-Eye Splice.** Initially position the cable so that the end will extend slightly beyond the sleeve, as the sleeve will elongate somewhat when it is compressed. If the cable end is inside the sleeve, the splice may not hold

Cable size	Copper oval sleeve stock No.		Manual tool No.	Sleeve length before compression (approx.) (inches)	Sleeve length after compression (approx.) (inches)	Number of presses	Tested strength (pounds)
	Plain	Plated *					
3/64	18–11–B4	28–11–B4	51–B4–887	3/8	7/16	1	340
1/16	18–1–C	28–1–C	51–C–887	3/8	7/16	1	550
3/32	18–2–G	28–2–G	51–G–887	7/16	1/2	1	1,180
1/8	18–3–M	28–3–M	51–M–850	9/16	3/4	3	2,300
5/32	18–4–P	28–4–P	51–P–850	5/8	7/8	3	3,050
3/16	18–6–X	28–6–X	51–X–850	1	1 1/4	4	4,350
7/32	18–8–F2	28–8–F2	51–F2–850	7/8	1 1/16	4	5,790
1/4	18–10–F6	28–10–F6	3–F6–950	1 1/8	1 1/2	3	7,180
5/16	18–13–G9	28–13–G9	3–G9–950	1 1/4	1 5/8	3	11,130
			No. 635 Hydraulic tool dies				
3/8	18–23–H5	28–23–H5	Oval H5	1 1/2	1 7/8	1	16,800
7/16	18–24–J8	28–24–J8	Oval J8	1 3/4	2 1/8	2	19,700
1/2	18–25–K8	28–25–K8	Oval K8	1 7/8	2 1/2	2	25,200
9/16	18–27–M1	28–27–M1	Oval M1	2	2 3/4	3	31,025
5/8	18–28–N5	28–28–N5	Oval N5	2 3/8	3 1/8	3	39,200

*Required on stainless cable.

FIGURE 4.8.—Copper oval sleeve data.

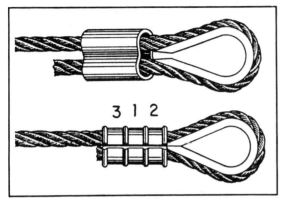

FIGURE 4.9.—Typical thimble-eye splice.

the full strength of the cable. It is desirable that the oval sleeve be placed in close proximity to the thimble points, so that when compressed the sleeve will contact the thimble as shown in figure 4.9. The sharp ends of the thimble may be cut off before being used; however, make certain the thimble is firmly secured in the cable loop after the splice has been completed. When using a sleeve requiring three compressions, make the center compression first, the compression next to the thimble second, and the one farthest from the thimble last.

(2) Lap Splice. Lap or running splices may also be made with copper oval sleeves. When making such splices, it is usually necessary to

Cable size (inch)	Sleeve No.	Tool No.	Sleeve length (inch)	Sleeve O.D. (inch)	Tested strength (pounds
$\frac{3}{64}$	871–12–B4	51–B4–887	$\frac{7}{32}$	$\frac{11}{64}$	280
$\frac{1}{16}$	871–1–C	51–C–887	$\frac{7}{32}$	$\frac{13}{64}$	525
$\frac{3}{32}$	871–17–J (Yellow)	51–MJ	$\frac{5}{16}$	$\frac{21}{64}$	600
$\frac{1}{8}$	871–18–J (Red)	51–MJ	$\frac{5}{16}$	$\frac{21}{64}$	800
$\frac{5}{32}$	871–19–M	51–MJ	$\frac{5}{16}$	$\frac{27}{64}$	1,200
$\frac{3}{16}$	871–20–M (Black)	51–MJ	$\frac{5}{16}$	$\frac{27}{64}$	1,600
$\frac{7}{32}$	871–22–M	51–MJ	$\frac{5}{8}$	$\frac{7}{16}$	2,300
$\frac{1}{4}$	871–23–F6	3–F6–950	$\frac{11}{16}$	$\frac{21}{32}$	3,500
$\frac{5}{16}$	871–26–F6	3–F6–950	$\frac{11}{16}$	$\frac{21}{32}$	3,800

NOTE: All stop sleeves are plain copper—certain sizes are colored for identification.

FIGURE 4.10.—Copper stop sleeve data.

making such splices, it is usually necessary to use two sleeves to develop the full strength of the cable. The sleeves should be positioned as shown in figure 4.6b, and the compressions made in the order shown. As in the case of eye splices, it is desirable to have the cable ends extend beyond the sleeves sufficiently to allow for the increased length of the compressed sleeves.

(3) Stop Sleeves. Stop sleeves may be used for special cable end and intermediate fittings and they are installed in the same manner as Nicopress oval sleeves.

NOTE: All stop sleeves are plain copper—certain sizes are colored for identification.

(4) Terminal Gauge. To make a satisfactory copper sleeve installation, it is important that the amount of sleeve pressure be kept uniform. The completed sleeves should be checked periodically with the proper gauge. Hold the gauge so that it contacts the major axis of the sleeve. The compressed portion at the center of the sleeve should enter the gauge opening with very little clearance, as shown in figure 4.11. If it does not, the tool must be adjusted accordingly.

(5) Other Applications. The preceding information regarding copper oval sleeves and stop sleeves is based on tests made with flexible aircraft cable. The sleeves may also be used on wire ropes of other constructon if each specific type of cable is proof tested initially. Because of variation in rope strengths, grades, construction, and actual diameters, the test is necessary to insure proper selection of materials, the correct pressing procedure, and an adequate margin of safety for the intended use.

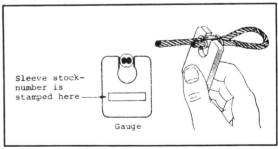

Sleeve stock-number is stamped here →

Gauge

FIGURE 4.11.—Typical terminal gauge.

197. HAND FABRICATED CABLE ASSEMBLIES.

a. Woven Splice Terminal. The 5-tuck woven splice may be utilized on 7×7 flexible and 7 ×19 extra-flexible cables of 3/32 inch diameter or greater; however, this type of terminal will only develop 75 percent of the cable strength. It should not be used to replace high efficiency terminals unless it is definitely determined the design load for the cable is not greater than 75 percent of the cable minimum breaking strength.

In some cases it will be necessary to splice one end of the cable on assembly. For this reason, investigate the original installation for pulleys and fair-leads that might restrict the passage of the splice. The procedure for the fabrication of a woven splice is as follows. (Refer to figure 4.12 for the designation of numbers and letters referred to in this sequence of operations.)

(1) Secure the cables around a bushing or thimble, by means of a splicing clamp in a vise, with the free end to the left of the standing wire and away from the operator. If a thimble is used as the end fitting, turn to point outward approximately 45°.

(2) Select the free strand (1) nearest standing length at the end of the fitting, and free this strand from the rest of the free ends. Next, insert a marlinspike under the first three strands (A, B, and C) of the standing length nearest the separated strand of the free end and separate them momentarily by twisting the marlinspike. Insert the free strand (1) under the three separated strands, through the opening created by the marlinspike. Pull the free end taut by means of pliers.

(3) Unlay a second strand (2), located to the left of the first strand tucked, and insert this second strand under the first two standing strands (A, B). Loosen the third free length (3), located to the left of the first two, and insert it under the first standing strand (A) of the original three (section AA).

(4) Remove the center or core strand (7) from the free end and insert it under the same standing strands (A, B). Temporarily secure the core strand to the body of the standing

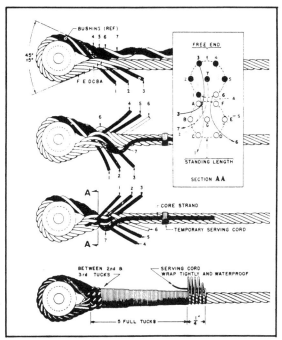

FIGURE 4.12.—Preparation of a woven cable splice.

cable. Loosen the last free strand (6) located just to the right of the first (1) and tuck it under the last two strands (E, F) of the standing cable. Tuck the free strand (5) around standing strand (E). Tuck the free end (4) around the sixth standing strand (F) (see figure 4.12 section AA). Pull all strands snug toward the end fitting with the pliers. This completes the first tuck.

(5) Begin with the first free strand (1) and work in a counterclockwise direction, tucking free strands under every other strand. After the completion of every tuck, pull the strands tight with pliers toward the end fitting. After the completion of the third complete tuck, cut in half the number of wires in each free strand. Make another complete tuck with the wires remaining. At the completion of the fourth tuck, again halve the number of wires in the free strands and make one final tuck with the wires remaining. Cut off all protruding strands and pound the splice with a wooden or rawhide mallet to relieve the strands in the wires.

(6) Serve the splice with waxed linen cord.

Start 1/4 inch from the end of the splice and carry the wrapping over the loose end of the cord and along the tapered splice to a point between the second and third tucks. Insert the end of the cord back through the last five wrappings and pull snug. Cut off the end, and if a thimble is used as an end fitting, bend down the points. Apply two coats of waterproofing to the cord, allowing two hours between coats. Carefully inspect the cable strands and splices for local failure. Weakness in a woven splice is made evident by a separation of the strand of serving cord.

b. Wrap-Soldered Terminal. The wrap-soldered splice terminal shown in figure 4.13 may be utilized on flexible cables less than 3/32 inch in diameter and on nonflexible single strand (19 wire) cable. This type of terminal will develop only 90 percent of the cable strength and should not be used to replace high efficiency terminals, unless it is definitely known that the design load for the cable is not greater than 90 percent of the cable minimum breaking strength. The method of making the wrapped and soldered splice is as follows.

(1) Use serving or wrapping wire made of commercial soft-annealed steel wire or commercial soft iron wire, thoroughly and smoothly tinned or galvanized.

(2) Use half tin and half lead solder conforming to Federal Specification QQ–S–571. The melting point of this solder varies from 320° to 390° F., and the tensile strength is approximately 5,700 pounds per square inch.

(3) Use solder flux consisting of stearic acid (there should be no mineral acid present) and resin, with a composition of 25 to 50 percent resin. A warming gluepot to keep the flux in fluid state is desirable.

(4) Before the cable is cut, solder the wires to prevent slipping. The preferred process is to tin and solder the cable thoroughly two to three inches by placing in a solder trough, finishing smooth with a soldering tool. The cable may be cut diagonally to conform to the required taper finish.

(5) After being soldered and cut, the cable

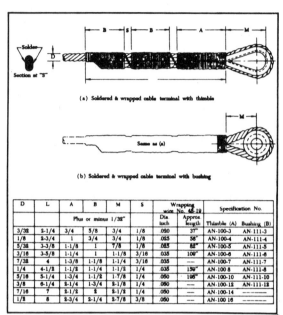

(a) Soldered & wrapped cable terminal with thimble

Same as (a)

(b) Soldered & wrapped cable terminal with bushing

D	L	A	B	M	S	Wrapping wire No. 4B-19		Specification No.	
		Plus or minus 1/32"				Dia. inch	Approx. length	Thimble (A)	Bushing (B)
3/32	2-1/4	3/4	5/8	3/4	1/8	.020	37"	AN-100-3	AN-111-3
1/8	2-3/4	1	3/4	3/4	1/8	.025	58"	AN-100-4	AN-111-4
5/32	3-3/8	1-1/8	1	7/8	1/8	.025	82"	AN-100-5	AN-111-5
3/16	3-5/8	1-1/4	1	1-1/8	3/16	.035	109"	AN-100-6	AN-111-6
7/32	4	1-3/8	1-1/8	1-1/4	3/16	.035	---	AN-100-7	AN-111-7
1/4	4-1/2	1-1/2	1-1/4	1-1/2	1/4	.035	150"	AN-100-8	AN-111-8
5/16	5-1/4	1-3/4	1-1/2	1-7/8	1/4	.050	195"	AN-100-10	AN-111-10
3/8	6-1/4	2-1/4	1-3/4	2-1/8	1/4	.050	---	AN-100-12	AN-111-12
7/16	7	2-1/2	2	2-1/2	1/4	.050	---	AN-100-14	-------
1/2	8	2-3/4	2-1/4	2-7/8	3/8	.050	---	AN-100-16	-------

FIGURE 4.13.—Preparation of a wrapped soldered terminal.

is securely bent around the proper size thimble, and clamped so that the cables lie close and flat and the taper end for finish lies on the outside. If it is necessary to trim the taper at this point in the process, it is preferable that it be done by nipping. Grinding is permissible, provided a steel guard at least 3 inches long and 1/32-inch thick is placed between the taper end and the main cable during the operation; and that the heat generated from the grinding does not melt the solder and loosen the wires.

(6) Serving may be done by hand or machine, but in either case each serving convolution must touch the adjoining one and be pulled tightly against the cable, with spaces for permitting a free flow of solder and inspection. (See figure 4.13a.)

(7) Prevent drawing of the temper of any cable resulting from excessive temperature or duration of applied heat. Use a soldering flux consisting of stearic acid and resin. The use, as a flux, of sal-ammoniac or any other compound having a corrosive effect is not acceptable.

(8) Soldering is accomplished by immersing the terminal alternately in the flux and in the

solder bath, repeating the operation until thorough tinning and filling with solder under the serving wire and thimble is obtained. The temperature of the solder bath and place where terminal is withdrawn should not be above 450° F. A soldering iron may be used in the final operation to give a secure and good-appearing terminal. Assure that the solder completely fills the space under the serving wire and thimble. A slightly hollowed cast-iron block to support the splice during soldering may help in securing the best results. The use of abrasive wheels or files for removing excess solder is not recommended.

(9) As an alternative process for making terminals for nonflexible cable, the oxyacetylene cutting method and the presoldering method (soldering before wrapping) are acceptable, but only under the following conditions:

(a) that the process of cutting securely welds all wires together;

(b) that the annealing of the cable does not extend more than one cable diameter from the end,

(c) that no filing is done either before or after soldering;

(d) that for protection during the operation of grinding the tapered end of the cable, a steel guard at least three inches in length and 1/32 inch thick should be placed between the taper and the main cable;

(e) that heat from grinding does not draw the temper of the cable.

(10) Do not use wrap-soldered splice terminals ahead of the firewall, or in other fire zones, or in other locations where they might be subjected to high temperature.

198. CABLE SYSTEM INSPECTION. Aircraft cable systems are subject to a variety of environmental conditions and forms of deterioration that ultimately may be easy to recognize as wire/strand breakage or the not-so-readily visible types of wear, corrosion, and/or distortion. The following data will aid in detecting the presence of these conditions:

a. Cable Damage. Critical areas for wire breakage are those sections of the cable which pass through fairleads and around pulleys. Examine cables for broken wires by passing a cloth along the length of the cable. This will clean the cable for a visual inspection, and detect broken wires if the cloth snags on the cable. When snags are found, closely examine the cable to determine the full extent of the damage.

The absence of snags is not positive evidence that broken wires do not exist. Figure 4.14a shows a cable with broken wires that were not detected by wiping, but were found during a visual inspection. The damage became readily apparent (figure 4.14b) when the cable was removed and bent using the technique depicted in figure 4.14c.

NOTE: Tests by various aeronautical agencies have indicated that a few broken wires spread over the length of a cable will not result in a critical loss of strength. Obtain specific information regarding acceptable wire breakage limits from the manufacturer of the aircraft involved.

(1) External Wear Patterns. Wear will normally extend along the cable equal to the distance the cable moves at that location and may occur on one side of the cable only or on its entire circumference. Replace flexible and nonflexible cables when the individual wires in each strand appear to blend together (outer

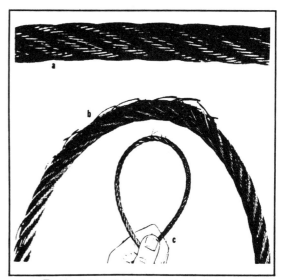

FIGURE 4.14.—Cable inspection technique.

125

INDIVIDUAL OUTER WIRES WORN MORE THAN 50%

INDIVIDUAL OUTER WIRES WORN 40-50%
(NOTE BLENDING OF WORN AREAS)

INDIVIDUAL OUTER WIRES WORN LESS THAN 40%
(WORN AREAS INDIVIDUALLY DISTINGUISHABLE)

FIGURE 4.15.—Cable wear patterns.

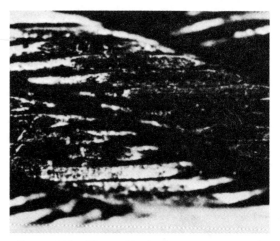

FIGURE 4.16.—Worn cable (replacement necessary).

wires worn 40–50 percent) as depicted in figure 4.15. Actual instances of cable wear beyond the recommended replacement point are shown in figures 4.16 and 4.17.

(2) Internal Cable Wear. As wear is taking place on the exterior surface of a cable, the same condition is taking place internally, particularly in the sections of the cable which pass over pulleys and quadrants. This condition (shown in figure 4.18) is not easily detected unless the strands of the cable are separated. Wear of this type is a result of the relative motion between inner wire surfaces. Under certain conditions the rate of this type wear can be greater than that occurring on the surface.

(3) Corrosion. Carefully examine any cable for corrosion that has a broken wire in a section not in contact with wear producing airframe components such as pulleys, fairleads, etc. It may be necessary to remove and bend the cable to properly inspect it for internal strand corrosion as this condition is usually not evident on the outer surface of the cable. Replace cable segments if internal strand rust or corrosion is found.

Areas especially conducive to cable corrosion are battery compartments, lavatories, wheel wells, etc., where concentrations of corrosive fumes, vapors, and liquids can accumulate.

NOTE: Check all exposed sections of cable for corrosion after a cleaning and/or metal-brightening operation has been accomplished in that area.

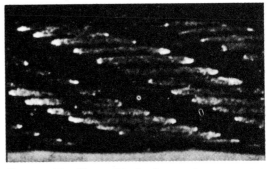

FIGURE 4.17.—Worn cable (replacement recommended).

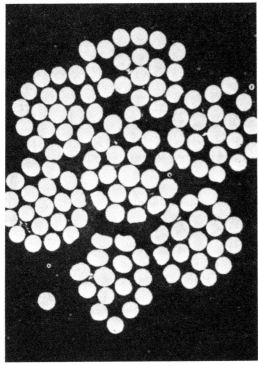

FIGURE 4.18.—Internal cable wear.

An example of cable corrosion, attributable to battery acid, is shown in figure 4.19.

b. **Wire Splices.** Standard manufacturing splices have been mistaken for defects in the cable because individual wire end splices were visible after assembly of a finished cable length. In some instances, the process of twist-

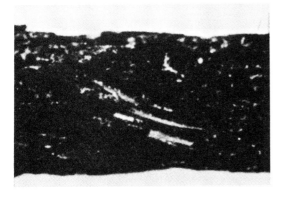

FIGURE 4.19.—Corrosion.

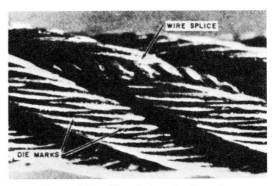

FIGURE 4.20.—Manufacturer's wire splice.

ing outer strands around the core strand may also slightly flatten individual outer wires, particularly in the area of a wire splice. This flattening is the result of die sizing the cable and does not affect the strength of the cable. These conditions, as shown in figure 4.20, are normal and are not a cause for cable rejection.

c. **Cable Maintenance.** Frequent inspections and preservation measures such as rust prevention treatments for bare cable areas will help to extend cable service life. Where cables pass through fairleads, pressure seals, or over pulleys, remove accumulated heavy coatings of corrosion prevention compound. Provide corrosion protection for these cable sections by lubricating with a light coat of graphite grease or general purpose, low-temperature oil.

CAUTION

Avoid the use of vapor degreasing, steam cleaning, methylethylketone (MEK) or other solvents to remove corrosion-preventative compounds, as these methods will also remove the cable internal lubricant.

d. **Routing.** Examine cable runs for incorrect routing, fraying, twisting, or wear at fairleads, pulleys, anti-abrasion strips, and guards. Look for interference with adjacent structure, equipment, wiring, plumbing, and other controls. Inspect cable systems for binding, full travel, and security of attaching hardware. Check for slack in the cable system by attempting to move the control column and/or pedals while the gust locks are installed on the control surfaces. With the gust locks removed, actuate the controls and check for friction or hard movement. These are indications that excessive cable tension exists.

NOTE: If the control movement is stiff after maintenance operations are performed on control surfaces, check for parallel cables twisted around each other or cables connected in reverse.

e. Cable Fittings. Check swaged terminal reference marks for an indication of cable slippage within the fitting. Inspect the fitting assembly for distortion and/or broken strands at the terminal. Assure that all bearings and swivel fittings (bolted or pinned) pivot freely to prevent binding and subsequent failure. Check turnbuckles for proper thread exposure and broken or missing safety wires/clips.

f. Pulleys. Inspect pulleys for roughness, sharp edges, and presence of foreign material embedded in the grooves. Examine pulley bearings to assure proper lubrication, smooth rotation, freedom from flat spots, dirt, and paint spray. Periodically rotate pulleys, which turn

through a small arc, to provide a new bearing surface for the cable. Maintain pulley alignment to prevent the cable from riding on the flanges and chafing against guards, covers, or adjacent structure. Check all pulley brackets and guards for damage, alignment, and security.

(1) Pulley Wear Patterns. Various cable system malfunctions may be detected by analyzing pulley conditions. These include such discrepancies as too much tension, misalignment, pulley bearing problems, and size mismatches between cables and pulleys. Examples of these conditions are shown in figure 4.21.

g. Fairleads, Guides, Anti-Abrasion Strips. Inspect fairleads for wear, breakage, alignment, cleanness, and security. Examine cable routing at fairleads to assure that deflection angles are no greater than 3° maximum. Determine that all guides and anti-abrasion strips are secure and in good condition.

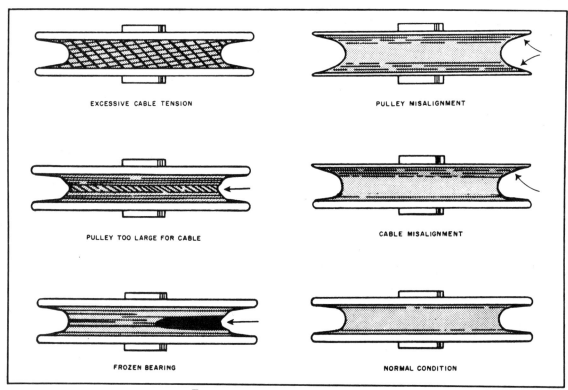

FIGURE 4.21.—Pulley wear patterns.

h. *Pressure Seals and Seal Guards.* Examine pressure seals for wear and/or material deterioration. Determine that the seal guards are positioned to prevent jamming of a pulley if a pressure seal fails and pieces slide along the cable.

199. CABLE TENSION ADJUSTMENT. Carefully adjust control cable tension in accordance with the airframe manufacturer's recommendations. On large aircraft, take the temperature of the immediate area into consideration when using a tensiometer. For long cable sections, use the average of two or three temperature readings to obtain accurate tension values. If necessary, compensate for extreme surface temperature variations that may be encountered if the aircraft is operated primarily in unusual geographic or climatic conditions such as arctic, arid, or tropic locations.

Use rigging pins and gust locks as necessary to assure satsifactory results. At the completion of rigging operations, check turnbuckle adjustment and safetying in accordance with Section 2 of this chapter.

200. CORROSION AND RUST PREVENTION. To insure a satisfactory service life for aircraft control cables, use a cable lubricant to reduce internal friction and prevent corrosion. Loose rust and surface corrosion may be removed with a stainless steel brush, being careful not to damage the cable. Care should be taken to remove all residue from the cable strands prior to rust prevention treatment. If the cable is made from tinned steel, coat the cable with rust preventive oil and wipe off any excess. It should be noted that corrosion-resistant steel cable does not require this treatment for rust prevention.

201.–211. RESERVED.

Section 2.   SAFETY METHODS FOR TURNBUCKLES

212. GENERAL. Safety all turnbuckles with safety wire using either the double or single wrap method, or with any appropriately approved special safetying device complying with the requirements of FAA Technical Standard Order TSO–C21. The swaged and unswaged turnbuckle assemblies are covered by AN Standard Drawings. For safety wire sizes and materials, refer to figure 4.22. Do not reuse safety wire. Adjust the turnbuckle to the correct cable tension so that no more than three threads are exposed on either side of the turnbuckle barrel. Do not lubricate turnbuckles.

213. DOUBLE WRAP METHOD. Of the methods using safety wire for safetying turnbuckles, the method described here is preferred, although either of the other methods described is satisfactory. The method of double wrap safetying is shown in figure 4.23(A). Use two separate lengths of the proper wire (see figure 4.22). Run one end of the wire through the hole in the barrel of the turnbuckle and bend the end of the wire towards opposite ends of

the turnbuckle. Then pass the second length of the wire into the hole in the barrel and bend

Cable size	Type of wrap	Diameter of safety wire	Material (annealed condition)
1/16	Single	0.040	Copper, brass.[1]
3/32	Single	0.040	Copper, brass.[1]
1/8	Single	0.040	Stainless steel, Monel and "K" Monel.
1/8	Double	0.040	Copper, brass.[1]
1/8	Single	0.057 min.	Copper, brass.[1]
5/32 and greater.	Double	0.040	Stainless steel, Monel and "K" Monel.[1]
5/32 and greater.	Single	0.057 min.	Stainless steel, Monel or "K" Monel.[1]
5/32 and greater.	Double	0.051 [2]	Copper, brass.

[1] Galvanized or tinned steel, or soft iron wires are also acceptable.
[2] The safety wire holes in 5/32-inch diameter and larger turnbuckle terminals for swaging may be drilled sufficiently to accommodate the double 0.051-inch diameter copper or brass wires when used.

FIGURE 4.22—Turnbuckle safetying guide.

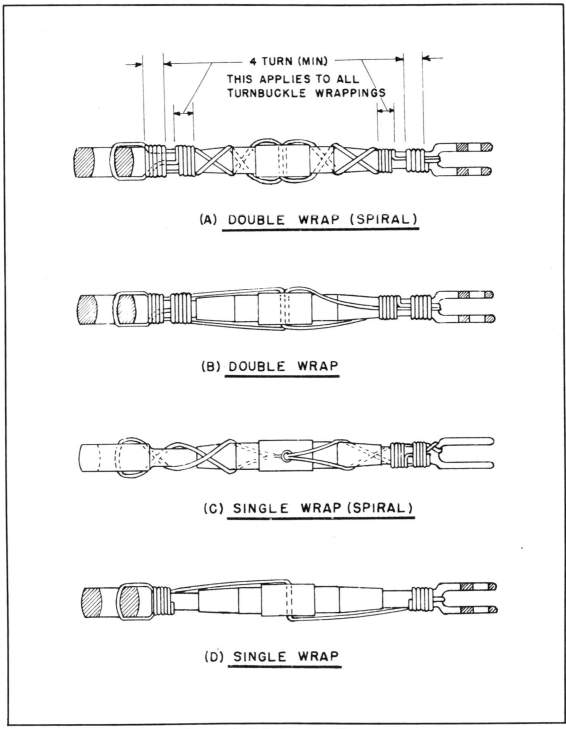

FIGURE 4.23.—Safetying turnbuckles.

the ends along the barrel on the side opposite the first. Spiral the two wires in opposite directions around the barrel to cross each other twice between the center hole and the ends. Then pass the wires at the end of the turnbuckle in opposite directions through the holes in the turnbuckle eyes or between the jaws of the turnbuckle fork, as applicable, laying one wire along the barrel and wrapping the other at least four times around the shank of the turnbuckle and binding the laid wires in place before cutting the wrapped wire off. Wrap the remaining length of safety wire at least four turns around the shank and cut it off. Repeat the procedure at the opposite end of the turnbuckle.

When a swaged terminal is being safetied, pass the ends of both wires, if possible, through the hole provided in the terminal for this purpose and wrap both ends around the shank as described above. When the hole in the terminal is not large enough to accommodate the ends of both wires, the hole may be enlarged in accordance with note 2 of figure 4.22 and the safetying completed as described above. If the hole is not large enough to allow passage of both wires, pass the wire through the hole and loop it over the free end of the other wire, and then wrap both ends around the shank as described.

a. Another satisfactory double wrap method is similar to the above, except that the spiraling of the wires is omitted as shown in figure 4.23(B).

b. The wrapping procedures described and shown on MS 33591 may be used in lieu of the safetying method shown herein.

214. SINGLE WRAP METHOD. The single wrap methods described in the following paragraphs and as illustrated in figures 4.23 (C) and (D) are acceptable but are not the equal of the double wrap methods.

a. Pass a single length of wire through the cable eye or fork, or through the hole in the swaged terminal at either end of the turnbuckle assembly. Spiral each of the wire ends in opposite directions around the first half of the turnbuckle barrel so as to cross each other twice. Thread both wire ends through the hole in the middle of the barrel so that the third crossing of the wire ends is in the hole. Again, spiral the two wire ends in opposite directions around the remaining half of the turnbuckle, crossing them twice. Then, pass one wire end through the cable eye or fork or through the hole in the swaged terminals, in the manner de-

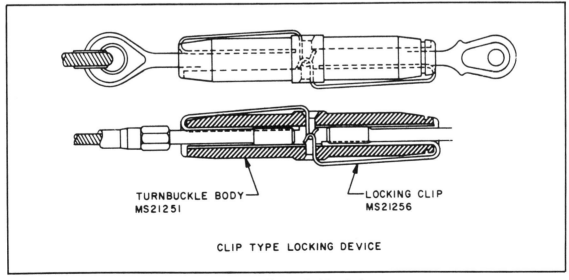

FIGURE 4.24.—Clip type locking device.

scribed above, wrap both wire ends around the shank for at least four turns each, cutting off excess wire. This method is shown in figure 4.23(C).

b. Pass one length of wire through the center hole of the turnbuckle and bend the wire ends toward opposite ends of the turnbuckle. Then pass each wire end through the cable eye or fork, or through the hole in the swaged terminal and wrap each wire end around the shank for at least four turns, cutting off excess wire. This method is shown in figure 4.23(D). After safetying, no more than three threads of the turnbuckle threaded terminal should be exposed.

215. SPECIAL LOCKING DEVICES. Several turnbuckle locking devices are available for securing turnbuckle barrels. Persons intending to use a special device must assure the turnbuckle assembly has been designed to accommodate such device. A typical unit is shown in figure 4.24. When special locking devices are not readily available, the use of safety wire is acceptable.

216.–226. RESERVED.

Aircraft Hardware

(Reprinted from FAA 43.13, Chapter 5)

Section 1. IDENTIFICATION AND USE OF AIRCRAFT HARDWARE

227. BOLTS. Most bolts used in aircraft structures are either general purpose AN bolts, or NAS (National Aircraft Standard) internal wrenching or close-tolerance bolts. In certain cases, aircraft manufacturers make up special bolts for a particular application and it is necessary to use them or their equivalent in replacement.

a. Identification. AN-type aircraft bolts can be identified by the code markings on the boltheads. The markings generally denote the bolt manufacturer, the material of which the bolt is made, and whether the bolt is a standard AN-type or a special purpose bolt. AN standard steel bolts are marked with either a raised dash or asterisk, corrosion-resistant steel is indicated by a single raised dash, and AN aluminum alloy bolts are marked with two raised dashes. The strength and dimensional details of AN bolts are specified on the Army/Navy Aeronautical Standard Drawings.

Special purpose bolts include the high-strength and low-strength types, close-tolerance types; such bolts are normally inspected by magnetic, fluorescent or equivalent inspection methods. Typical markings include "SPEC" (usually highly heat treated), an aircraft manufacturer's part number stamped on the head, or plain heads (low strength). Close-tolerance National Aircraft Standards (NAS) bolts are marked with either a raised or recessed triangle. The material markings for NAS bolts are the same as for AN bolts, except that they may be either raised or recessed. Bolts inspected magnetically (Magnaflux) or by fluorescent means (Zyglo) are identified by means of colored lacquer, or a head marking of a distinctive type. Figure 5.1 shows the typical coding used on aircraft boltheads.

b. Grip Length. In general, bolt-grip lengths should equal the material thickness. However, bolts of slightly greater grip length may be used provided washers are placed under the nut or the bolthead. In the case of plate nuts,

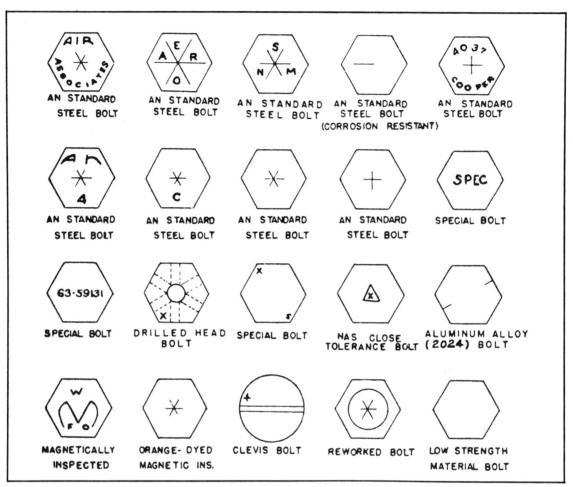

FIGURE 5.1.—Bolt identification.

add shims under the plate. For proper washers, refer to paragraph 231.

c. Locking or Safetying of Bolts. Lock or safety all bolts and/or nuts, except self-locking nuts. Do not reuse cotter pins and safety wire.

d. Bolt Fit. Many boltholes, particularly those in primary connecting elements, have close tolerances. Generally, it is permissible to use the first lettered drill size larger than the normal bolt diameter, except where the AN hexagon bolts are used in light-drive fit (reamed) applications and where NAS close-tolerance bolts or AN clevis bolts are used. Boltholes are to be normal to the surface involved to provide full bearing surface for the bolthead and nut, and

not be oversized or elongated. In case of oversized or elongated holes in critical members, obtain advice from an FAA inspector or engineer, or the aircraft manufacturer before drilling or reaming the hole to take the next larger bolt, as usually, items such as edge distance, clearance, etc., must be considered.

e. Torques. The importance of correct applicacation can not be overemphasized. Undertorque can result in unnecessary wear of nuts and bolts as well as the parts they are holding together. When insufficient pressures are applied, uneven loads will be transmitted throughout the assembly which may result in excessive wear or premature failure due to fatigue. Overtorque can be equally damaging because of failure of a bolt or nut from overstressing the threaded areas. There are a few simple, but very important, procedures that should be followed to assure that correct torque is applied:

(1) Calibrate the torque wrench periodically to assure accuracy; and re-check frequently.

(2) Be sure that bolt and nut threads are clean and dry (unless otherwise specified by the manufacturer).

(3) Run nut down to near contact with the washer or bearing surface and check "friction drag torque" required to turn the nut.

(4) Add the friction drag torque to the desired torque recommended by the manufacturer, or obtain desired torque as shown in figure 5.2. This is referred to as final torque which should register on the indicator or the setting for a snapover type wrench.

(5) Apply a smooth even pull when applying torque pressure. If chattering or a jerking motion occurs during final torque, back off and re-torque.

(6) When installing a castle nut, start alignment with the cotter pin hole at minimum recommended torque, plus friction drag torque, and do not exceed maximum plus friction drag. If the hole and nut castellation do not align, change washers and try again. Exceeding the maximum recommended torque is not recommended.

(7) If torque is applied to capscrews or boltheads, apply recommended torque plus friction drag torque as determined in step (3).

(8) If special adapters are used which will change the effective length of the torque wrench, the final torque indication or wrench setting must be adjusted accordingly. Determine the torque wrench indication or setting with adapter installed as shown in figure 5.3. Figure 5.2 is a composite chart of recommended torque to be used when specific torque is not recommended by the manufacturer. The chart includes standard nut and bolt combinations currently used in aviation maintenance.

f. *Hex-Head Bolts (AN–3 through AN–20).* The hex-head aircraft bolt is an all-purpose structural bolt used for general applications involving tension or shear loads. Alloy steel bolts smaller than No. 10–32 and aluminum alloy bolts smaller than 1/4-inch diameter are not to be used in primary structure. Do not use aluminum alloy bolts and nuts where they will be repeatedly removed for purposes of maintenance and inspection. Aluminum alloy nuts may be used with cadmiumplated steel bolts loaded in shear on land airplanes, but are not to be used on seaplanes due to the possibility of dissimilar metals corrosion.

g. *Close-Tolerance Bolts (AN–173 through AN–186 (Hex-Head), NAS–80 through NAS–86 (100° Countersunk)).* Close-tolerance bolts are used in high-performance aircraft in applications where the bolted joint is subject to severe load reversals and vibration. The standard AN hex-head bolts may be used for the same applications provided a light-drive fit is accomplished.

h. *Internal Wrenching Bolts (MS–20004 through MS–20024 or NAS–495).* These bolts are suitable for use both in tension and shear applications. In steel parts, countersink the bolthole to seat the large radius of the shank at the head or, as in aluminum alloys, use a special heat-treated washer (NAS–143C) that fits the head to provide adequate bearing area. A special heat-treated plain washer (NAS–143) is used under the nut. Use special high-strength nuts on these bolts. (Refer to paragraph 230c(7).) Replace all internal wrenching bolts by another internal wrenching bolt. Standard AN hexhead bolts and washers cannot be substituted for them, as they do not have the required strength.

i. *Drilled-Head Bolts (AN–73).* The AN drilled-head bolt is similar to the standard hex-bolt, but has a deeper head which is drilled to receive wire for safetying. The AN–3 and the AN–73 series of bolts are interchangeable for all practical purposes from the standpoint of tension and shear strengths.

228. SCREWS. In general, screws differ from

BOLTS Steel Tension	BOLTS Steel Tension	BOLTS Aluminum
AN 3 thru AN 20	MS 20004 thru MS 20024	AN 3DD thru AN 20DD
AN 42 thru AN 49	NAS 144 thru NAS 158	AN 173DD thru AN 186DD
AN 73 thru AN 81	NAS 333 thru NAS 340	AN 509DD
AN 173 thru AN 186	NAS 583 thru NAS 590	AN 525D
MS 20033 thru MS 20046	NAS 624 thru NAS 644	MS 27039D
MS 20073	NAS 1303 thru NAS 1320	MS 24694DD
MS 20074	NAS 172	
AN 509 NK9	NAS 174	
MS 24694	NAS 517	
AN 525 NK525	Steel shear bolt	
MS 27039	NAS 464	

NUTS		NUTS		NUTS	
Steel Tension	Steel Shear	Steel Tension	Steel Shear	Aluminum Tension	Aluminum Shear
AN 310	AN 320	AN 310	AN 320	AN 365D	AN 320D
AN 315	AN 364	AN 315	AN 364	AN 310D	AN 364D
AN 363	NAS 1022	AN 363	NAS 1022	NAS 1021D	NAS 1022D
AN 365	MS 17826	AN 365	MS 17826		
NAS 1021	MS 20364	MS 17825	MS 20364		
MS 17825		MS 20365			
MS 21045		MS 21045			
MS 20365		NAS 1021			
MS 20500		NAS 679			
NAS 679		NAS 1291			

FINE THREAD SERIES

Nut-bolt size	Torque Limits in.-lbs.		Torque Limits in.-lbs.		Torque Limits in.-lbs.		Torque Limits in.-lbs.		Torque Limits in.-lbs.		Torque Limits in.-lbs.	
	Min.	Max.	Min.	Max.	Min.	Max.	Min.	Max.	Min.	Max.	Min.	Max.
8 −36	12	15	7	9	--------	--------	--------	--------	5	10	3	6
10 −32	20	25	12	15	25	30	15	20	10	15	5	10
¼−28	50	70	30	40	80	100	50	60	30	45	15	30
5⁄16−24	100	140	60	85	120	145	70	90	40	65	25	40
⅜−24	160	190	95	110	200	250	120	150	75	110	45	70
7⁄16−20	450	500	270	300	520	630	300	400	180	280	110	170
½−20	480	690	290	410	770	950	450	550	280	410	160	260
9⁄16−18	800	1,000	480	600	1,100	1,300	650	800	380	580	230	360
⅝−18	1,100	1,300	660	780	1,250	1,550	750	950	550	670	270	420
¾−16	2,300	2,500	1,300	1,500	2,650	3,200	1,600	1,900	950	1,250	560	880
⅞−14	2,500	3,000	1,500	1,800	3,550	4,350	2,100	2,600	1,250	1,900	750	1,200
1 −14	3,700	4,500	2,200	3,300	4,500	5,500	2,700	3,300	1,600	2,400	950	1,500
1⅛ −12	5,000	7,000	3,000	4,200	6,000	7,300	3,600	4,400	2,100	3,200	1,250	2,000
1¼ −12	9,000	11,000	5,400	6,600	11,000	13,400	6,600	8,000	3,900	5,600	2,300	3,650

COARSE THREAD SERIES

Nut-bolt size	Min.	Max.	Min.	Max.	Min.	Max.	Min.	Max.	Min.	Max.	Min.	Max.
8 −32	12	15	7	9								
10 −24	20	25	12	15								
¼ −20	40	50	25	30								
5⁄16−18	80	90	48	55								
⅜ −16	160	185	95	110								
7⁄16−14	235	255	140	155								
½ −13	400	480	240	290								
9⁄16−12	500	700	300	420								
⅝ −11	700	900	420	540								
¾ −10	1,150	1,600	700	950								
⅞ − 9	2,200	3,000	1,300	1,800								
1 − 8	3,700	5,000	2,200	3,000								
1⅛ − 8	5,500	6,500	3,300	4,000								
1¼ − 8	6,500	8,000	4,000	5,000								

FIGURE 5.2.—Recommended torque values
for nut-bolt combinations— (without lubrication).

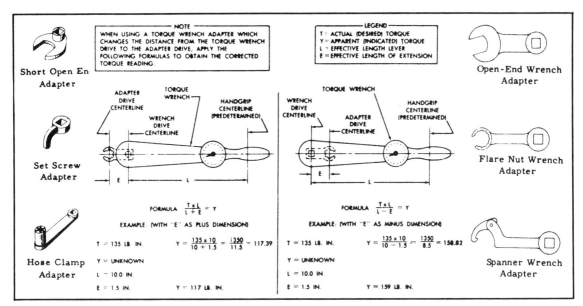

NOTE — WHEN USING A TORQUE WRENCH ADAPTER WHICH CHANGES THE DISTANCE FROM THE TORQUE WRENCH DRIVE TO THE ADAPTER DRIVE, APPLY THE FOLLOWING FORMULAS TO OBTAIN THE CORRECTED TORQUE READING:

LEGEND —
T = ACTUAL (DESIRED) TORQUE
Y = APPARENT (INDICATED) TORQUE
L = EFFECTIVE LENGTH LEVER
E = EFFECTIVE LENGTH OF EXTENSION

Short Open End Adapter

Set Screw Adapter

Hose Clamp Adapter

Open-End Wrench Adapter

Flare Nut Wrench Adapter

Spanner Wrench Adapter

FORMULA $\frac{T \times L}{L + E} = Y$

EXAMPLE: (WITH "E" AS PLUS DIMENSION)

T = 135 LB. IN. $Y = \frac{135 \times 10}{10 + 1.5} = \frac{1350}{11.5} = 117.39$
Y = UNKNOWN
L = 10.0 IN.
E = 1.5 IN.   Y = 117 LB. IN.

FORMULA $\frac{T \times L}{L - E} = Y$

EXAMPLE: (WITH "E" AS MINUS DIMENSION)

T = 135 LB. IN. $Y = \frac{135 \times 10}{10 - 1.5} = \frac{1350}{8.5} = 158.82$
Y = UNKNOWN
L = 10.0 IN.
E = 1.5 IN.   Y = 159 LB. IN.

FIGURE 5.3.—Torque wrench with various adapters.

bolts by the following characteristics: Usually lower material strength, a looser thread fit (No. 2), head shapes formed to engage a screwdriver, and the shank threaded along its entire length without a clearly defined grip. However, several types of structural screws are available that differ from the standard structural bolts only in the type of head.

The material is equivalent and a definite grip is provided. The AN–525 washerhead screws, the AN 509–100° countersunk structural screws, and the NAS–204 through NAS–235 are such parts. The material markings are the same as those used on AN standard bolts.

a. Structural Screws (NAS–204 through NAS–235, AN–509 and AN–525). This type of screw, when made of alloy steel such as SAE–4130, NE–8630, or equivalent, and heat-treated from 125,000 p.s.i., may be used for structural assembly in shear applications similar to structural bolts.

b. Self-Tapping Screws. The AN–504 and AN–506 screws are used for attaching minor removable parts such as nameplates and the like. AN–530 and AN–531 are used in blind applications for the temporary attachment of sheet

metal for riveting and the permanent assembly of nonstructural assemblies. AN–535 is a plain head self-tapping screw used in the attachment of nameplates or in sealing drainholes in corrosion-proofing tubular structures, and is not intended to be removed after installation. Never use self-tapping screws to replace standard screws, nuts, bolts, or rivets in the original structure.

229. TAPER PINS (AN–385 AND AN–386). Plain and threaded taper pins are used in joints which carry shear loads and where absence of play is essential. The plain taper pin is drilled and usually safetied with wire. The threaded taper pin is used with a taper-pin washer (AN–975) and shear nut (safetied with cotter pin) or self-locking nut.

a. The Flathead Pin (MS–20392). Commonly called a clevis pin, the flathead pin is used in conjunction with tie rod terminals and in secondary controls which are not subject to continuous operation. The pin is customarily installed with the head up so that if the cotter pin fails or works out, the pin will remain in place.

b. The AN–380 Cotter Pin. This is used for

safetying bolts, screws, nuts, other pins, and in various applications where such safetying is necessary. Use AN–381 cotter pins in locations where nonmagnetic material is required or in locations where resistance to corrosion is desired.

230. NUTS.

a. Self-Locking Nuts. Self-locking nuts are acceptable for use on certificated aircraft subject to the restrictions on the pertinent manufacturer's recommended practice sheets. Self-locking nuts are used on aircraft to provide tight connections which will not shake loose under severe vibration. Two types of self-locking nuts are currently in use, the all-metal type and the fiber or nylon lock type. Do not use self-locking nuts at joints which subject either the nut or bolt to rotation. They may be used with antifriction bearings and control pulleys, provided the inner race of the bearing is clamped to the supporting structure by the nut and bolt. Attach nuts to the structure in a positive manner to eliminate rotation or misalignment when tightening the bolts or screws.

(1) All-metal locknuts are constructed with either the threads in the locking insert out-of-phase with the load-carrying section, or with a saw-cut insert with a pinched-in thread in the locking section. The locking action of the all-metal nut depends upon the resiliency of the metal when the locking section and load-carrying section are engaged by screw threads.

(2) Fiber or nylon locknuts are constructed with an unthreaded fiber-locking insert held securely in place. The fiber or nylon has a smaller diameter than the nut, and when a bolt or screw is entered, it taps into the insert, producing a locking action. After the nut has been tightened, make sure the rounded or chamfered end bolts, studs, or screws extend at least the full round or chamfer through the nut. Flat end bolts, studs, or screws should extend at least 1/32 inch through the nut. When fiber-type self-locking nuts are reused, check the fiber carefully to make sure it has not lost its locking friction or become brittle. Do not reuse locknuts if they can be run up finger-

tight. Bolts 5/16-inch diameter and over with cotter pinholes may be used with self-locking nuts but only if free from burrs around the holes. Bolts with damaged threads and rough ends are not acceptable. Do not tap the fiber-locking insert.

(3) Self-locking nut bases are made in a number of forms and materials for riveting and welding to aircraft structure or parts. Certain applications require the installation of self-locking nuts in channels, an arrangement which permits the attachment of many nuts with only a few rivets. These channels are track-like bases with regularly spaced nuts which are either removable or nonremovable. The removable type carries a floating nut, which can be snapped in or out of the channel, thus making possible the ready removal of damaged nuts. Nuts such as the clinch-type and spline-type which depend on friction for their anchorage are not acceptable for use in aircraft structures.

(4) Self-locking nuts may be used on aircraft engines and accessories when their use is specified by the engine manufacturer in his bulletins or manuals.

b. Aircraft Castle Nut (AN–310). The castle nut is used with drilled-shank AN hex-head bolts, clevis bolts, eye bolts, drilled-head bolts or studs, and is designed to accommodate a cotter pin or lockwire as a means of safetying.

c. Miscellaneous Aircraft Nuts.

(1) The plain nut (AN–315 and AN–335) has limited use on aircraft structures and requires an auxiliary locking device such as a checknut or lockwasher.

(2) Light hex-nuts (AN–340 and AN–345) are used in miscellaneous applications and must be locked by an auxiliary device.

(3) The checknut (AN–316) is used as a locking device for plain nuts, screws, threaded rod ends, and other devices.

(4) The castellated shear nut (AN–320) is designed for use with clevis bolts and threaded taper pins, which are normally subjected to shearing stress only.

(5) Wing nuts (AN–350) are intended for use on hose clamps and battery connections,

etc., where the desired tightness is ordinarily obtained by the use of the fingers or hand tools.

(6) Sheet spring nuts, such as speed nuts, are used with standard and sheet metal self-tapping screws in nonstructural locations. They find various uses in supporting line clamps, conduit clamps, electrical equipment, access doors, and the like, and are available in several types.

(7) Two commercial types of high-strength internal or external wrenching nuts are available, the internal and external wrenching elastic-stop nut and the Unbrako internal and external wrenching nut. Both are of the self-locking type, are heat-treated, and are capable of carrying the high-strength bolt-tension load.

231. WASHERS. The types of washers used in aircraft structure are: plain washers, lock-washers, and special washers.

a. Plain washers (AN–960 and AN–970) are widely used under hex nuts to provide a smoothbearing surface, to act as a shim and to adjust holes in bolts. Use plain washers under lockwashers to prevent damage to surfaces. Cadmiumplated steel washers are recommended for use under boltheads or nuts on aluminum alloy or magnesium structures where corrosion, if it occurs, will then be between the washer and the steel. The AN–970 steel washer provides a greater bearing area than the plain type, and is used in wooden structures under both boltheads and nuts to prevent local crushing of the surface.

b. Lock washers (AN–935 and AN–936) may be used with machine screws or bolts whenever the self-locking or castellated type of nut is not applicable. They are not to be used as fastenings to primary or secondary structures, or where subject to frequent removal or corrosive conditions.

c. Ball-socket and seat-washers (AN–950 and AN–955) are used in special applications where the bolt is installed at an angle to the surface, or when perfect alinement with the surface is required at all times. These washers are used together.

d. Taper-pin washers (AN–975) are used with the threaded taper pin.

e. NAS–143 washers are used with NAS internal wrenching bolts and internal wrenching nuts. Type "C" is countersunk to seat the bolt-head shank radius and a plain-type washer is used under the nut. Both of these washers are heat treated from 125,000 to 145,000 p.s.i.

232. TYPES OF RIVETS.

a. Standard solid-shank rivets and the universal head rivets (AN–470) are used in aircraft construction in both interior and exterior locations.

b. Roundhead rivets (AN–430) are used in the interior of aircraft except where clearance is required for adjacent members.

c. Flathead rivets (AN–442) are used in the interior of the aircraft where interference of adjacent members does not permit the use of roundhead rivets.

d. Brazierhead rivets (AN–455 and AN–456) are used on the exterior surfaces of aircraft where flush riveting is not essential.

e. All protruding head rivets may be replaced by MS–20470 (supersedes AN–470) rivets. This has been adopted as the standard for protruding head rivets in this country.

f. Countersunk head rivets MS–20426 (supersedes AN–426 100°) are used on the exterior surfaces of aircraft to provide a smooth aerodynamic surface, and in other applications where a smooth finish is desired. The 100° countersunk head has been adopted as the standard in this country.

233. MATERIAL APPLICATIONS.

a. 2117–T3 is the most commonly used rivet material utilized in aluminum alloy structures. Its main advantage lies in the fact that it may be used in the condition received without further treatment.

b. The 2017–T3, 2017–T31, and 2024–T4 rivets are used in aluminum alloy structures where strength higher than that of the 2117–T3 rivet is needed. See Handbook MIL–HDBK–5 for differences between the two types of 17ST rivets specified here.

c. **The 1100 rivets of pure aluminum** are used for riveting nonstructural parts fabricated from the softer aluminum alloys, such as 1100, 3003, and 5052.

d. **When riveting magnesium alloy structures,** 5056 rivets are used exclusively due to their corrosion-resistant qualities in combination with the magnesium alloys.

e. **Mild steel rivets** are used primarily in riveting steel parts. Do not use galvanized rivets on steel parts subjected to high heat.

f. **Corrosion-resistant steel rivets** are used primarily in riveting corrosion-resistant steel parts such as firewalls, exhaust stack bracket attachments, and similar structures.

g. **Monel rivets** are used in special cases for riveting high-nickel steel alloys and nickel alloys. They may be used interchangeably with stainless steel rivets as they are more easily driven. However, it is preferable to use stainless steel rivets in stainless steel parts.

h. **Copper rivets** are used for riveting copper alloys, leather, and other nonmetallic materials. This rivet has only limited usage in aircraft.

i. **Hi-shear rivets** are sometimes used in connections where the shearing loads are the primary design consideration. Its use is restricted to such connections. It should be noted that hi-shear rivet patterns are not to be used for the installation of control surface hinges and hinge brackets. Do not paint the rivets prior to assembly, even where dissimilar metals are being joined. However, it is advisable to touch up each end of the driven rivet with zinc chromate primer to allow the later application of the general airplane finish.

j. **Blind rivets** in the MS–20600 through MS–20603 series rivets and the mechanically-locked stem NAS 1398, 1399, 1738, and 1739 rivets may be substituted for solid rivets in accordance with the blind rivet manufacturer's recommendations. They should not be used where the looseness or failure of a few rivets will impair the airworthiness of the aircraft. Design allowables for blind rivets are specified in MIL-HDBK–5, "Metallic Materials and Elements for Flight Vehicle Structures." Specific structural applications are outlined in MS–33522. Nonstructural applications for such blind rivets as MS–20604 and MS–20605 are contained in MS–33557.

234. FASTENERS (COWL AND FAIRING). A number of patented fasteners are in use on aircraft. A variety of these fasteners are commercially available and the manufacturer's recommendations concerning the proper use of these types of fasteners should always be considered in other than replacement application.

235. UNCONVENTIONAL ATTACHMENTS. Do not use unconventional or new attachment devices in the primary structure unless approved by a representative of the Federal Aviation Administration.

236.–246. RESERVED.

Chapter 6

Windshields, Enclosures, and Exits

(Reprinted from FAA 43.13, Chapter 9)

Note: FAA 43.13 Chapters 6 (Corrosion Protection), 7 (Identification, Testing, and Inspection of Materials) and 8 (Aircraft Equipment) have been omitted from this text. These areas are best left to the professional airframe & powerplant mechanic.

375. GENERAL. These repairs are applicable to plastic windshields, enclosures, and windows in nonpressurized airplanes. For pressurized airplanes replace or repair plastic elements in accordance with the manufacturer's recommendation.

a. *Types of Plastics.* Two types of plastics are commonly used in transparent enclosures of aircraft. These materials are known as acrylic plastics and polyester plastics.

376. REPLACEMENT PANELS. Use material equivalent to that originally used by the manufacturer of the aircraft for replacement panels. There are many types of transparent plastics on the market. Their properties vary greatly, particularly in regard to expansion characteristics, brittleness under low temperatures, re-sistance to discoloration when exposed to sun-light, surface checking, etc. Information on these properties is in MIL–HDBK–17, *Plastics for Flight Vehicles, Part II—Transparent Glazing Materials,* available from the Government Printing Office. These properties have been considered by aircraft manufacturers in selecting materials to be used in their designs and the use of substitutes having different characteristics may result in subsequent difficulties.

377. INSTALLATION PROCEDURES. When installing a replacement panel, use the same mounting method employed by the manufacturer of the airplane. While the actual installation will vary from one type of aircraft to another, consider the following major principles when installing any replacement panel:

a. *Never force a plastic panel* out of shape to make it fit a frame. If a replacement panel does not fit easily into the mounting, obtain a new replacement or heat the whole panel and

141

reform. When possible, cut and fit a new panel at ordinary room temperature.

b. *In clamping or bolting plastic panels* into their mountings, do not place the plastic under excessive compressive stress. It is easy to develop more than 1,000 pounds per square inch on the plastic by overtorquing a nut and bolt. Tighten each nut to a firm fit, then back off one full turn.

c. *In bolt installations*, use spacers, collars, shoulders, or stopnuts to prevent tightening the bolt excessively. Whenever such devices are used by the airplane manufacturer, retain them in the replacement installation. It is important that the original number of bolts, complete with washers, spacers, etc., be used. When rivets are used, provide adequate spacers or other satisfactory means to prevent excessive tightening of the frame to the plastic.

d. *Mount plastic panels* between rubbed, cork, or other gasket material to make the installation waterproof, to reduce vibration, and to help to distribute compressive stresses on the plastic.

e. *Plastics expand and contract* considerably more than the metal channels in which they are mounted. Mount windshield panels to a sufficient depth in the channel to prevent it from falling out when the panel contracts at low temperatures or deforms under load. When the manufacturer's original design permits, mount panels to a minimum depth of 1 1/8 inch and with a clearance of 1/8 inch between the plastic and the bottom of the channel.

f. *In installations involving bolts or rivets*, make the holes through the plastic oversize 1/8 inch diameter and center so that the plastic will not bind or crack at the edge of the holes. The use of slotted holes is also recommended.

378. REPAIR OF PLASTICS. Replace extensively damaged transparent plastic rather than repair whenever possible since even a carefully patched part is not the equal of a new section either optically or structurally. At the first sign of crack development, drill a small hole at the extreme ends of the cracks as shown in figure 9.1. This serves to localize the cracks and to prevent further splitting by distributing the strain over a large area. If the cracks are small, stopping them with drilled holes will usually suffice until replacement or more permanent repair can be made. The following repairs are permissible; however, they are not to be located in the pilot's line of vision during landing or normal flight.

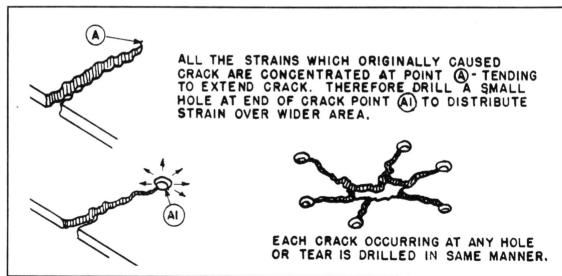

ALL THE STRAINS WHICH ORIGINALLY CAUSED CRACK ARE CONCENTRATED AT POINT (A) - TENDING TO EXTEND CRACK. THEREFORE DRILL A SMALL HOLE AT END OF CRACK POINT (A1) TO DISTRIBUTE STRAIN OVER WIDER AREA.

EACH CRACK OCCURRING AT ANY HOLE OR TEAR IS DRILLED IN SAME MANNER.

FIGURE 9.1.—Stop-drilling cracks.

a. *Surface Patch.* If a surface patch is to be installed, trim away the damaged area and round all corners. Cut a piece of plastic of sufficient size to cover the damaged area and extend at least 3/4 inch on each side of the crack or hole. Bevel the edges as shown in figure 9.2. If the section to be repaired is curved, shape the patch to the same contour by heating it in an oil bath at a temperature of 248° to 302° F., or it may be heated on a hotplate until soft. Boiling water should not be used for heating. Coat the patch evenly with plastic solvent adhesive and place immediately over the hole. Maintain a uniform pressure of from 5 to 10 pounds per square inch on the patch for a minimum of 3 hours. Allow the patch to dry 24 to 36 hours before sanding or polishing is attempted.

b. *Plug Patch.* In using inserted patches to repair holes in plastic structures, trim the holes

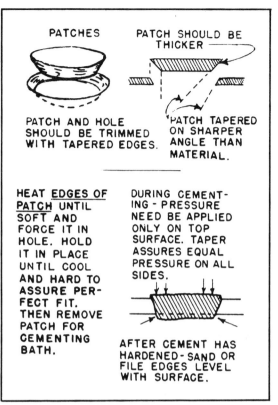

FIGURE 9.3.—Plug patch repair.

to a perfect circle or oval and bevel the edges slightly. Make the patch slightly thicker than the material being repaired and similarly bevel the edges. Install patches in accordance with figure 9.3. Heat the plug until soft and press into the hole without cement and allow to cool to make a perfect fit. Remove the plug, coat the edges with adhesive, and then reinsert in the hole. Maintain a firm light pressure until the cement has set, then sand or file the edges level with the surface; buff and polish.

379. CLEANING AND POLISHING TRANSPARENT PLASTIC. Plastics have many advantages over glass for aircraft use, but they lack the surface hardness of glass, and care must be exercised while servicing the aircraft to avoid scratching or otherwise damaging the surface.

a. *Cleaning.* Clean the plastic by washing with plenty of water and mild soap, using a clean, soft, grit-free cloth, sponge, or bare hands. Do

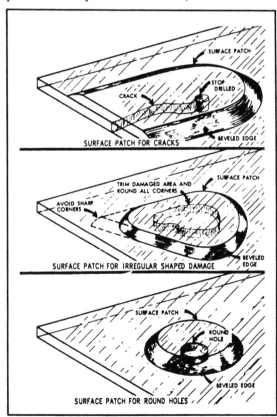

FIGURE 9.2.—Surface patches.

not use gasoline, alcohol, benzene, acetone, carbon tetracholoride, fire extinguisher or deicing fluids, lacquer thinners, or window cleaning sprays because they will soften the plastic and cause crazing.

b. **Plastics should not be rubbed** with a dry cloth since this is likely to cause scratches, and also build up an electrostatic charge which attracts dust particles to the surface. If after removing dirt and grease no great amount of scratching is visible, finish the plastic with a good grade of commercial wax. Apply the wax in a thin even coat and bring to a high polish by rubbing lightly with a soft cloth.

c. **Polishing.** Do not attempt hand polishing or buffing until the surface is clean. A soft, open-type cotton or flannel buffing wheel is suggested. Minor scratches may be removed by vigorously rubbing the affected area by hand, using a soft clean cloth dampened with a mixture of turpentine and chalk, or by applying automobile cleanser with a damp cloth. Remove the cleaner and polish with a soft, dry cloth. Acrylic and cellulose acetate plastics are thermoplastic. Friction created by buffing or polishing too long in one spot can generate sufficient heat to soften the surface. This will produce visual distortion and is to be guarded against.

380. EMERGENCY EXITS. The following material is intended as a guide for the inspection and maintenance of aircraft emergency exit provisions. Schedule inspections to coincide with all 100-hour/annual, progressive inspections or the maintenance procedures that have been approved by the Administrator. Before beginning inspection or maintenance activities of any type, consult the appropriate manufacturer's service manual for information specifying the type of exit release mechanism used.

a. *Inspection.* Examine the emergency exits and all associated hardware closely for deformation, excessive wear, security of attachment, lubrication, and cleanness.

(1) **Doors.**

(a) Inspect the door structure and skin for wrinkles, cracks, alignment with the fuselage, deep scratches, dents, loose rivets, corrosion, or any other indication of structural irregularity.

(b) Examine rubber seals for cuts, tears, excessive wear, proper contact with the entire door frame, and general deterioration.

(c) Inspect bearings, hinges, hinge fairings, latches, springs, pins, rods, handles, and related parts for wear and general condition.

(d) Examine the door jamb, frame, and supporting structure for cracks, loose fasteners, condition of stops, and corrosion or damage.

(e) Check the door for ease of operation and freedom of movement through its full range of travel.

(f) If a door warning light is provided, test it for proper operation and adjustment.

(g) Check the door locking mechanism for positive fit and at least the minimum lock pin engagement as specified in the applicable aircraft manual.

(2) **Passenger Escape Hatches.**

(a) Remove the escape hatch. Check for ease of removal and correct functioning of the release mechanism through all angles of pull likely to be encountered during emergency conditions.

CAUTION

If applicable, position one man outside the aircraft to catch the hatch, thereby preventing it from falling and damaging the wing and/or hatch.

(b) Examine the escape hatch structure for cracks, dents, deep scratches, alignment, loose rivets and/or bolts, corrosion, or any other indication of structural irregularity.

(c) Inspect the rubber seals for excessive wear, deterioration, cuts, tears, and proper contact with the fuselage.

(d) Check the operating mechanisms for wear, cracks, and general condition; springs for proper tension, alignment, and security.

(e) If applicable, inspect external release mechanisms for wear, cracks, and proper operation. Check for presence and legibility of external placards and exit location markings.

(f) Examine the escape hatch opening jamb, frame, stops, and skin for cracks and other evidence of damage or failure.

(g) If an emergency escape rope is provided, check it for accessibility, attachment, freedom of operation, rot, broken strands, and general condition. Inspect the storage container or tube for sharp edges or moisture.

(3) Crew Compartment Sliding Windows.

(a) Inspect the window frame for cracks, dents, questionable scratches, loose rivets, corrosion, or any other indication of structural irregularity.

(b) Examine the extrusion seal for wear, general deterioration, and proper contact with the fuselage canopy.

(c) Check the window teleflex mechanism for loose bearings, wear, corrosion, and proper operation.

(d) Inspect the windows for cracks, scratches, nicks, crazing, fogging or moisture between panes, delaminations, hot spots or discoloration.

NOTE: Fogging or delaminations of windows other than windshields are generally not cause for replacement unless visibility is impaired. It is suggested the manufacturer be consulted on any question concerning windows installed in pressurized aircraft.

b. Maintenance.

(1) Lubrication. Lubricate all moving parts of the exit latching mechanisms. The following practices will generally apply when specific procedures are not available.

(a) Piano hinges and operating mechanism pivot points—oil lightly and wipe off excess. Use only oil that is compatible with the type of seal used on that specific aircraft. Do not allow the oil to contact fabrics or finished surfaces.

(b) Latch bolts and sliding surfaces— apply a light film from a graphite stick or latch lubricant (door ease).

(2) Seal Replacement. Information pertaining to special handling procedures for seals, gaskets, lubricants (dry or liquid), age limitations (shelf life), and types of adhesives may be found in the manufacturer's maintenance and overhaul manuals. Check the thickness of the seal or gasket for uniformity to prevent warping of the component, i.e., hatch or door. Exercise care when using adhesives to cement seals to the hatch frame or exit door as spillage or excessive amounts could cause the exit to bind.

NOTE: Replace seals and gaskets with materials recommended by the manufacturer. Many times these materials have been changed due to service experience, therefore a check of manufacturers' service information should be made to ascertain that any replacement parts, materials, etc., are those currently recommended.

(3) Hatch/Window Replacement. Check replacement hatches or windows for proper size and fit to preclude opening problems. Improper loading of the aircraft or an accident may cause binding of the hatch/window if inadequate clearance exists.

(4) Emergency Exit Service Difficulties. Emergency exits that fail to open unless extreme force is exerted are usually caused by one of the following:

(a) Paint or primers on the mating surfaces of the exit which are not allowed to dry completely. As a result, the surfaces will stick to each other.

(b) Latches that bind or fail to work unless pulled straight out.

(c) Failure to lubricate mating or rubbing surfaces.

(d) Failure to operate exits after final assembly. The exits may perform satisfactorily before the airplane is painted, but the finishing process results in the application of solvents, cleaners, primers, and paint finishes that may tend to make the exit inoperable. Check the exit for ease of release after painting and finishing of an aircraft.

c. Operational Considerations.

(1) Placards. Check to assure that all required placards and markings are installed (FAR 23.1557 (d) or 25.811). Make certain that curtains, drapes, clothes racks, etc. do not cover the placard or the exit operating handle.

When the normal exit identification signs are obstructed by compartmentation, galleys or other similar furnishings, use signs which contain the word "EXIT" and appropriate arrows to direct the attention of occupants to the exit locations.

(2) Precautions. Following any cabin interior modifications or configuration changes, check the accessability and operation of emergency exits by actual operation of the exit.

(a) Certain types of escape hatches have release handles which will not reinstall the lock pins into their locked position. If this type of release handle is pulled to any degree, either intentionally or inadvertently, it is necessary to ascertain that the locking pins are in position and safetied.

(b) Safety wire used to secure aircraft egress provisions should be of the type recommended by the manufacturer. Do not use stainless steel or other types of stiff wire. Acceptable substitutes would be either .011" copper or .020" aluminum soft safety wire.

(c) Some aircraft have inflatable door seals which assure a positive sealing capability during pressurization. Check these systems for proper operation in accordance with the manufacturer's maintenance instructions.

(d) Ascertain that seatbacks, tables, cabinets and other furnishings cannot interfere with the accessibility and opening of any exit either from inside or outside of the aircraft.

(3) Power Assist Devices. Some aircraft are presently equipped with powered systems to assist in door opening. It is imperative that the manufacturers' service instructions and manuals be reviewed before any maintenance is performed on such systems. These devices are usually hydraulically powered and, during an emergency condition, utilize a high-pressure bottle system as an alternate source (pneumatic or CO_2). Future designs will quite possibly involve various combinations of hydraulic, electrical, or pneumatic units. Strict attention to all servicing procedures will be essential to assure proper functioning of the power-assist device when needed in an emergency.

381.–391. RESERVED.

Comment: We draw upon the FAA publication AC 65.9, *Airframe and Powerplant Mechanics General Handbook,* for additional data on aircraft plastics:

TRANSPARENT PLASTICS

Transparent plastic materials used in aircraft canopies, windshields, and other similar transparent enclosures may be divided into two major classes according to their reaction to heat. These are *thermoplastic* and *thermosetting.*

Thermoplastic materials will soften when heated and harden when cooled. These materials can be heated until soft and then formed into the desired shape. When cooled, they will retain this shape. The same piece of plastic can be reheated and reshaped any number of times without changing the chemical composition of the material.

Thermosetting plastics harden upon heating, and reheating has no softening effect. These plastics cannot be reshaped after once being fully cured by the application of heat.

In addition to the above classes, transparent plastics are manufactured in two forms, monolithic (solid) and laminated. Laminated transparent plastics are made from transparent face sheets bonded by an inner-layer material, usually polyvinyl butyral. Because of its shatter-resistant qualities, laminated plastic is superior to solid plastics and is used in many pressurized aircraft. Most of the transparent sheet used in aviation is manufactured in accordance with military specifications.

Another development in transparent plastics is stretched acrylic. This is a type of plastic which, before being shaped, is pulled in both directions to rearrange its molecular structure. Stretched acrylic panels have greater resistance to impact and are less subject to shatter; its chemical resistance is greater, edging is simpler, and crazing and scratches are less detrimental.

Individual sheets of transparent plastic are covered with a heavy paper to which a pressure-sensitive adhesive has been added. This paper helps to prevent accidental scratching during storage and handling.

Sheets should be stored in bins that are tilted approximately 10 degrees from vertical. If they must be stored horizontally, piles should not be over 18 inches high, and small sheets should be placed atop larger ones to avoid unsupported overhang. Storage should be in a cool, dry place away from solvent fumes, heating coils, radiators and steam pipes. The temperature in the storage room should not exceed 120 degrees F.

While direct sunlight does not harm acrylic plastic, it will cause drying and hardening of the masking adhesive, making removal of the paper difficult. If the paper will not roll off easily, place the sheet in an oven at 250 degrees F for one minute, maximum. The heat will soften the adhesive for easy removal of the paper.

If an oven is not available, hardened masking paper may be removed by softening the adhesive with aliphatic naphtha. Sheets so treated must be washed immediately with clean water, taking care not to scratch the surface.

Note: Aliphatic naphtha is not to be confused with aromatic naphtha and other dry cleaning solvents that are definitely harmful to plastic. However, aliphatic naphatha is flammable and all precautions regarding the use of flammable liquids must be observed when handling it.

REINFORCED PLASTIC

Reinforced plastic is a thermosetting material used in the manufacture of radomes, antenna covers, wingtips, and as insulation for various pieces of electrical equipment and fuel cells. It has excellent dielectric characteristics that make it ideal for radomes, however, its high strength-to-weight ratio, resistance to mildew, rust, and rot, and ease of fabrication make it equally suitable for other parts of an aircraft.

Reinforced plastic components of aircraft are formed of either solid laminates or sandwich-type laminates. Resins used to impregnate glass cloths are of the contact-pressure type (requiring little or no pressure during cure). These resins are supplied as a liquid which can vary in viscosity from a waterlike consistency to a thick syrup. Cure or polymerization is effected by the use of a catalyst, usually benzoyl peroxide.

Solid laminates are constructed of three or more layers of resin-impregnated cloths "wet laminated" together to form a solid sheet facing or molded shape.

Sandwich-type laminates are constructed of two or more solid sheet facings or a molded shape enclosing a fiberglass honeycomb or foam-type core. Honeycomb cores are made of glass cloths impregnated with a polyester or a combination of nylon and phenolic resins. The specific density and cell size of honeycomb cores varies over a considerable latitude. Honeycomb cores are normally fabricated in blocks that are later cut to the desired thickness on a band saw.

Foam-type cores are formulated from combinations of alkyd resins and metatoluene di-isocyanate. Sandwich-type fiberglass components filled with foam cores are manufactured to exceedingly close tolerances on overall thickness of the molded facing and core material. To achieve this accuracy, the resin is poured into a close-tolerance, molded shape. The resin formulation immediately foams up to fill the void in the molded shape and forms a bond between the facing and the core.

Chapter 7

Weight and Balance

(Reprinted from FAA 43.13, Chapter 13)

Note: FAA 43.13 Chapters 10 (Hydraulic and Pneumatic Systems), 11 (Electrical Systems) and 12 (Propellers, Rotors, and Associated Equipment) have been omitted from this text. These areas are best left to the professional airframe & powerplant mechanic.

656. GENERAL. The removal or addition of equipment results in changes to the center of gravity and empty weight of the aircraft, and the permissible useful load is affected accordingly. Investigate the effects of these changes, otherwise the aircraft flight characteristics may be adversely affected. Information on which to base the record of weight and balance changes to the aircraft may be obtained from the pertinent aircraft specification, the prescribed aircraft operating limitations, airplane flight manual, and the aircraft weight and balance report.

Removal or addition of minor items of equipment such as nuts, bolts, rivets, washers, and similar standard parts of negligible weight on fixed-wing aircraft do not require a weight and balance check. Since rotorcraft are in general more critical with respect to control with

changes in c.g. positions, the procedures and instructions in the particular model maintenance or flight manual should be followed.

657. TERMINOLOGY. The following terminology is used in the practical application of weight and balance control.

a. *Maximum Weight*. The maximum weight is the maximum authorized weight of the aircraft and its contents as listed in the specifications.

b. *Empty Weight*. The empty weight of an aircraft includes all operating equipment that has a fixed location and is actually installed in the aircraft. It includes the weight of the airframe, powerplant, required equipment, optional and special equipment, fixed ballast, full engine coolant, hydraulic fluid, and the fuel and oil as explained in paragraph 658 f and g. Additional information regarding fluids which may be contained in the aircraft systems and which must be included in the empty weight will be indicated in the pertinent aircraft specifications whenever deemed necessary.

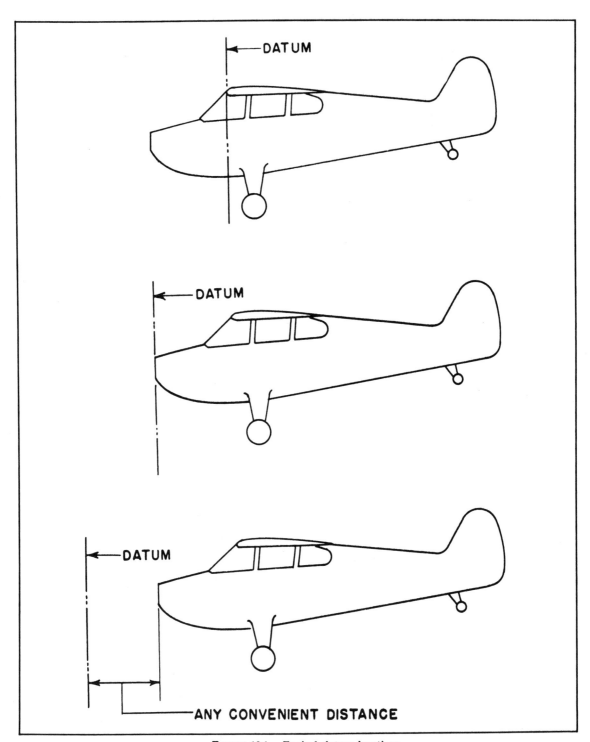

FIGURE 13.1.—Typical datum locations.

c. Useful Load. The useful load is the empty weight subtracted from the maximum weight of the aircraft. This load consists of the pilot, crew if applicable, maximum oil, fuel, passengers, and baggage, unless otherwise noted.

d. Weight Check. A weight check consists of checking the sum of the weights of all items of useful load against the authorized useful load (maximum weight less empty weight) of the aircraft.

e. Datum. The datum is an imaginary vertical plane from which all horizontal measurements are taken for balance purposes with the aircraft in level flight attitude. The datum is indicated on most FAA Aircraft Specifications. On some of the older aircraft, where the datum is not indicated, any convenient datum may be selected. However, once the datum is selected, all moment arms and the location of the permissible c.g. range must be taken with reference to it. Examples of typical locations of the datum are shown in figure 13.1.

f. Arm (or Moment Arm). The arm is the horizontal distance in inches from the datum to the center of gravity of an item. The algebraic sign is plus (+), if measured aft of the datum, and minus (−) if measured forward of the datum. Examples of plus and minus arms are shown in figure 13.2.

g. Moment. Moment is the product of a weight multiplied by its arm. The moment of an item about the datum is obtained by multiplying the weight of the item by its horizontal distance from the datum. A typical moment calculation is given in figure 13.3.

h. Center of Gravity. The center of gravity is a point about which the nose-heavy and tail-heavy moments are exactly equal in magnitude. If the aircraft were suspended from there, it would have no tendency to pitch in either direction (nose up or down). The weight of the aircraft (or any object) may be assumed to be concentrated at its center of gravity. (See figure 13.3.)

i. Empty Weight Center of Gravity. The empty weight c.g. is the center of gravity of an aircraft in its empty weight condition, and is an essential part of the weight-and-balance record. Formulas for determining the center of gravity for tail and nosewheel type aircraft are given in figure 13.4. Typical examples of computing the empty weight and empty weight

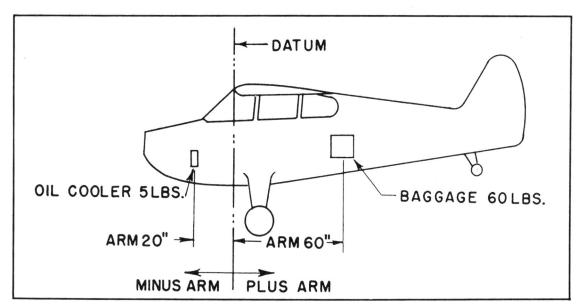

FIGURE 13.2.—Illustration of arm (or moment arm).

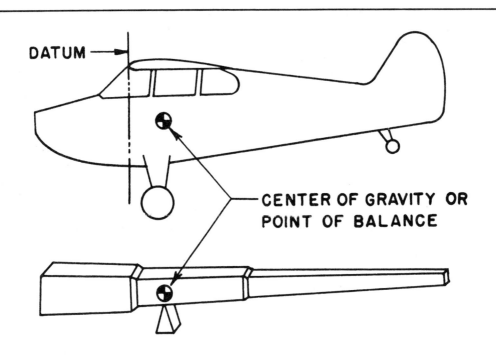

DATUM

CENTER OF GRAVITY OR
POINT OF BALANCE

The entire aircraft weight may be considered to be concentrated at the center of gravity. Therefore, the moment
of the aircraft about the datum is the weight of the aircraft times the horizontal distance between the C.G. and
the datum.

Example: If the weight of this airplane is 2000 lbs. and
the arm from the datum to the center of gravity is 16
inches, the moment of the aircraft about the datum is
2000 x 16 or 32,000 in. lbs.

FIGURE 13.3.—Example of moment computation.

c.g. for aircraft are shown in figures 13.5 and 13.6.

i. *Empty Weight Center-of-Gravity Range.* The empty weight center-of-gravity range is deter-mined so that the empty weight c.g. limits will not be exceeded under standard specification loading arrangements. In cases where it is pos-sible to load an aircraft in a manner not cov-ered in the Aircraft Specification (i.e., extra tanks, extra seats, etc.), complete calculations as outlined in paragraph 661. The empty weight c.g. range, when applicable, is listed on the Aircraft Specifications. Calculation of empty weight c.g. is shown in figures 13.5 and 13.6.

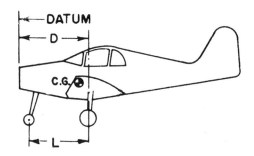

NOSE WHEEL TYPE AIRCRAFT

DATUM LOCATED FORWARD OF THE
MAIN WHEELS

$$C.G. = D - \left(\frac{F \times L}{W}\right)$$

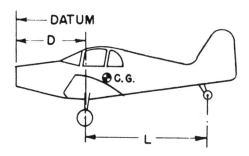

TAIL WHEEL TYPE AIRCRAFT

DATUM LOCATED FORWARD OF THE
MAIN WHEELS

$$C.G. = D + \left(\frac{R \times L}{W}\right)$$

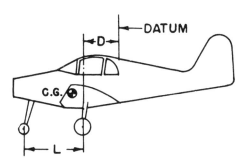

NOSE WHEEL TYPE AIRCRAFT

DATUM LOCATED AFT OF THE MAIN
WHEELS

$$C.G. = -\left(D + \frac{F \times L}{W}\right)$$

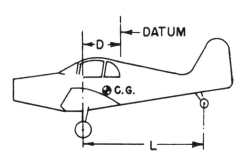

TAIL WHEEL TYPE AIRCRAFT

DATUM LOCATED AFT OF THE MAIN
WHEELS

$$C.G. = -D + \left(\frac{R \times L}{W}\right)$$

CG = Distance from datum to center of gravity of the aircraft.
W = The weight of the aircraft at the time of weighing.
D = The horizontal distance measured from the datum to the main wheel weighing point.
L = The horizontal distance measured from the main wheel weighing point to the nose or tail weighing point.
F = The weight at the nose weighing point.
R = The weight at the tail weighing point.

FIGURE 13.4.—Empty weight center-of-gravity formulas.

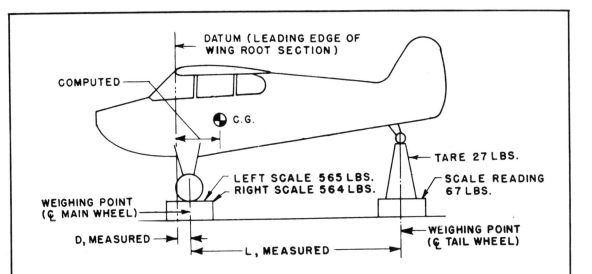

DATUM (LEADING EDGE OF WING ROOT SECTION)

COMPUTED

C.G.

TARE 27 LBS.

LEFT SCALE 565 LBS.
RIGHT SCALE 564 LBS.

SCALE READING 67 LBS.

WEIGHING POINT (₵ MAIN WHEEL)

D, MEASURED

L, MEASURED

WEIGHING POINT (₵ TAIL WHEEL)

TO FIND: EMPTY WEIGHT AND EMPTY WEIGHT CENTER OF GRAVITY

Datum is the leading edge of the wing (from aircraft specification)

(D) Actual measured horizontal distance from the main wheel weighing point ₵ main wheel) to the Datum--3"

(L) Actual measured horizontal distance from the rear wheel weighing point (₵ rear wheel) to the main wheel weighing point--222"

SOLVING: EMPTY WEIGHT

Weighing Point	Scale Reading #	Tare #	Net Weight #
Right	564	0	564
Left	565	0	565
Rear	67	27	40
Empty Weight (W)			1169

SOLVING: EMPTY WEIGHT CENTER OF GRAVITY

Formula: $C.G. = D + \dfrac{R \times L}{W} = 3" + \dfrac{40 \times 222}{1169} = 3" + 7.6" = 10.6"$

Reference for formula, Figure 13.4

This case is shown properly entered on a sample weight and balance report form, Figure 13.17

FIGURE 13.5.—Empty weight and empty weight center of gravity—tail-wheel type aircraft.

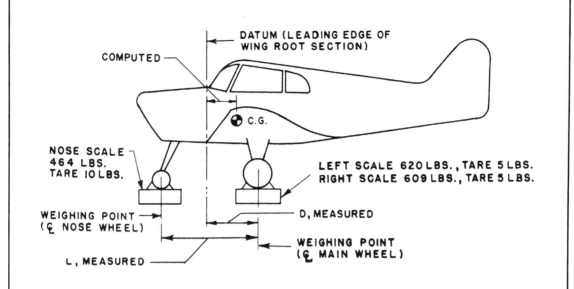

TO FIND: EMPTY WEIGHT AND EMPTY WEIGHT CENTER OF GRAVITY

Datum is the leading edge of the wing (from aircraft specification)
(D) Actual measured horizontal distance from the main wheel weight point (℄ main wheel) to the Datum-- 34.0''
(L) Actual measured horizontal distance from the front wheel weighing point (℄ front wheel) to the main wheel weighing point---------------------------------- 67.8''

SOLVING: EMPTY WEIGHT

Weighing Point	Scale Reading #	Tare #	Net Weight
Right	609	5	604
Left	620	5	615
Front	464	10	454
Empty Weight (W)			1673

SOLVING: EMPTY WEIGHT CENTER OF GRAVITY

Formula: $C.G. = D - \dfrac{F \times L}{W} = 34'' - \dfrac{454 \times 67.8}{1673} = 34'' - 18.3'' = 15.7''$

Reference for formula, Figure 13.4.

FIGURE 18.6.—Empty weight and empty weight center-of-gravity—nose-wheel type aircraft.

k. *Operating Center-of-Gravity Range.* The operating c.g. range is the distance between the forward and rearward center of gravity limits indicated on the pertinent aircraft specification. These limits were determined as to the most forward and most rearward loaded c.g. positions at which the aircraft meets the requirements of the Federal Aviation Regulations. The limits are indicated on the specification in either percent of mean aerodynamic chord or inches from the datum. The c.g. of the loaded aircraft must be within these limits at all times as illustrated in figure 13.7.

l. *Mean Aerodynamic Chord (MAC).* For weight and balance purposes it is used to locate the c.g. range of the aircraft. The location and dimensions of the MAC will be found in the Aircraft Specifications, Aircraft Flight Manual, or the Aircraft Weight and Balance Report.

m. *Weighing Point.* If the c.g. location is determined by weighing, it is necessary to obtain horizontal measurements between the points on the scale at which the aircraft's weight is concentrated. If weighed, using scales under the landing gear tires, a vertical line passing through the centerline of the axle will locate the point on the scale at which the weight is concentrated. This point is called the "weighing point." Other structural locations capable of supporting the aircraft, such as jack pads on the main spar, may also be used if the aircraft weight is resting on the jack pads. Indicate these points clearly in the weight and balance report when used in lieu of the landing gear. Typical locations of the weighing points are shown in figure 13.8.

n. *Zero fuel weight* is the maximum permissible weight of a loaded aircraft (passengers, crew, cargo, etc.) less its fuel. All weights in excess of maximum zero fuel weight must consist of usable fuel.

o. *Minimum Fuel.* Minimum fuel for balance purposes is no more than the quantity of fuel necessary for one-half hour of operation at rated maximum continuous power, and is the maximum amount of fuel used in weight and balance computation when low fuel may adversely affect the most critical balance condition.

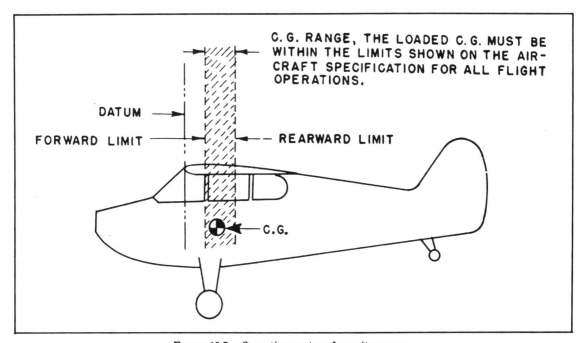

FIGURE 13.7.—Operating center-of-gravity range.

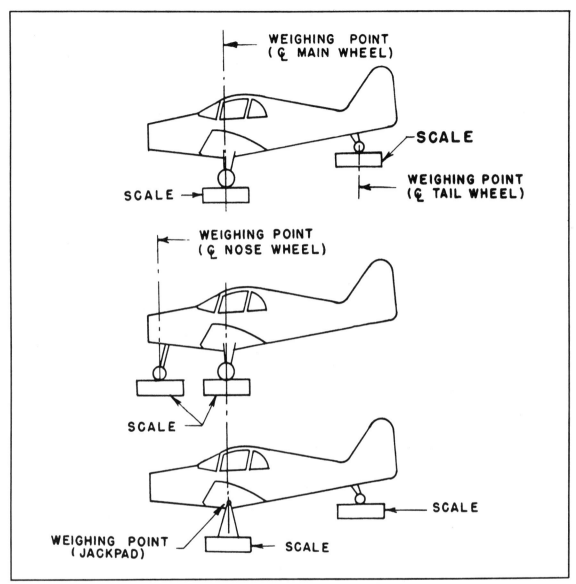

FIGURE 13.8.—Weighing point centerline.

p. *Full Oil.* Full oil is the quantity of oil shown in the aircraft specifications as oil capacity. Use full oil as the quantity of oil when making the loaded weight and balance computations.

q. *Tare.* Tare is the weight of chocks, blocks, stands, etc., used when weighing aircraft, and is included in the scale readings. Tare is deducted from the scale reading at each respective weighing point where tare is involved to obtain the actual aircraft weight.

658. WEIGHING PROCEDURE. Accepted procedures when weighing an aircraft are:

a. Remove excessive dirt, grease, moisture, etc., from the aircraft before weighing.

b. Weigh the aircraft inside a closed building

to prevent error in scale reading due to wind.

c. To determine the center of gravity, place the aircraft in a level flight attitude.

d. Have all items of equipment included in the certificated empty weight installed in the aircraft when weighing. These items of equipment are a part of the current weight and balance report. (See paragraph 662.)

e. Properly calibrate, zero, and use the scales in accordance with the scale manufacturer's instructions. The scales and suitable support for the aircraft, if necessary, are usually placed under the wheels of a landplane, the keel of a seaplane float, or the skis of a skiplane. Other structural locations capable of supporting the aircraft, such as jack pads, may be used.

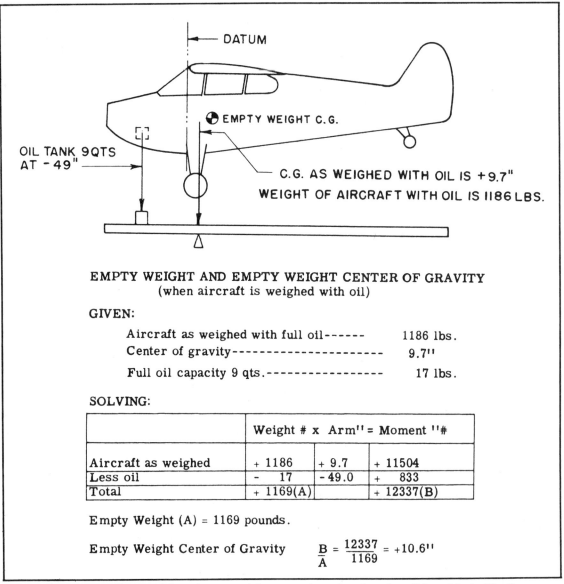

EMPTY WEIGHT AND EMPTY WEIGHT CENTER OF GRAVITY
(when aircraft is weighed with oil)

GIVEN:

Aircraft as weighed with full oil------	1186 lbs.
Center of gravity---------------------	9.7"
Full oil capacity 9 qts.----------------	17 lbs.

SOLVING:

	Weight # x	Arm" =	Moment "#
Aircraft as weighed	+ 1186	+ 9.7	+ 11504
Less oil	- 17	- 49.0	+ 833
Total	+ 1169(A)		+ 12337(B)

Empty Weight (A) = 1169 pounds.

Empty Weight Center of Gravity $\quad \dfrac{B}{A} = \dfrac{12337}{1169} = +10.6"$

FIGURE 13.9.—Empty weight and empty weight center-of-gravity when aircraft is weighed with oil.

Clearly indicate these points in the weight and balance report.

f. Unless otherwise noted in the aircraft specification, drain the fuel system until the quantity indicator reads "zero" or empty with the aircraft in level flight attitude. The amount of fuel remaining in the tank, lines, and engine is termed "residual fuel" and it is to be included in the empty weight. In special cases, the aircraft may be weighed with full fuel in tanks provided a definite means of determining the exact weight of the fuel is available.

g. Unless otherwise noted in the aircraft specification, the oil system should be completely drained with all drain cocks open. Under these conditions, the amount of oil remaining in the oil tank, lines and engine is termed "residual oil," and it will be included in the empty weight. When weighed with full oil, actual empty weight equals the actual recorded weight less the weight of the oil in the oil tank (oil weight = oil capacity in gallons × 7.5 pounds). Indicate in all weight and balance reports whether weights include full oil or oil drained (see figure 13.9).

h. Do not set brakes while taking scale reading.

i. Note tare when the aircraft is removed from the scales.

659. WEIGHT AND BALANCE COMPUTATIONS. It is often necessary, after completing an extensive alteration, to establish by computation that the authorized weight or c.g. limits as shown on the FAA Aircraft Specifications are not exceeded. Paragraph b. explains the significance of algebraic signs used in balance computations.

The Aircraft Specifications contain the following information relating to the subject:

1. Center of gravity range.
2. Empty weight c.g. range when applicable.
3. Leveling means.
4. Datum.
5. Maximum weights.
6. Number of seats and arm.
7. Maximum baggage and arm.

8. Fuel capacity and arm.
9. Oil capacity and arm.
10. Equipment items and arm.

FAA Type Certificate Data Sheets do not list the basic required equipment prescribed by the applicable airworthiness regulations for certification. Refer to the manufacturer's equipment list for such information.

a. Unit Weight for Weight and Balance Purposes.

Gasoline _____ 6 pounds per U.S. gal.
Turbine fuel _____ 6.7 pounds per U.S. gal.
Lubricating oil ____ 7.5 pounds per U.S. gal.
Crew and
    passengers _____ 170 pounds per person.

b. Algebraic Signs. It is important to retain the proper algebraic sign (+ or −) through all balance computations. For the sake of uniformity in these computations, visualize the aircraft with the nose to the left. In this position any arm to the left (forward) of the datum is "minus" and any arm to the right (rearward) of the datum is "plus." Any item of weight added to the aircraft either side of the datum is plus weight. Any weight item removed is a minus weight. When multiplying weights by arms, the answer is plus if the signs are alike, and minus if the signs are unlike.

The following combinations are possible:
Items added forward of the datum—
  (+) weight × (−) arm = (−) moment.
Items added to the rear of the datum—
  (+) weight × (+) arm = (+) moment.
Items removed forward of the datum—
  (−) weight × (−) arm = (+) moment.
Items removed rear of the datum—
  (−) weight × (+) arm = (−) moment.

The total weight of the airplane is equal to the weight of the empty aircraft plus the weight of the items added, minus the weight of the items removed.

The total moment of the aircraft is the algebraic sum of the empty weight moment of the aircraft and all of the individual moments of the items added and/or removed.

660. WEIGHT AND BALANCE EXTREME CONDI-

TIONS. The weight and balance extreme conditions represent the maximum forward and rearward c.g. position for the aircraft. Include in the weight and balance data information showing that the c.g. of the aircraft (usually in the fully loaded condition) falls between the extreme conditions.

a. Forward Weight and Balance Check. When a forward weight and balance check is made, establish that neither the maximum weight nor the forward c.g. limit listed in the Aircraft Specifications is exceeded. To make this check, the following information is needed:

(1) The weights, arms, and moment of the empty aircraft.

(2) The maximum weights, arms, and moments of the items of useful load which are located ahead of the forward c.g. limit; and

(3) The minimum weights, arms, and moments of the items of useful load which are located aft of the forward c.g. limit.

A typical example of the computation necessary to make this check, using the above data, is shown in figure 13.10.

b. Rearward Weight and Balance Check. When a rearward weight and balance check is made, establish that neither the maximum weight nor the rearward c.g. limit listed in the aircraft specification is exceeded. To make this check, the following information is needed:

(1) The weight, arms, and moments of empty aircraft;

(2) The maximum weights, arms, and moments of the items of useful load which are located aft of the rearward c.g. limit; and

(3) The minimum weights, arms, and moments of the items of useful load which are located ahead of the rearward c.g. limit.

A typical example of the computation necessary to make this check, using the above data, is shown in figure 13.11.

661. LOADING CONDITIONS AND/OR PLACARDS. If the following items have not been covered in the weight and balance extreme condition checks, or are not covered by suitable placards in the aircraft, additional computations are necessary.

These computations should indicate the permissible distribution of fuel, passengers, and baggage which may be carried in the aircraft at any one time without exceeding either the maximum weight or c.g. range. The conditions to check are:

a. With full fuel, determine the number of passengers and baggage permissible.

b. With maximum passengers, determine the fuel and baggage permissible.

(1) Examples of the computations for the above items are given in figures 13.12, 13.13, and 13.14 respectively. The above cases are mainly applicable to the lighter type personal aircraft. In the case of the larger type transport aircraft, a variety of loading conditions is possible and it is necessary to have a loading schedule.

662. EQUIPMENT LIST. A list of the equipment included in the certificated empty weight may be found in either the approved Airplane Flight Manual or the weight and balance report. Enter in the weight and balance report all required, optional and special equipment installed in the aircraft at time of weighing and/or subsequent equipment changes.

a. Required equipment items are items so listed in the pertinent aircraft specification.

b. Optional equipment items are so listed in the pertinent aircraft specification and may be installed in the aircraft at the option of the owner.

c. Special equipment is any item not corresponding exactly to the descriptive information in the aircraft specification. This includes such items as flares, instruments, ashtrays, radios, navigation lights, carpets, etc.

d. Required and optional equipment may be shown on the equipment list making reference to the pertinent item number listed in the applicable specification only when they are identical to that number item with reference to description, weight, and arm given in the specification.

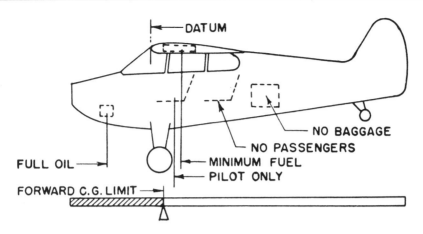

TO CHECK: MOST FORWARD WEIGHT AND BALANCE EXTREME.

GIVEN: Actual empty weight of the airplane------------- 1169#
Empty weight center of gravity ----------------- +10.6''
*Maximum weight ------------------------- 2100#
*Forward C.G. limit ------------------------ + 8.5''
*Oil, capacity 9 qts. ----------------------- 17# at - 49
*Pilot in farthest forward seat equipped with
controls (unless otherwise placarded) ----------- 170# at + 16''
*Since the fuel tank is located to the rear of
the forward C.G. limit, minimum fuel should be
included. $\dfrac{\text{METO HP}}{12} = \dfrac{165}{12} = 13.75$ gal. x 6# ------- 83# at + 22''

*Information should be obtained from the aircraft specification.

Note: Any items or passengers must be used if they are located
ahead of the forward C.G. limit.
Full fuel must be used if the tank is located ahead of the
forward C.G. limit.

CHECK OF FORWARD WEIGHT AND BALANCE EXTREME

	Weight (#)	x Arm ('')	= Moment (''#)
Aircraft Empty	+ 1169	+ 10.6	+ 12391
Oil	+ 17	- 49	- 833
Pilot	+ 170	+ 16	+ 2720
Fuel	+ 83	+ 22	+ 1826
Total	+ 1439 (TW)		+ 16104 (TM)

Divide the TM (Total Moment) by the TW (Total Weight) to obtain
the forward weight and balance extreme.
$$\dfrac{\text{TM}}{\text{TW}} = \dfrac{16104}{1439} = + 11.2''$$

Since the forward C.G. limit and the maximum weight are not
exceeded, the forward weight and balance extreme condition is
satisfactory.

FIGURE 13.10.—Example of check of most forward weight and balance extreme.

161

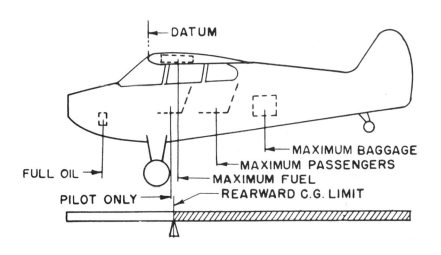

DATUM

MAXIMUM BAGGAGE
MAXIMUM PASSENGERS
MAXIMUM FUEL
REARWARD C.G. LIMIT

FULL OIL

PILOT ONLY

TO CHECK: MOST REARWARD WEIGHT AND BALANCE EXTREME.

```
GIVEN:  Actual empty weight of the airplane --------   1169#
        Empty weight center of gravity -------------   10.6''
        *Maximum weight ----------------------------   2100#
        *Rearward C.G. limit -----------------------   21.9''
        *Oil capacity 9 qts. ------------------------    17# at - 49''
        *Baggage, placarded do not exceed 100 lbs. ---  100# at + 75.5''
        *Two passengers in rear seats, 170 x 2 ------   340# at + 48''
        *Pilot in most rearward seat equipped with
         controls (unless otherwise placarded) -------  170# at + 16''
        *Since the fuel tank is located aft of the
         rearward C.G. limit full fuel must be used ---  240# at + 22''
```

* Information should be obtained from the aircraft specification.

Note: If fuel tanks are located ahead of the rearward C.G. limit
minimum fuel should be used.

CHECK OF REARWARD WEIGHT AND BALANCE EXTREME

	Weight (#)	x Arm ('')	= Moment (''#)
Aircraft empty	+ 1169	+ 10.6	+ 12391
Oil	+ 17	- 49	- 833
Pilot (1)	+ 170	+ 16	+ 2720
Passengers (2)	+ 340	+ 48	+ 16320
Fuel (40 gals.)	+ 240	+ 22	+ 5280
Baggage	+ 100	+ 75.5	+ 7550
Total	+ 2036 (TW)		+ 43428 (TM)

Divide the TM (Total Moment) by the TW (Total Weight) to obtain the
rearward weight and balance extreme.

$$\frac{TM}{TW} = \frac{43428}{2036} = + 21.3''$$

Since the rearward C.G. limit and the maximum weight are not exceeded,
the rearward weight and balance extreme condition is satisfactory.

FIGURE 13.11.—Example of check of most rearward weight and balance extreme.

EXAMPLE OF THE DETERMINATION OF THE NUMBER OF PASSENGERS AND BAGGAGE PERMISSIBLE WITH FULL FUEL

GIVEN:

Actual empty weight of the aircraft ------------------- 1169#
Empty weight center of gravity ---------------------— 10.6"
Maximum weight ------------------------------------- 2100#
Datum is leading edge of the wing
Forward center of gravity limit --------------------— 8.5"
Rearward center of gravity limit -------------------- 21.9"
Oil capacity, 9 qts.; show full capacity --------------- 17# at -49"
Baggage, maximum ------------------------------- 100# at +75.5"
Two passengers in rear seat, 170# x 2 --------------- 340# at +48"
Pilot in most rearward seat equipped with
controls (unless otherwise placarded) --------------- 170# at +16"
Full fuel, 40 gals. x 6# --------------------------- 240# at +22"

	Weight(#)	x Arm(")	= Moment("#)
Aircraft empty	+ 1169	+10.6	+ 12391
Oil	+ 17	- 49	- 833
Full fuel	+ 240	+ 22	+ 5280
Passengers, 2 rear	+ 340 *	+ 48	+ 16320
Pilot	+ 170	+ 16	+ 2720
Baggage	+ 100	+ 75.5	+ 7550
Total	+ 2036 (TW)		+ 43428 (TM)

Divide the TM (total moment) by the TW (total weight) to obtain the loaded center of gravity.

$$\frac{TM}{TW} = \frac{43428}{2036} = +21.3''$$

The above computations show that with full fuel, 100 pounds of baggage and two passengers in the rear seat may be carried in this aircraft without exceeding either the maximum weight or the approved C.G. range.

This condition may be entered in the loading schedule as follows:

GALLONS OF FUEL	NUMBER OF PASSENGERS	POUNDS OF BAGGAGE
Full	2 Rear	100

* Only two passengers are listed to prevent the maximum weight of 2100 lbs. from being exceeded.

FIGURE 18.12.—Loading conditions: determination of the number of passengers and baggage permissible with full fuel.

EXAMPLE OF THE DETERMINATION OF THE POUNDS OF FUEL AND BAGGAGE PERMISSIBLE WITH MAXIMUM PASSENGERS

	Weight (#)	x Arm (")	= Moment ("#)
Aircraft empty	+ 1169	+ 10.6	+ 12391
Oil	+ 17	- 49	- 833
Pilot	+ 170	+ 16	+ 2720
Passenger, 1 front	+ 170	+ 16	+ 2720
Passengers, 2 rear	+ 340	+ 48	+ 16320
Fuel (39 gals.)	+ 234	+ 22	+ 5148
Baggage	---	---	---
Total	+ 2100		+ 38466

Divide the TM (total moment) by the TW (total weight) to obtain the loaded center of gravity.

$$\frac{TM}{TW} = \frac{38466}{2100} = + 18.3''$$

The above computations show that with the maximum number of passengers, 39 gallons of fuel and zero pounds of baggage may be carried in this aircraft without exceeding either the maximum weight or the approved C.G. range.

This condition may be entered in the loading schedule as follows:

GALLONS OF FUEL	NUMBER OF PASSENGERS	POUNDS OF BAGGAGE
* FULL	*2 rear	* 100
39	1(F) 2(R)	None

* Conditions as entered from Figure 13.12
(F) Front seat
(R) Rear seat

FIGURE 13.13.—Loading conditions: determination of the fuel and baggage permissible with maximum passengers.

Show all special equipment items by making reference to the item by name, make, model, weight, and arm. When the arm for such an item is not available, determine by actual measurement.

(1) **Equipment Changes.** The person making an equipment change is obligated to make an entry on the equipment list indicating items added, removed, or relocated with the date accomplished, and identify himself by name and certificate number in the aircraft records.

Examples of items so affected are the installation of extra fuel tanks, seats, or baggage compartments. Figure 13.15 illustrates the effect on balance when equipment items are added within the acceptable c.g. limits and fore

EXAMPLE OF THE DETERMINATION OF THE FUEL AND THE NUMBER AND
LOCATION OF PASSENGERS PERMISSIBLE WITH MAXIMUM BAGGAGE

	Weight (#) x	Arm ('') =	Moment (''#)
Aircraft empty	+ 1169	+ 10.6	+ 12391
Oil	+ 17	- 49	- 833
Pilot	+ 170	+ 16	+ 2720
Passenger (1) rear	+ 170	+ 48	+ 8160
Passenger (1) front	+ 170	+ 16	+ 2720
Fuel (40 gals.)	+ 240	+ 22	+ 5280
Baggage	+ 100	+ 75.5	+ 7550
Total	+ 2036		+ 37988

Divide the TM (total moment) by the TW (total weight) to
obtain the loaded center of gravity.

$$\frac{TM}{TW} = \frac{37988}{2036} = + 18.7$$

The above computations show that with maximum baggage, full
fuel and 2 passengers (1 in the front seat and 1 in the rear seat)
may be carried in this aircraft without exceeding either the
maximum weight or the approved C.G. range.

This condition may be entered in the loading schedule as
follows:

GALLONS OF FUEL	NUMBER OF PASSENGERS	POUNDS OF BAGGAGE
* Full	* 2 Rear	*100
** 39	*1 (F) 2 (R)	**None
Full	1 (F) 1 (R)	Full

  * Conditions as entered from Figure 13.12
 ** Conditions as entered from Figure 13.13
  (F) Front seat
  (R) Rear seat

FIGURE 13.14.—Loading conditions: determination of the
fuel and the number and location of passengers permissible with maximum baggage.

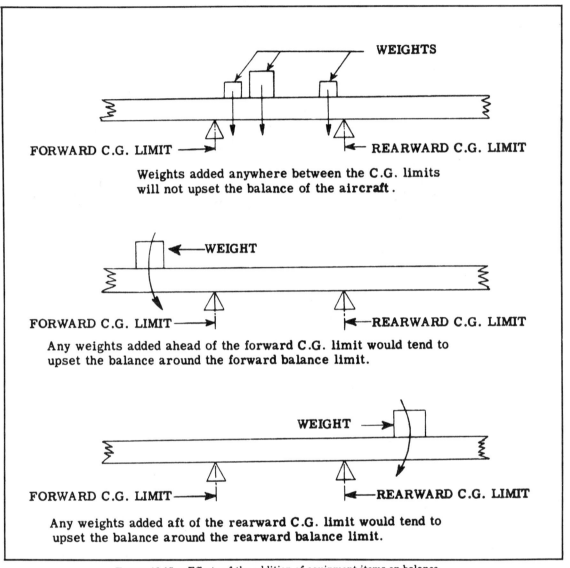

FIGURE 13.15.—Effects of the addition of equipment items on balance.

and aft of the established c.g. limits. Moment computations for typical equipment changes are given in figure 13.17 and are also included in the sample weight and balance sheet in figure 13.18.

663. SAMPLE WEIGHT AND BALANCE REPORT. Suggested methods of tabulating the various data and computations for determining the c.g., both in the empty weight condition and fully loaded condition, are given in figures 13.17 and 13.18, respectively, and represent a suggested means of recording this information. The data presented in figure 13.17 have previously been computed in figures 13.10 and 13.11 for the extreme load conditions, and figure 13.16 for equipment change and represent suggested means of recording this information.

664. INSTALLATION OF BALLAST. Ballast is sometimes permanently installed for c.g. balance purposes as a result of installation or removal of equipment items and is not used to correct a nose-up or nose-down tendency of an aircraft. It is usually located as far aft or as far forward as possible in order to bring the c.g. position within acceptable limits with a minimum of weight increase. Permanent ballast is often in the form of lead plate wrapped around and/or bolted to the fuselage primary structure (tail-post, longerons, or bulkhead members). Permanent ballast invariably constitutes a concentrated load; therefore, the strength of the local structure and the attachment of the ballast thereto should be investigated for the design loading conditions pertinent to the particular aircraft. Placard permanent ballast

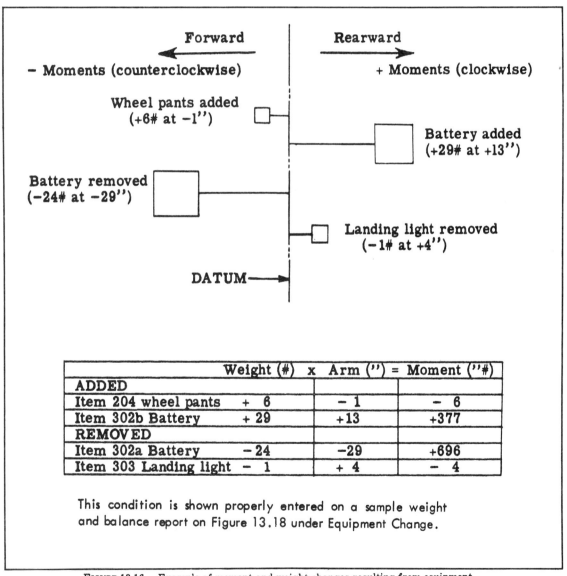

	Weight (#) x	Arm (″) =	Moment (″#)
ADDED			
Item 204 wheel pants	+ 6	− 1	− 6
Item 302b Battery	+ 29	+13	+377
REMOVED			
Item 302a Battery	− 24	−29	+696
Item 303 Landing light	− 1	+ 4	− 4

This condition is shown properly entered on a sample weight and balance report on Figure 13.18 under Equipment Change.

FIGURE 13.16.—Example of moment and weight changes resulting from equipment changes.

MAKE __MA-700__ MODEL __A__ SERIAL # __0000__ REGISTRATION # __N1234__
DATUM IS __leading edge of wing.__

COMPUTE AS FOLLOWS IF AIRCRAFT WEIGHED

1. Leveling means: __level top longeron between front and rear seats.__
2. Main wheel weighing point is located (_____"FORWARD)(+__3__" AFT) of datum.
3. Actual measured distance from the main weight point centerline to the tail (or nose) point centerline __222__".
4. Oil over and above "ZERO" tank reading = (a.__—__ Gals.)(b.__—__Lbs.)(c.__—__In.)

ACTUAL EMPTY WEIGHT

	Weight Point	Scale Reading	−	Tare	=	Net Weight
5.	Right	564		0		564
6.	Left	565		0		565
7.	Tail	67		27		40
8.	Nose	——		—		——
9.	Total Net Weight					1169

CENTER OF GRAVITY AS WEIGHED

10. C.G. relative to main wheel weighing point:
    (a) Tail wheel airc. $\dfrac{\text{(item 3, 222)} \quad X \quad \text{(Item 7, 40)}}{\text{(Item 9, 1169)}}$ = + __7.6__ = C.G.

    (b) Nose wheel airc. $\dfrac{\text{(Item 3 —)} \quad X \quad \text{(Item 8 —)}}{\text{(Item 9 —)}}$ = _____ = C.G.

11. C.G. relative to datum:
    (a) Tail wheel airc. (Item 10a, + 7.6) added to (Item 2, + 3) = + 10.6" = C.G.
    (b) Nose wheel airc. (Item 10b, ____) added to (Item 2, ____) = _____ = C.G.

COMPUTE IF AIRCRAFT WEIGHED WITH OIL (Item 4)

	Weight	X	Arm	=	Moment
Aircraft	(9)		(11)		
Less Oil	(4b)		(4c)		
Empty Totals	(a)				(b)

$\underline{(b)}$ —————— = (c)—————" = Empty weight C.G.

12. (a)

REPAIR AGENCY_____ _____ DATE_____
              Name   Number

FIGURE 13.17.—Sample weight and balance report to determine empty weight center-of-gravity.

EQUIPMENT LIST

*Required or Optional Item Numbers as Shown in Aircraft Specification						
1	2	101	102	103	104	105
106	201	202	203	301	302(a)	303
401(a)	402	——	——	——	——	——

Special Equipment				
Item	Make	Model	Weight	Arm
3 Flares 1½ Min.	XYZ	03	25#	150"

Enter above those items included in the empty weight.

WEIGHT AND BALANCE EXTREME CONDITIONS

Approved fwd limit _8.5_ "   Approved max. weight _2100#_   Approved aft limit _21.9"_

Item	FORWARD CHECK			REARWARD CHECK		
	Weight X	Arm =	Moment	Weight X	Arm =	Moment
Airc. Empty	+ 1169 (9 or 12a)	+ 10.6 (11 or 12c)	+ 12391	+ 1169 (9 or 12a)	+ 10.6 (11 or 12c)	+ 12391
Oil	+ 17	- 49	- 833	+ 17	- 49	- 833
Pilot	+ 170	+ 16	+ 2720	+ 170	+ 16	+ 2720
Fuel	+ 83	+ 22	+ 1826	+ 240	+ 22	+ 5280
Passenger(s)				+ 340	+ 48	+ 16320
Baggage				+ 100	+ 75.5	+ 7550
TOTAL	+ 1439= TW		+ 16104 = TM	+ 2036=TW		+ 43428=TM

$$\frac{TM}{TW} = \frac{16104}{1439} = +11.2" =$$ Most Forward C.G. location

$$\frac{TM}{TW} = \frac{43428}{2036} = +21.3" =$$ Most rearward C.G. location

LOADING SCHEDULE

Gallons of Fuel	Number of Passengers	Pounds of Baggage
40	2(R)	100

The above includes pilot and capacity oil.

EQUIPMENT CHANGE

Computing New C.G.			
Item, Make, and Model*	Weight X	Arm =	Moment
Airc. Empty	+ 1169 (9 or 12a)	+ 10.6 (11 or 12c)	+ 12391
204 added	+ 6	- 1	- 6
302(b) added	+ 29	+ 13	+ 377
302(a) removed	- 24	- 29	+ 696
303 removed	- 1	+ 4	- 4
NET TOTALS	- 1179 = NW		+ 13454 = NM

$$\frac{NM}{NW} = \frac{13454}{1179} = +11.4" =$$ New C.G.

*ITEM NUMBERS WHEN LISTED IN PERTINENT AIRCRAFT SPECIFICATION MAY BE USED IN LIEU OF "ITEM, MAKE, AND MODEL".

PREPARED BY _____   DATE_____

FIGURE 13.18.—Sample weight and balance report including an equipment change for aircraft fully loaded.

169

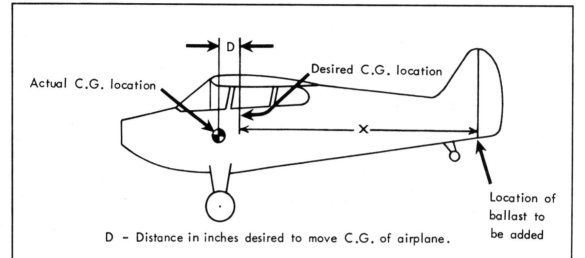

D – Distance in inches desired to move C.G. of airplane.

W – Weight of airplane as loaded.

X – Distance in inches from point where ballast is to be installed, to the desired location of the new C.G.

B – Weight of ballast required in pounds.

$$B = \frac{D \times W}{X}$$

Compute the new C.G. of the aircraft with ballast installed.

NOTE: If greater accuracy is desired, repeat the entire formula using the NEW aircraft weight and the NEW C.G. in the second operation.

FIGURE 13.19.—Permanent ballast computation formula.

"Permanent ballast—do not remove." It is not desirable to install permanent ballast by pouring melted lead into the tail-post or longerons, due to difficulties that may be encountered in subsequent welding repair operations. It should be noted that the installation of permanent ballast results in an increase of aircraft empty weight. See figure 13.19 for ballast computation. When disposable ballast is carried, the local strength of the compartment in which the ballast is carried and the effect of the ballast on aircraft balance and weight should be investigated.

665. LOADING SCHEDULE. The loading schedule should be kept with the aircraft and usually forms a part of the airplane flight manual. It includes instructions on the proper load distribution, such as filling of fuel and oil tanks, passenger seating, restrictions of passenger movement; distribution of cargo, etc.

a. Other means of determining safe loading

conditions, such as the use of a graphical index, load adjuster, etc., are acceptable and may be used in lieu of the information in paragraph 661.

b. Compute a separate loading condition when the aircraft is to be loaded in other than the specified conditions shown in the loading schedule.

666.–676. RESERVED.

Chapter 8

Engines and Fuel Systems

(Reprinted from FAA 43.13, Chapter 14)

Section 1. ENGINES

677. GENERAL. Persons should avail themselves of the manufacturer's manuals, service bulletins, and instruction books regarding the repair and overhaul, inspection, installation, and maintenance of aircraft engines. The repair and overhaul of engines are too many and varied for the different types and models of engines to mention here in specific detail.

678. INSPECTION. All moving and/or highly-stressed parts and those subjected to high temperature should have a critical visual inspection at the time of overhaul. It is often necessary to supplement the visual inspection by employing one of the following procedures:

a. Wet or dry magnetic dust inspection of magnetic materials,

b. Wet or dry penetrant inspection of non-magnetic materials,

c. X-ray or sonic inspection of any material, or

d. Hydrostatic inspection testing of fluid lines and internal passages and assemblies such as cylinder heads.

679. POWERPLANT SUDDEN STOPPAGE. For the purpose of this section, powerplant sudden stoppage refers to any momentary slowdown or complete stoppage of the main shaft of an aircraft powerplant; when the stoppage of a reciprocating or turboprop engine is the result of the rotating propeller striking a foreign object; or when the stoppage of a turbine engine is the result of ingestion of foreign objects or material. Any aircraft powerplant that has been subjected to sudden stoppage should be inspected to the extent necessary to assure continued safe operation. These procedures will serve as a guide for locating damage that may occur whenever an aircraft powerplant has been subjected to sudden deceleration or stoppage.

To fully evaluate any unsatisfactory findings resulting from this type of inspection, it will be necessary to refer to the applicable manufacturer's service and overhaul data. In addition, many of the prime aeronautical engine manufacturers now have specific recommendations on the subject of sudden stoppage involving their products. To assure continued airworthiness and reliability, it is essential that such data be used. In the event the manufacturer has not specified an instruction to follow, the following may be used as a guideline.

a. *Reciprocating Engine (Direct Drive).*

(1) **Powerplant Exterior Inspection.** Remove the engine cowling and examine the engine for visible external damage and audible internal damage.

(a) Rotate the propeller shaft to determine any evidence of abnormal grinding or sounds.

(b) With the propeller removed, inspect the crankshaft flange or splines for signs of twisting, cracks, or other deformation. Remove the thrust-bearing nut and seal and thoroughly inspect the threaded area of the shaft for evidence of cracks.

(c) Rotate the shaft slowly in 90° increments while using a dial indicator or an equivalent instrument to check the concentricity of the shaft.

(d) Remove the oil sump drain plug and check for metal chips and foreign material.

(e) Remove and inspect the oil screens for metal particles and contamination.

(f) Visually inspect engine case exterior for signs of oil leakage and cracks. Give particular attention to the propeller thrust-bearing area of the nose case section.

(g) Inspect cylinders and cylinder holddown area for cracks and oil leaks. Thoroughly investigate any indication of cracks, oil leaks or other damage.

(2) **Powerplant Internal Inspection.**

(a) On engines equipped with crankshaft vibration dampers, remove the cylinders necessary to inspect the dampers and inspect in accordance with the engine manufacturer's inspection and overhaul manual. When engine design permits, remove the damper pins, and examine the pins and damper liners for signs of nicks or brinelling.

(b) After removing the engine-driven ac-

cessories remove the accessory drive case and examine the accessory and supercharger drive gear train, couplings, and drive case for evidence of damage.

1. Check for cracks in the case in the area of accessory mount pads and gear shaft bosses.

2. Check the gear train for signs of cracked, broken, or brinelled teeth.

3. Check the accessory drive shaft couplings for twisted splines, misalignment and runout.

(3) **Accessory and Drive Inspection.** Check the drive shaft of each accessory, i.e., magnetos, generators, external supercharger, and pumps for evidence of damage.

(4) **Engine Mount Inspection.**

(a) Examine the engine flex mounts when applicable for looseness, distortion, or signs of tear.

(b) Inspect the engine mount structure for bent, cracked, or buckled tubes.

(c) Check the adjacent airframe structure for cracks, distortion, or wrinkles.

(d) Remove engine mount bolts and mount holddown bolts and inspect for shear, cracks, or distortion.

(5) **Exhaust-driven Supercharger (Turbo) Inspection.** Sudden stoppage of the powerplant can cause the heat in turbine parts to heat soak the turbine seals and bearings. This excessive heat causes carbon to develop in the seal area and varnish to form on the turbine bearings and journals.

(a) Inspect all air ducts and connections for air leaks, warpage, or cracks.

(b) Remove compressor housing and check the turbine wheel for rubbing or binding.

(6) **Propeller Inspection Repair.** Any propeller that has struck a foreign object during service should be promptly inspected in accordance with the propeller manufacturer's prescribed procedures for possible damage resulting from this contact with the foreign object and, if necessary, repaired according to the manufacturer's instructions. If the propeller is damaged beyond the repair limits established by the propeller manufacturer and a replacement

is necessary, install the same make/model or alternate approved for this installation. Refer to the aircraft manufacturer's optional equipment list, applicable FAA Aircraft Specification, Data Sheet, or Supplemental Type Certificate Data.

b. *Reciprocating Engine (Geared Drive).* Inspect the engine, propeller and components as in preceding paragraphs.

(1) Remove the propeller reduction gear housing and inspect for:

(a) Loose, sheared, or spalled cap screws or bolts.

(b) Cracks in the case.

(2) Disassemble the gear train and inspect the propeller shaft, reduction gears and accessory drive gears for nicks, cracks, or spalling.

c. *Turbine, Engine, Ingestion Inspection.* When the components of the compressor assembly or turbine section are subjected to ingestion damage, refer to the engine manufacturer's inspection and overhaul manual for specific inspection procedures and allowable tolerances. In general, an inspection after ingestion of foreign materials consists of the following areas:

(1) Inspect the external areas of the engine cases, attached parts and engine mounts for cracks, distortion, or other damage.

(2) Inspect the turbine disc for warpage or distortion.

(3) Inspect turbine disc seal for damage from rubbing or improper clearance.

(4) Inspect compressor rotor blades and stators for nicks, cracks, or distortion.

(5) Check rotor and main shaft for misalignment.

(6) Inspect shaft bearing area for oil leaks.

(7) Inspect the hot section for cracks or hot spots.

(8) Inspect the accessory drives as prescribed under paragraph a(2)(b).

NOTE: Turbine disc seal rubbing is not unusual and may be a normal condition. Consult the engine manufacturer's inspection procedures and table of limits.

d. *Turboprop Engine Inspection.*

(1) When sudden stoppage is the result of

compressor ingestion of foreign material, inspect the engine as follows:

(a) Inspect the powerplant as described in paragraph c, "Turbine Engine, Ingestion Inspection."

(b) Inspect the reduction gear section as described in paragraph b(1) and b(2) where reduction gear damage is suspected.

(2) When sudden stoppage is the result of the propeller striking foreign objects, inspect the engine as follow:

(a) Inspect the reduction gear section as described in paragraph b(1) and b(2).

(b) Inspect mainline shafts and coupling shafts for runout and spiral cracks.

(c) Inspect bearings for brinelling.

(d) Inspect engine compressor and turbine blades for tip clearance.

e. *Approval for Returning Engine to Service.*

(1) Correct all discrepancies found in the foregoing inspection in accordance with the engine manufacturer's service instructions.

(2) Test run the engine to determine that the engine, propeller, and accessories are functioning properly.

(3) After shutdown, check the engine for oil leak and check oil screens for signs of contaminants.

(4) If everything is normal the engine is ready for preflight runup and test flight.

680. CRANKSHAFTS. Carefully inspect for misalignment and replace if bent beyond the manufacturer's permissible service limit. Make no attempt to straighten crankshafts damaged in service without consulting the engine manufacturer for appropriate instructions. Worn journals may be repaired by regrinding in accordance with manufacturers' instructions. It is recommended that grinding operations be performed by appropriately rated repair stations or the original engine manufacturer to assure adherence to aeronautical standards. Common errors that occur in crankshaft grinding are the removal of nitrided journal surface, improper journal radii, unsatisfactory surfaces, and grinding tool marks on the journals. If the fillets are altered, do not reduce their radii. Polish the reworked surfaces to assure removal of all tool marks. Most opposed engines have nitrided crankshafts and manufacturers specify that these crankshafts must be nitrided after grinding.

681. REPLACEMENT PARTS IN CERTIFICATED ENGINES. Only those parts which are approved under FAR Part 21 should be used. Serviceable parts obtained from the engine manufacturer, his authorized service facility, and those which are FAA/PMA approved meet the requirements of FAR Part 21 and are acceptable for use as replacement parts. It is suggested that the latest type parts as reflected on the current parts list be obtained. Parts from military surplus stocks, which are applicable to the specific engine may be used provided they were originally accepted under the military procurement agency's standards, are found to be serviceable, and are not prohibited from use by the Administrator.

a. *Parts for obsolete engines* for which new parts are no longer obtainable from the original manufacturer or his successor are sometimes fabricated locally. When it becomes necessary to do this, physical tests and careful measurements of the old part may provide adequate technical information. This procedure is usually regarded as a major change which requires engine testing and is not recommended except as a last alternative.

b. *Parts from certain military surplus* tank or ground power unit engines are used on engines used in restricted aircraft and amateur-built aircraft. Users of such parts are cautioned to determine that they do not exceed the design limits of the engine. For example, a particular tank engine utilized a piston design that developed a compression ratio well in excess of the crankshaft absorption rate of the aircraft engine counterpart—result, crankshaft failure.

682. CYLINDER HOLDDOWN NUTS AND CAPSCREWS. Great care is required in tightening cylinder holddown nuts and capscrews. They must be tightened to recommended torque limits to prevent improper stressing and to insure even loading on the cylinder flange. The installation of baffles, brackets, clips, and other extraneous parts under nuts and capscrews is not considered good practice and should be discouraged. If these baffles, brackets, etc., are not properly fabricated or made of suitable material, they may cause loosening of the nuts or capscrews even though the nuts or capscrews were properly tightened and locked at installation. Either improper prestressing or loosening of any one of these nuts or capscrews will introduce the danger of progressive stud failure with the possible loss of the engine cylinder in flight. Do not install parts made from aluminum alloy or other soft metals under cylinder holddown nuts or capscrews.

683. REUSE OF SAFETYING DEVICES. Do not use cotter pins and safety wire a second time. Flat steel-type wristpin retainers and thin lockwashers likewise should be replaced at overhaul unless the manufacturer's recommendations permit their reuse.

684. SELF-LOCKING NUTS FOR AIRCRAFT ENGINES AND ACCESSORIES. Self-locking nuts may be used on aircraft engines provided the following criteria are met:

a. Where their use is specified by the engine manufacturer in his assembly drawing, parts list, and bills of material,

b. When the nuts will not fall inside the engine should they loosen and come off,

c. When there is at least one full thread protruding beyond the nut,

d. When the edges of cotter pin or lockwire holes are well rounded to preclude damage to the locknut,

e. Prior to reuse, the effectiveness of the self-locking feature is found to be satisfactory,

f. Where the temperature will not exceed the maximum limits established for the self-locking material used in the nut. On many engines the cylinder baffles, rocker box covers, drive covers and pads, and accessory and supercharger housings are fastened with fiber insert locknuts which are limited to a maximum temperature of 250° F. Above this temperature the fiber insert will usually char and consequently lose its locking characteristic. For locations such as the exhaust pipe attachment to the cylinder, a locknut which has good locking features at elevated temperatures will give invaluable service. In a few instances, fiber insert locknuts have been approved for use on cylinder holddown studs. This practice is not generally recommended, since especially tight stud fits to the crankcase must be provided, and extremely good cooling must prevail so that low temperatures exist at this location on the specific engine for which such use is approved.

g. All proposed applications of new types of locknuts or new applications of currently used self-locking nuts must be investigated since many engines require specifically designed nuts. Such specifically designed nuts are usually required for one or more of the following reasons to provide:

(1) Heat resistance,

(2) Adequate clearance for installation and removal,

(3) For the required degree of tightening or locking ability which sometimes requires a stronger, specifically heat-treated material, a heavier cross-section, or a special locking means,

(4) Ample bearing area under the nut to reduce unit loading on softer metals, and

(5) To prevent loosening of studs when nuts are removed.

h. Information concerning approved self-locking nuts and their use on specific engines is usually found in engine manufacturer's manuals or bulletins. If the desired information is not available, it is suggested that the engine manufacturer be contacted.

685. WELDING OF HIGHLY STRESSED ENGINE PARTS. In general, welding of highly-stressed engine parts is not recommended for parts that were not originally welded. However, under the conditions given below, welding may be accomplished if it can be reasonably expected that the welded repair will not adversely affect the airworthiness of the engine when:

a. The weld is externally situated and can be inspected easily,

b. The part has been cracked or broken as the result of unusual loads not encountered in normal operation,

c. A new replacement part of obsolete type engine is not available,

d. The welder's experience and equipment employed will insure a first-quality weld in the type of material to be repaired and will insure restoration of the original heat treat in heat-treated parts. Refer to Chapter 2 for information on process details.

686. WELDING OF MINOR ENGINE PARTS. Many minor parts not subjected to high stresses may be safely repaired by welding. Mounting lugs, cowl lugs, cylinder fins, covers, and many parts originally fabricated by welding are in this category. The welded part should be suitably stress-relieved after welding.

687. METALLIZING. Metallizing internal parts of aircraft engines is not acceptable unless it is proven to the Federal Aviation Administration that the metallized part will not adversely affect the airworthiness of the engine. Metallizing the finned surfaces of steel cylinder barrels with aluminum is acceptable, since many engines are originally manufactured in this manner.

688. PLATING. Restore plating on engine parts in accordance with the manufacturer's instructions. In general, chromium plating should not be applied to highly stressed engine parts. Certain applications of this nature have been found to be satisfactory; however, engineering evaluation of the details for the processes used should be obtained.

a. *Dense chromium plating* of the crankpin and main journals of some small engine crankshafts has been found satisfactory, except where the crankshaft is already marginal in strength. Plating to restore worn low-stress engine parts such as accessory driven shafts and splines, propeller shaft ends, and seating surfaces of roller- and ball-type bearing races is acceptable.

b. *Porous chromium plated* walls of cylinder barrels have been found to be satisfactory for practically all types of engines. Dense or smooth chromium plating without roughened surfaces, on the other hand, has not been found to be generally satisfactory.

(1) Cylinder barrel pregrinding and chromium plating techniques used by the military are considered acceptable for all engines, and military approved facilities engaged in doing this work in accordance with military specifications are eligible for approval by the Federal Aviation Administration.

(2) Chromium plated cylinder barrels have been required for some time to be identified in such a manner that the markings are visible with the cylinder installed. Military processed cylinders are banded with orange enamel above the mounting flange. It has been the practice to etch on either the flange edge or on the barrel skirt the processer's initials and cylinder oversize. Most plating facilities use the orange band as well as the permanent identification marks.

(3) A current list of engine and maximum permissible cylinder barrel oversize follows:

Engine manufacturer	Engine series	Maximum oversize (in.)
Air Cooled Motors (Franklin).	No oversize for sleeved cylinders.	
	Solid cylinders	0.020
Continental Motors	R–670, W–670, R9A	0.020
	All others	0.015
Jacobs	All	0.020
Kinner	All	0.015
Pigman, LeBlond, Rearwin, Ken Royce.	All	0.025
Lycoming	All	0.015
Menasco	All	0.010
Pratt & Whitney	R–2800B, C, CA, CB	0.025
	*R–985 and R–1830	0.030
	All others	0.020
Ranger	6–410 early cyls. 6–390	0.010
	6–410 late cyls. 6–440 (L–440) series.	0.020
Warner	All	0.015
Wright	All	0.020

*(The above oversize limits correspond to the manufacturer's requirements, except for P&W R–985 and R–1830 series engines.)

(4) The following is a list of known agencies, and their identifying initials, performing cylinder barrel plating for the military service.

Agencies	Initials
Hol-Chrome Corporation	HCC
San Antonio Air Materiel Area	SAX
Koppers Co. (American Hammered Piston Ring).	KC
McQuay-Norris	MQN
VanDer Horst Corporation	VDH
Terry Industries	TIX
Lement Chromium	LC
Pennington Channel Chrome	PCC
Spar-Tan Engineering Company	SEC
Superior Aero Chrome	SAC

(5) Cylinder barrels which have been plated by an agency whose process is approved by the FAA and which have not been preground beyond maximum permissible limits will be considered acceptable for installation on certificated engines. It will be the responsibility of the owner or the repairing agency to provide this proof. In some cases, it may be necessary to remove cylinders to determine the amount of oversize since this information may be etched on the mating surface of the cylinder base flange.

689. ENGINE ACCESSORIES. Overhaul and repair of engine accessories in accord with the engine and the accessory manufacturers' instructions are recommended.

690. CORROSION. Accomplish corrosion preventive measures for temporary and dead storage in accord with the instructions issued by the pertinent engine manufacturer. Avoid the use of strong solutions which contain strong caustic compounds and all solutions, polishes, cleaners, abrasives, etc., which might possibly promote corrosive action.

691. ENGINE RUN-IN. After an aircraft engine has been overhauled, it is recommended the pertinent aircraft engine manufacturer's run-in instructions be followed. Observe the manufacturer's recommendations concerning engine temperatures and other criteria.

Repair processes employed during overhaul often necessitate amending the manufacturer's run-in procedures. Follow the approved amended run-in procedures in such instances.

692. COMPRESSION TESTING OF AIRCRAFT ENGINE CYLINDERS. The purpose of testing cylinder compression is to determine the internal condition of the combustion chamber by ascertaining if any appreciable leakage is occurring.

a. *Types of Compression Testers.* The two basic types of compression testers currently in use are the direct compression and the differential pressure type testers. The optimum procedure would be to utilize both types of testers when checking the compression of aircraft cylinders. In this respect, it is suggested that the direct compression method be used first and the findings substantiated with the differential pressure method. This provides a cross-reference to validate the readings obtained by each method and tends to assure that the cylinder is defective before it is removed. Before beginning a compression test, consider the following points:

(1) When the spark plugs are removed, identify them to coincide with the cylinder. Close examination of the plugs will reveal the actual operating conditions and aid in diagnosing problems within the cylinder. Paragraph 693d. of this section contains more information on this subject.

(2) The operating and maintenance records of the engine should be reviewed. Records of previous compression tests are of assistance in determining progressive wear conditions and help to establish the necessary maintenance actions.

(3) Before beginning a compression check, precautions should be taken to prevent the accidental starting of the engine.

b. *Direct Compression Check.* This type of compression test indicates the actual pressures within the cylinder. Although the particular defective component within the cylinder is difficult to determine with this method, the consistency of the readings for all cylinders is an indication of the condition of the engine as a whole. The following are suggested guidelines for performing a direct compression test.

(1) Thoroughly warm up the engine to operating temperatures and perform the test as soon as possible after shutdown.

(2) Remove the most accessible spark plug from each cylinder.

(3) Rotate the engine with the starter to expel any excess oil or loose carbon in the cylinders.

(4) If a complete set of compression testers is available, install one tester in each cylinder; however, if only one tester is being used, check each cylinder in turn.

(5) Rotate the engine at least three complete revolutions using the engine starter and record the compression reading.

NOTE: It is recommended that an external power source be used, if possible, as a low battery will result in a slow engine-turning rate and lower readings. This will noticeably affect the validity of the second engine test on a twin-engine aircraft.

(6) Recheck any cylinder which shows an abnormal reading when compared with the others. Any cylinder having a reading approximately 15 p.s.i. lower than the others should be suspected of being defective.

(7) If a compression tester is suspected of being defective, replace it with one known to be accurate, and recheck the compression of the affected cylinders.

c. *Differential Pressure Compression Check.* The differential pressure tester is designed to check the compression of aircraft engines by measuring the leakage through the cylinders caused by worn or damaged components. The operation of the compression tester is based on the principle that, for any given airflow through a fixed orifice, a constant pressure drop across that orifice will result. The restrictor orifice dimensions in the differential pressure tester should be sized for the particular engine as follows:

1. Engines up to 1,000 cubic inch displacement .040 orifice diameter, .250 inch long, 60° approach angle.

2. Engines in excess of 1,000 cubic inch displacement .060 orifice diameter, .250 inch long, 60° approach angle.

A typical schematic diagram of the differential pressure tester is shown in figure 14.1.

As the regulated air pressure is applied to one side of the restrictor orifice with the air valve closed, there will be no leakage on the other side of the orifice and both pressure gauges will read the same. However, when the air valve is opened and leakage through the cylinder increases, the cylinder pressure gauge will record a proportionally lower reading.

(1) **Performing the Check.** The following procedures are listed to outline the principles involved, and are intended to supplement the manufacturer's instructions for the particular tester being utilized.

(a) Perform the compression test as soon as possible after the engine is shut down to ensure that the piston rings, cylinder walls, and other engine parts are well lubricated.

(b) Remove the most accessible spark plug from each cylinder.

(c) With the air valve closed, apply an external source of clean air (approximately 100 to 120 p.s.i.) to the tester.

(d) Install an adapter in the spark plug bushing and connect the compression tester to the cylinder.

(e) Adjust the pressure regulator to obtain a reading of 80 p.s.i. on the regulator pressure gauge. At this time, the cylinder pressure gauge should also register 80 p.s.i.

(f) Turn the crankshaft by hand in the direction of rotation until the piston (in the cylinder being checked) is coming up on its compression stroke. Slowly open the air valve and pressurize the cylinder to approximately 20 p.s.i.

CAUTION
Care must be exercised in opening the air valve since sufficient air pressure will have built up in the cylinder to cause it to rotate the crankshaft if the piston is not at TDC.

Continue rotating the engine against this pressure until the piston reaches top dead center (TDC). Reaching TDC is indicated by a flat spot or sudden decrease in force required to turn the crankshaft. If the crankshaft is rotated too far, back up at least one-half revolution and start over again to eliminate the effect of backlash in the valve operating mechanism and to keep piston rings seated on the lower ring lands.

(g) Open the air valve completely. Check the regulated pressure and adjust, if necessary, to 80 p.s.i.

(h) Observe the pressure indication on the cylinder pressure gauge. The difference between this pressure and the pressure shown by the regulator pressure gauge is the amount of leakage through the cylinder. A loss in excess of 25 percent of the input air pressure is cause to suspect the cylinder of being defective; however, recheck the readings after operating the engine for at least 3 minutes to allow for sealing of the rings with oil.

(i) If leakage is still occurring after a

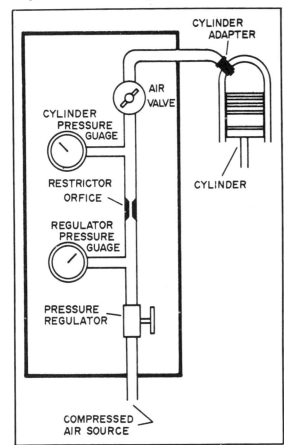

FIGURE 14.1.—Schematic of typical differential pressure compression tester.

recheck, it may be possible to correct a low reading. This is accomplished by placing a fiber drift on the rocker arm directly over the valve stem and tapping the drift several times with a hammer to dislodge any foreign material between the valve face and seat.

NOTE: When correcting a low reading in this manner, rotate the propeller so the piston will not be at TDC. This is necessary to prevent the valve from striking the top of the piston in some engines. Rotate the engine before rechecking compression to reseat the valves in the normal manner.

693. SPARK PLUGS. The spark plug provides the high voltage electrical spark to ignite the fuel/air mixture in the cylinder. The types of spark plugs used in different engines will vary in regard to heat range, reach, thread size and other characteristics required by the particular installation.

a. Heat Range. The heat range of a spark plug is a measure of its ability to transfer heat to the cylinder head. The plug must operate hot enough to burn off the residue deposits which can cause fouling, yet remain cool enough to prevent a preignition condition from occurring. The length of the nose core is the principal factor in establishing the plug's heat range. "Hot" plugs have a long insulator nose thereby creating a long heat transfer path, whereas "cold" plugs have a relatively short insulator to provide a rapid transfer of heat to the cylinder head. (See figure 14.2.)

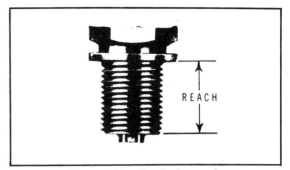

FIGURE 14.3.—Spark plug reach.

b. Reach. The spark plug reach (figure 14.3) is the threaded portion which is inserted into the spark plug bushing of the cylinder. A plug with the proper reach will insure that the electrode end inside the cylinder is in the best position to achieve ignition. Spark plug seizure or improper combustion within the cylinder will probably occur if a plug with the wrong reach is used.

c. Installation Procedures. When installing spark plugs, observe the following procedure:

(1) Visually inspect the plug for cleanliness and condition of the threads, ceramic, and electrodes.

NOTE: Never install a spark plug which has been dropped.

(2) Check the plug for the proper gap setting using a round wire feeler gauge as shown in figure 14.4. In the case of used plugs,

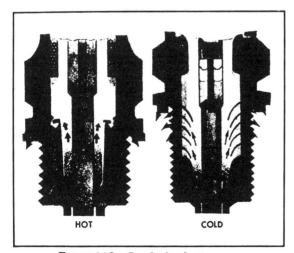

FIGURE 14.2.—Spark plug heat ranges.

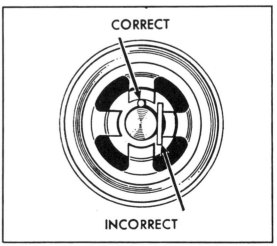

FIGURE 14.4.—Method of checking spark plug gap.

procedures for cleaning and regapping are usually contained in the various manufacturers' manuals.

(3) Check the plug and cylinder bushing to ascertain that only one gasket is used per spark plug. When a thermocouple-type gasket is used, no other gasket is required.

(4) Apply antiseize compound sparingly to the shell threads, but do not allow the compound to contact the electrodes as the material is conductive and will short out the plug. If desired, the use of antiseize compound may be eliminated on engines equipped with stainless steel spark plug bushings or inserts.

(5) Screw the plug into the cylinder head as far as possible by hand. If the plug will not turn easily to within 2 or 3 threads of the gasket, it may be necessary to clean the threads.
NOTE: Cleaning inserts with a tap is not recommended as permanent damage to the insert may result.

(6) Seat the proper socket securely on the spark plug and tighten to the torque limit specified by the engine manufacturer before proceeding to the next plug.

CAUTION

A loose spark plug will not transfer heat properly and, during engine operation, may overheat to the point where the nose ceramic will become a "hot spot" and cause preignition. However, avoid overtightening as damage to the plug and bushing may result.

(7) Connect the ignition lead after wiping clean with methylethylketone (MEK), acetone, or similar material. Insert the terminal assembly into the spark plug in a straight line. (Care should be taken as improper techniques can damage the terminal sleeves.) Screw the connector nut into place until finger tight; then tighten an additional one-quarter turn while holding the elbow in the proper position.

(8) Perform an engine runup after installing a new set of spark plugs. When the engine has reached normal operating temperatures, check the magnetos and spark plugs in accordance with the manufacturer's instructions.

d. Operational Problems. Whenever problems develop during engine operation which appear to be caused by the ignition system, it is recommended that the spark plugs and ignition har-

nesses be checked first before working on the magnetos. The following are the most common spark plug malfunctions and are relatively easy to identify:

(1) Fouling.

(a) Carbon fouling (figure 14.5a) is identified by the dull black, sooty deposits on the electrode end of the plug. Although the primary causes are excessive ground idling and rich idle mixtures, plugs with a cold heat range may also be a contributing factor.

(b) Lead fouling is characterized by hard, dark, cinderlike globules which gradually fill up the electrode cavity and short out the plug. (See figure 14.5b). The primary cause for this condition is poor fuel vaporization combined with a high tetraethyl-lead content fuel. Plugs with a cold heat range may also contribute to this condition.

(c) Oil fouling is identified by a wet, black carbon deposit over the entire firing end of the plug as shown in figure 14.5c. This condition is fairly common on the lower plugs in horizontally opposed engines, and both plugs in the lower cylinders of radial engines. Oil fouling is normally caused by oil drainage past the piston rings after shutdown. However, when both spark plugs removed from the same cylinder are badly fouled with oil and carbon, some form of engine damage should be suspected, and the cylinder more closely inspected. Mild forms of oil fouling can usually be cleared up

FIGURE 14.5a.—Typical carbon fouled spark plug.

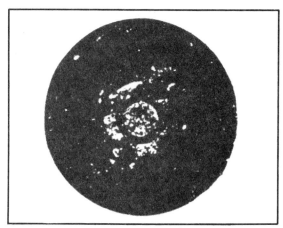

FIGURE 14.5b.—Typical lead fouled spark plug.

by slowly increasing power while running the engine until the deposits are burned off and the misfiring stops.

(2) Fused Electrodes. There are many different types of malfunctions which result in fused spark plug electrodes; however, most are associated with preignition either as the cause or the effect. For this reason, any time a spark plug is found with the following defects, further investigation of the cylinder and piston should be conducted.

(a) Cracked Nose Ceramics. Occasionally, the ceramic nose core will crack, break away, and remain trapped behind the ground electrode. This piece of insulation material will then build up heat to the point where it will ignite the fuel/air mixture prematurely. The

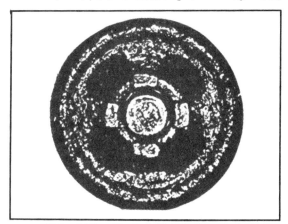

FIGURE 14.5c.—Typical oil fouled spark plug.

FIGURE 14.6a.—Typical eroded spark plug.

high temperatures and pressures encountered during this condition can cause damage to the cylinder and piston and ultimately lead to fusing and shorting out of the plug.

(b) Copper Runout. Some erosion or "cupping" of the exposed center electrode copper core is normal and will gradually decrease with the service life of the plug until it practically ceases. This condition, depicted in figure 14.6a, is not a cause for rejection until the erosion has progressed to a point more than 3/32 inch below the tip of the center electrode.

The high temperatures and pressures associated with preignition can cause the condition shown in figure 14.6b. In this instance, the copper center electrode melted and flowed out, bridged the electrodes, and caused a shorted condition.

(3) Bridged Electrodes. Occasionally, free combustion chamber particles will settle on the electrodes of a spark plug and gradually bridge the electrode gap, resulting in a shorted

FIGURE 14.6b.—Typical spark plug with copper runout.

plug. Small particles may be dislodged by slowly cycling the engine as described for the oil-fouled condition; however, the only remedy for more advanced cases is removal and replacement of the spark plug. This condition is shown in figure 14.7.

(4) Metal Deposits. Whenever metal spray is found on the electrodes of a spark plug, it is an indication that a failure of some part of the engine is in progress. The location of the cylinder in which the spray is found is important in diagnosing the problem, as various types of failures will cause the metal spray to appear differently. For example, if the metal spray is located evenly in every cylinder, the problem will be in the induction system, such as an impeller failure. If the metal spray is only found on the spark plugs in one cylinder, the problem is isolated to that cylinder and will generally be a piston failure. In view of the secondary damage which occurs whenever an engine part fails, any preliminary indication such as metal spray should be thoroughly investigated to establish the cause and correct it.

(5) Flashover. It is important that spark plug terminal contact springs and moisture seals be checked regularly for condition and cleanness to prevent "flashover" in the connector well. Foreign matter or moisture in the terminal connector well can reduce the insulation value of the connector to the point where ignition system voltages at higher power settings

FIGURE 14.8.—Spark plug well flashover.

may flash over the connector well surface to ground and cause the plug to misfire. If moisture is the cause, hard starting can also result. The cutaway spark plug shown in figure 14.8 illustrates this malfunction. Any spark plug found with a dirty connector well may have this condition, and should be reconditioned before reuse.

e. Pre-reconditioning Inspection. All spark plugs should be inspected visually prior to reconditioning to eliminate any plug with obvious defects. A partial checklist of common defects includes:

(1) Ceramic chipped or cracked either at the nose core or in the connector well.

(2) Damaged or badly worn electrodes.

(3) Badly nicked, damaged, or corroded threads on shell or shielding barrel.

(4) Shielding barrel dented, bent, or cracked.

(5) Connector seat at the top of the shielding barrel badly nicked or corroded.

694. IGNITION HARNESSES. Aircraft quality ignition harness is usually made of either medium or high temperature wire. The type used will depend upon the manufacturing specification for the particular engine. In addition to the applicable manufacturer's maintenance and repair procedures, the following is a quick-reference checklist for isolating some of the malfunctions inherent to ignition harnesses.

a. Carefully inspect the lead conduit or shielding. A few broken strands will not affect serviceability, but if the insulation in general looks worn, replace the lead.

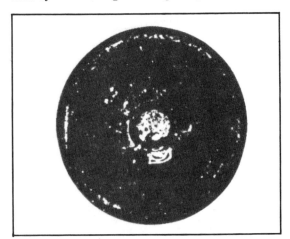

FIGURE 14.7.—Typical spark plug with bridged electrodes.

b. When replacing a lead, if the dressing procedure is not accomplished properly, strands of shielding may be forced through the conductor insulation. If this occurs, a short will exist in the conductor; therefore, it is essential this task be performed properly.

c. The high temperature coating used on some lightweight harnesses is provided for vibration abrasion resistance and moisture protection. Slight flaking or peeling of this coating is not serious, and a harness assembly need not be removed from service because of this condition.

d. Check the spark plug contact springs for breaks, corrosion, or deformation. If possible, check the lead continuity from the distributor block to the contact spring.

e. Check the insulators at the spark plug end of the lead for cracks, breaks, or evidence of old age. Make sure they are clean.

f. Check to see that the leads are positioned as far away from the exhaust manifold as possible and are supported to prevent any whipping action.

g. When lightweight harnesses are used and the conduit enters the spark plug at a severe angle, use clamps as shown in figure 14.9 to prevent overstressing the lead.

695. MAGNETO INSPECTION. Whenever ignition problems develop and it is determined that the magneto is the cause of the difficulty, the following are a few simple inspection procedures which may locate the malfunction quickly. However, conduct any internal inspection or repair of a magneto in accordance with the manufacturer's maintenance and overhaul manuals.

a. Inspect the distributor block contact springs. If broken or corroded, replace.

b. Inspect the felt oil washer if applicable. It should be saturated with oil. If it is dry, check for a worn bushing.

c. Inspect the distributor block for cracks or a burned area. The wax coating on the block should not be removed. Do not use any solvents for cleaning.

d. Look for excess oil in the breaker compartment. If oil is present, it may mean a bad oil seal or bushing at the drive end. This condition could require complete overhaul, as too much oil may foul and cause excessive burning of the contact points.

e. Look for frayed insulation on the leads in the breaker compartment of the magneto. See that all terminals are secure. Be sure that wires are properly positioned.

f. Inspect the capacitor visually for general condition, and check the mounting bracket for cracks or looseness. If possible, check the capacitor for leakage, capacity, and series resistance.

g. Examine the points for excessive wear or burning. Discard points which have deep pits or excessively burned areas. Desired contact surfaces have a dull gray, sandblasted (almost rough) or frosted appearance over the area where electrical contact is made. Figure 14.10 shows how the normal contact point will look when surfaces are separated for inspection. Minor irregularities or roughness of point surfaces are not harmful (see figure 14.11); neither are small pits or mounds, if not too pronounced. If there is a possibility of the pit

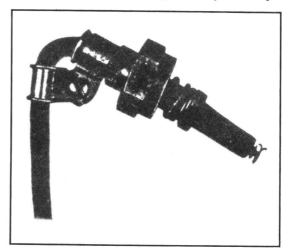

FIGURE 14.9.—Typical method of clamping leads.

185

FIGURE 14.10.—Normal contact point.

becoming deep enough to penetrate the pad (figure 14.12), reject the contact assembly.

Generally, no attempt should be made to dress or stone contact point assemblies; however, if provided, procedures and limits contained in the manufacturer's manuals may be followed.

CAUTION

When inspecting the contact points for condition, do not open further than absolutely necessary. Excess tension on the spring will weaken it and adversely affect the performance of the magneto.

h. Adjustment of magneto point gap must be correct for proper internal timing of magneto. (See applicable manufacturer's publications for internal timing procedures.)

i. Check breaker cam to assure cleanness and smoothness. Check cam screw for tightness. If new points have been installed, blot a little oil on the cam. In addition, check contact point assembly to ascertain that the cam follower is securely fastened.

j. If the impulse coupling is accessible, inspect for excessive wear on the contact edges

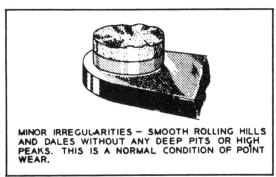

FIGURE 14.11.—Point with minor irregularities.

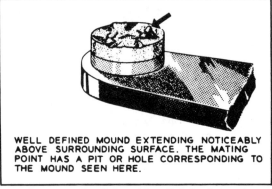

FIGURE 14.12.—Point with well-defined mound.

of the body and flyweights. In addition, check the flyweights for looseness on the axles.

k. Further examination of the impulse coupling body may disclose cracks caused by exceedingly tight flyweight axle rivets.

l. Check the magneto ventilators for proper functioning and obstructions. If drilled plugs are used, they should be in the lowest vent hole of the magneto to serve as a drain for condensation and oil.

696. MAGNETO-TO-ENGINE TIMING. While the actual process of timing magnetos to an engine is covered in the engine manufacturer's technical manuals, the following general procedures may be applied:

a. Before installing a new magneto, the correct "E" gap setting specified by the magneto manufacturer should be verified.

b. When setting or checking the magneto-to-engine timing, always turn the crankshaft steadily in the normal direction of rotation to eliminate any error caused by gear backlash.

c. Recheck magneto-to-engine timing after any point gap adjustment, or after replacement of the breaker points.

d. Never advance the magneto timing beyond the engine timing specification recommended by the engine manufacturer.

e. The possibility of a timing error exists if a timing indicator which attaches to the propeller shaft or spinner of geared engines is used. Engine timing specifications are always given in degrees of crankshaft travel, and cannot be applied directly to geared propeller shafts because of the gear ratio. Therefore, the correct position of the propeller shaft, if used for timing, must be determined by multiplying the crankshaft timing angle in degrees before top center (BTC) by the propeller gear ratio.

697.–707. RESERVED.

Section 2. FUEL SYSTEMS

708. GENERAL. Maintain, service, and adjust aircraft fuel systems and fuel system components in accordance with the applicable manufacturer's maintenance instructions. Certain general fuel system maintenance principles are outlined below.

709. FUEL LINES AND FITTINGS. When fuel system lines are to be replaced or repaired, consider the following fundamentals in addition to the applicable airworthiness requirements. Additional inspection and repair practices for aircraft tubing systems may be found in paragraph 393.

    a. Compatibility of Fittings. All fittings are to be compatible with their mating parts. Although various types of fittings appear to be interchangeable in many cases they have different thread pitch or minor design differences which prevent proper mating and may cause the joint to leak or fail.

    b. Routing. Make sure that the line does not chafe against control cables, airframe structure, etc., or come in contact with electrical wiring or conduit. Where physical separation of the fuel lines from electrical wiring or conduit is impracticable, locate the fuel line below the wiring and clamp it securely to the airframe structure. In no case may wiring be supported by the fuel line.

    c. Alignment. Locate bends accurately so that the tubing is aligned with all support clamps and end fittings and is not drawn, pulled, or otherwise forced into place by them. Never install a straight length of tubing between two rigidly mounted fittings. Always incorporate at least one bend between such fittings to absorb strain caused by vibration and temperature changes.

    d. Bonding. Bond metallic fuel lines at each point where they are clamped to the structure. Integrally bonded and cushioned line support clamps are preferred to other clamping and bonding methods.

    e. Support of Line Units. To prevent possible failure, all fittings heavy enough to cause the line to sag should be supported by means other than the tubing.

    f. Support Clamps.

    (1) Place support clamps or brackets for metallic lines as follows:

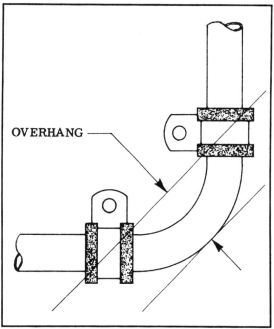

OVERHANG

FIGURE 14.13.—Location of clamps at tube bends.

Tube O.D.		*Approximate distance between supports*
1/8″–3/16″	--------------------------	9″
1/4″–5/16″	--------------------------	12″
3/8″–1/2″	--------------------------	16″
5/8″–3/4″	--------------------------	22″
1″–1 1/4″	--------------------------	30″
1 1/2″–2″	--------------------------	40″

(2) Locate clamps or brackets as close to bends as possible to reduce overhang (see figure 14.13).

710. FUEL TANKS AND CELLS. Welded or riveted fuel tanks that are made of commercially pure aluminum, 3003, 5052, or similar alloys, may be repaired by welding. Tanks made from heat-treatable aluminum alloys are generally assembled by riveting. In case it is necessary to rivet a new piece in a tank, use the same material as used in the tank undergoing repair, and seal the seams with a compound that is insoluble in gasoline. Special sealing compounds are available and should be used in the repair of tanks. Inspect fuel tanks and cells for general condition, security of attachment, and evidence of leakage. Examine fuel tank or cell vent line, fuel line, and sump drain attachment fittings closely.

CAUTION

Purge defueled tanks of explosive fuel/air mixtures in accordance with the manufacturers' service instructions. In the absence of such instructions, utilize an inert gas such as CO_2 as a purgative to assure the total deletion of fuel/air mixtures.

a. Integral Tanks. Examine the interior surfaces and seams for sealant deterioration and corrosion (especially in the sump area). Follow the manufacturer's instructions for repair and cleaning procedures.

b. Internal Metal Tanks. Check the exterior for corrosion and chafing. Dents or other distortion, such as a partially collapsed tank caused by an obstructed fuel tank vent, can adversely affect fuel quantity gauge accuracy and tank capacity. Check the interior surfaces for corrosion. Pay particular attention to the sump area, especially those which are made of cast material. Repairs to the tank may be accomplished in accordance with the practices outlined in Chapter 2 of this handbook.

c. Removal of Flux After Welding. It is especially important, after repair by welding, to completely remove all flux in order to avoid possible corrosion. Promptly upon completion of welding, wash the inside and outside of the tank with liberal quantities of hot water and then drain. Next, immerse the tank in either a 5 percent nitric or 5 percent sulfuric acid solution. If the tank cannot be immersed, fill the tank with either solution, and wash the outside with the same solution. Permit the acid to remain in contact with the weld about one hour and then rinse thoroughly with clean water. Test the efficiency of the cleaning operation by applying some acidified 5 percent silver nitrate solution to a small quantity of the rinse water used last to wash the tank. If a heavy white precipitate is formed, the cleaning is insufficient and the washing should be repeated.

d. Flexible Fuel Cells. Inspect the interior for checking, cracking, porosity, or other signs of deterioration. Make sure the cell retaining fasteners are properly positioned. If repair or further inspection is required, follow the manufacturer's instructions for cell removal, repair, and installation. Do not allow flexible fuel cells to dry out. Preserve them in accordance with the manufacturer's instructions.

711. FUEL TANK CAPS, VENTS, AND OVERFLOW LINES. Inspect the fuel tank caps to determine that they are the correct type and size for the installation.

a. Vented caps, substituted for unvented caps, may cause loss of fuel or fuel starvation. Similarly, an improperly installed cap that has a special venting arrangement can also cause malfunctions.

b. Unvented caps, substituted for vented caps, will cause fuel starvation and possible collapse of the fuel tank or cell. Malfunctioning of this type occurs when the pressure within the tank decreases as the fuel is withdrawn. Eventually, a point is reached where the fuel will no longer flow, and/or the outside atmospheric pressure collapses the tank. Thus, the effects will occur sooner with a full fuel tank than with one partially filled.

c. *Check tank vents and overflow lines* thoroughly for condition, obstructions, correct installation, and proper operation of any check valves and ice protection units. Pay particular attention to the location of the tank vents when such information is provided in the manufacturer's service instructions. Inspect for cracked or deteriorated filler opening recess drains, which may allow spilled fuel to accumulate within the wing or fuselage. One method of inspection is to plug the fuel line at the outlet and observe fuel placed in the filler opening recess. If drainage takes place, investigate condition of the line and purge any excess fuel from the wing.

d. *Assure that filler opening markings* are stated according to the applicable airworthiness requirements and are complete and legible.

712. FUEL CROSSFEED, FIREWALL SHUTOFF, AND TANK SELECTOR VALVES. Inspect these valves for leakage and proper operation as follows:

a. *Internal leakage* can be checked by placing the appropriate valve in the "off" position, draining the fuel strainer bowl, and observing if fuel continues to flow into it. Check all valves located downstream of boost pumps with the pump(s) operating. Do not operate the pump(s) longer than necessary.

b. *External leakage* from these units can be a severe fire hazard, especially if the unit is located under the cabin floor or within a similarly confined area. Correct the cause of any fuel stains associated with fuel leakage.

c. *Selector Handles.* Check the operation of each handle or control to see that it indicates the actual position of the selector valve. Assure that stops and detents have positive action and

feel. Worn or missing detents and stops can cause unreliable positioning of the fuel selector valve.

d. *Worn Linkage.* Inaccurate positioning of fuel selector valves can also be caused by worn mechanical linkage between the selector handle and the valve unit. An improper fuel valve position setting can seriously reduce engine power by restricting the available fuel flow. Check universal joints, pins, gears, splines, cams, levers, etc., for wear and excessive clearance, which prevent the valve from positioning accurately or from obtaining fully "off" and "on" positions.

e. *Assure that required placards* are complete and legible. Replace those that are missing or cannot be read easily.

713. FUEL PUMPS. Inspect, repair, and overhaul boost pumps, emergency pumps, auxiliary pumps, and engine-driven pumps in accordance with the appropriate manufacturer's instructions.

714. FUEL FILTERS, STRAINERS, AND DRAINS. Check each strainer and filter element for contamination. Determine and correct the source of any contaminants found. Replace throwaway filter elements with the recommended type. Examine fuel strainer bowls to see that they are properly installed according to direction of fuel flow. Check the operation of all drain devices to see that they operate properly and have positive shutoff action.

715. INDICATOR SYSTEMS. Inspect, service, and adjust the fuel indicator systems according to the manufacturer's instructions. Determine that the required placards and instrument markings are complete and legible.

Appendix
Aircraft Welding

(Reprinted from FAA AC 65-15, Chapter 6)

Welding

Welding is the process of joining metal by fusing the materials while they are in a plastic or molten state. There are three general types of welding: (1) Gas, (2) electric arc, and (3) electric resistance welding. Each of these types of welding has several variations which are used in aircraft construction.

Welding is used extensively in the repair and manufacture of aircraft. Such parts as engine mounts and landing gear are often fabricated in this manner, and many fuselages, control surfaces, fittings, tanks, etc., are also of welded construction. Structures that have been welded in manufacture may generally be repaired economically by using the same welding process. Careful workmanship, both in preparation and actual welding, is of utmost importance.

Welding is one of the most practical of the many metal-joining processes available. The welded joint offers rigidity, simplicity, low weight, and high strength. Consequently, welding has been universally adopted in the manufacture and repair of all types of aircraft. Many structural parts as well as nonstructural parts are joined by some form of welding, and the repair of many of these parts is an indispensable part of aircraft maintenance.

It is equally important to know when not to weld, as it is to know when. Many of the alloy steels or high-carbon steel parts that have been hardened or strengthened by heat treatment cannot be restored to 100% of their former hardness and strength after they have been welded.

Gas Welding

Gas welding is accomplished by heating the ends or edges of metal parts to a molten state with a high-temperature flame. This flame is produced with a torch burning a special gas such as acetylene or hydrogen with pure oxygen. The metals, when in a molten state, flow together to form a union without the application of mechanical pressure or blows.

Aircraft parts fabricated from chrome-molybdenum or mild carbon steel are often gas welded. There are two types of gas welding in common use: (1) Oxyacetylene and (2) oxyhydrogen. Nearly all gas welding in aircraft construction is done with an oxyacetylene flame, although some manufacturers prefer an oxyhydrogen flame for welding aluminum alloys.

Electric Arc Welding

Electric arc welding is used extensively in both the manufacture and repair of aircraft, and can be satisfactorily used in the joining of all weldable metals. The process is based on using the heat generated by an electric arc. Variations of the process are: (1) Metallic arc welding, (2) carbon arc welding, (3) atomic hydrogen welding, (4) inert-gas (helium) welding, and (5) multi-arc welding. Metallic arc and inert-gas welding are the two electric arc welding processes most widely used in aircraft construction.

Electric Resistance Welding

Electric resistance welding is a welding process in which a low-voltage, high-amperage current is applied to the metals to be welded through a heavy, low-resistance copper conductor. The materials to be welded offer a high resistance to the flow of current, and the heat generated by this resistance fuses (welds) the parts together at their point of contact.

Three commonly used types of electric resistance welding are butt, spot, and seam welding. Butt welding is used in aircraft work to weld terminals to control rods. Spot welding is frequently used in airframe construction. It is the only welding method used for joining structural corrosion-resistant steel. Seam welding is similar to spot welding, except that power-driven rollers are used as electrodes. A continuous airtight weld can be obtained using seam welding.

OXYACETYLENE WELDING EQUIPMENT

Oxyacetylene welding equipment may be either stationary or portable. A portable equipment rig consists of the following:

    (1) Two cylinders, one containing oxygen and one acetylene.

    (2) Acetylene and oxygen pressure regulators, complete with pressure gages and connections.

    (3) A welding torch, with a mixing head, extra tips and connections.

    (4) Two lengths of colored hose, with adapter connections for the torch and regulators.

    (5) A special wrench.

    (6) A pair of welding goggles.

    (7) A flint lighter.

    (8) A fire extinguisher.

Figure 6–1 shows some of the equipment in a typical portable acetylene welding rig.

Stationary oxyacetylene welding equipment is similar to portable equipment, except that acetylene and oxygen are piped to one or several welding stations from a central supply. The central supply usually consists of several cylinders connected to a common manifold. A master regulator controls the pressure in each manifold to ensure a constant pressure to the welding torch.

Acetylene Gas

Acetylene gas is a flammable, colorless gas which has a distinctive, disagreeable odor, readily detectable even when the gas is heavily diluted with air. Unlike oxygen, acetylene does not exist free in the

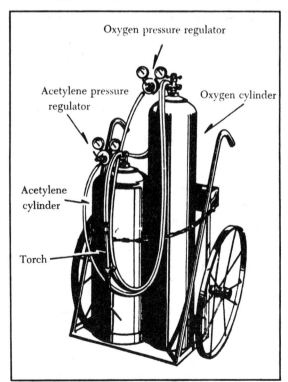

FIGURE 6–1. Typical portable acetylene welding rig.

atmosphere; it must be manufactured. The process is neither difficult nor expensive. Calcium carbide is made to react chemically with water to produce acetylene.

Acetylene is either used directly in a manifold system or stored in cylinders. If ignited, the result is a yellow, smoky flame with a low temperature. When the gas is mixed with oxygen in the proper proportions and ignited, the result is a blue-white flame with temperatures which range from approximately 5,700° to 6,300° F.

Under low pressure at normal temperatures, acetylene is a stable compound. But when compressed in a container to pressures greater than 15 p.s.i., it becomes dangerously unstable. For this reason, manufacturers fill the acetylene storage cylinders with a porous substance (generally a mixture of asbestos and charcoal) and saturate this substance with acetone. Since acetone is capable of absorbing approximately 25 times its own volume of acetylene gas, a cylinder containing the correct amount of acetone can be pressurized to 250 p.s.i.

Acetylene Cylinders

The acetylene cylinder is usually a seamless steel shell with welded ends, approximately 12 in. in diameter and 36 in. long. It is usually painted a distinctive color, and the name of the gas is stenciled or painted on the sides of the cylinder. A fully charged acetylene cylinder of this size contains approximately 225 cu. ft. of gas at pressures up to 250 p.s.i. In the event of fire or any excessive temperature rise, special safety fuse plugs installed in the cylinder will melt, allowing the excess gas to escape or burn, thus minimizing the chances of an explosion. The holes in the safety plugs are made small to prevent the flames from burning back into the cylinder. Acetylene cylinders should not be completely emptied, or a loss of filler material may result.

Oxygen Cylinders

The oxygen cylinders used in welding operations are made of seamless steel of different sizes. A typical small cylinder holds 200 cu. ft. of oxygen at 1,800 p.s.i. pressure. A large size holds 250 cu. ft. of oxygen at 2,265 p.s.i. pressure. Oxygen cylinders are usually painted green for identification The cylinder has a high-pressure valve located at the top of the cylinder. This valve is protected by a metal safety cap which should always be in place when the cylinder is not in use.

Oxygen should never come in contact with oil or grease. In the presence of pure oxygen, these substances become highly combustible. Oxygen hose and valve fittings should never be oiled or greased, or handled with oily or greasy hands. Even grease spots on clothing may flare up or explode if struck by a stream of oxygen. Beeswax is a commonly used lubricant for oxygen equipment and fittings.

Pressure Regulators

Acetylene and oxygen regulators reduce pressures and control the flow of gases from the cylinders to the torch. Acetylene and oxygen regulators are of the same general type, although those designed for acetylene are not made to withstand such high pressures as those designed for use with oxygen. To prevent interchange of oxygen and acetylene hoses, the regulators are built with different threads on the outlet fitting. The oxygen regulator has a right-hand thread, and the acetylene regulator has a left-hand thread.

On most portable welding units, each regulator is equipped with two pressure gages, a high-pressure gage which indicates the cylinder pressure and a low-pressure gage which indicates the pressure in the hose leading to the torch (working pressure).

In a stationary installation, where the gases are piped to individual welding stations, only one gage for oxygen and one for acetylene are required for each welding station, since it is necessary to indicate only the working pressure of the gases flowing through the hose to the welding torch.

A typical regulator, complete with pressure gages and connections, is shown in figure 6–2. The adjusting screw shown on the front of the regulator is for adjusting the working pressure. When this adjusting screw is turned to the left (counterclockwise) until it turns easily, the valve mechanism inside the regulator is closed. No gas can then flow to the torch. As the handle is turned to the right (clockwise), the screw presses against the regulat-

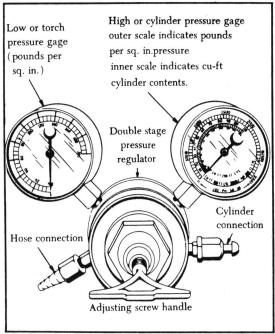

FIGURE 6-2. Typical oxygen pressure regulator.

ing mechanism, the valve opens, and gas passes to the torch at the pressure shown on the working pressure gage. Changes in the working pressure can be made by adjusting the handle until the desired pressure is registered.

Before opening the high-pressure valve on a cylinder, the adjusting screw on the regulator should be fully released by turning it counterclockwise. This closes the valve inside the regulator, protecting the mechanism against possible damage.

Welding Torch

The welding torch is the unit used to mix the oxygen and acetylene together in correct proportions. The torch also provides a means of directing and controlling the size and quality of the flame produced. The torches are designed with two needle valves, one for adjusting the flow of acetylene and the other for adjusting the flow of oxygen.

Welding torches are manufactured in different sizes and styles, thereby providing a suitable type for different applications. They are also available with several different sizes of interchangeable tips in order that a suitable amount of heat can be obtained for welding the various kinds and thicknesses of metals.

Welding torches can be divided into two classes: (1) The injector type and (2) the balanced-pressure type. The injector-type torch (figure 6-3A) is designed to operate with very low acetylene pressure as compared to the oxygen pressure.

A narrow passageway or nozzle within the torch, called the injector, through which the oxygen passes, causes the speed of oxygen flow to increase to a high velocity with a corresponding drop in pressure. This pressure drop across the injector creates a pressure differential which acts to draw the required amount of acetylene into the mixing chamber in the torch head.

In the balanced-pressure torch, the oxygen and acetylene are both fed to the torch at the same pressure (figure 6-3B). The openings to the mixing chamber for each gas are equal in size, and the delivery of each gas is independently controlled. This type of torch is generally better suited for aircraft welding than the injector type because of the ease of adjustment.

Welding Torch Tips

The torch tip delivers and controls the final flow of gases. It is important that the correct tip be selected and used with the proper gas pressures if a job is to be welded satisfactorily. The nature of the weld, the material, the experience of the welder, and the position in which the weld is to be made, all determine the correct size of the tip opening. The size of tip opening, in turn, determines the amount of heat (not the temperature) applied to the work. If a tip which is too small is used, the heat provided will be insufficient to produce penetration to the proper depth. If the tip is too large, the heat will be too great, and holes will be burned in the metal.

The torch tip sizes are designated by numbers, and each manufacturer has his own arrangement for classifying them. As an example, a number two tip is made with an orifice of approximately 0.040 in. diameter. The diameter of the tip orifice is related to the volume of heat it will deliver.

Torch tips are made of copper or copper alloy and are made so that they seat well when tightened

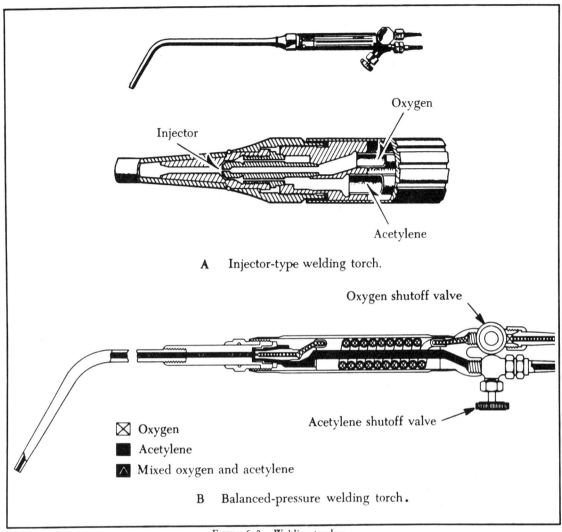

Injector

Oxygen

Acetylene

A   Injector-type welding torch.

Oxygen shutoff valve

⊠ Oxygen
■ Acetylene
⚠ Mixed oxygen and acetylene

Acetylene shutoff valve

B   Balanced-pressure welding torch.

FIGURE 6–3.   Welding torches.

handtight. Torch tips should not be rubbed across fire brick or used as tongs to position work.

With use, the torch tip will become clogged with carbon deposits and, if it is brought in contact with the molten pool, particles of slag may lodge in the opening. A split or distorted flame is an indication of a clogged tip. Tips should be cleaned with the proper size tip cleaners or with a piece of copper or soft brass wire. Fine steel wool may be used to remove oxides from the outside of the tip. These oxides hinder the heat dissipation and cause the tip to overheat.

A flint lighter is provided for igniting the torch. The lighter consists of a file-shaped piece of steel, usually recessed in a cuplike device, and a piece of flint that can be drawn across the steel, producing the sparks required to light the torch. Matches should never be used to ignite a torch since their length requires bringing the hand in close to the tip to ignite the gas. Accumulated gas may envelop the hand and, when ignited, cause a severe burn.

Goggles

Welding goggles, fitted with colored lenses, are

worn to protect the eyes from heat, light rays, sparks, and molten metal. A shade or density of color that is best suited for the particular situation should be selected. The darkest shade of lens which will show a clear definition of the work without eyestrain is the most desirable. Goggles should fit closely around the eyes and should be worn at all times during welding and cutting operations.

Welding (Filler) Rods

The use of the proper type filler rod is very important in oxyacetylene welding operations. This material not only adds reinforcement to the weld area, but also adds desired properties to the finished weld. By selecting the proper rod, either tensile strength or ductility can be secured in a weld, or both can be secured to a reasonably high degree. Similarly, rods can be selected which will help retain the desired amount of corrosion resistance. In some cases, a suitable rod with a lower melting point will eliminate possible cracks caused by expansion and contraction.

Welding rods may be classified as ferrous or nonferrous. The ferrous rods include carbon and alloy steel rods as well as cast-iron rods. Nonferrous rods include brazing and bronze rods, aluminum and aluminum alloy rods, magnesium and magnesium alloy rods, copper rods, and silver rods.

Welding rods are manufactured in standard 36-in. lengths and in diameters from $\frac{1}{16}$ in. to $\frac{3}{8}$ in. The diameter of the rod to be used is governed by the thickness of the metals being joined. If the rod is too small, it will not conduct heat away from the puddle rapidly enough, and a burned weld will result. A rod that is too large will chill the puddle. As in selecting the proper size welding torch tip, experience enables the welder to select the proper diameter welding rod.

Setting Up Acetylene Welding Equipment

Setting up acetylene welding equipment and preparing for welding should be done systematically and in a definite order to avoid costly mistakes. The following procedures and instructions are typical of those used to assure safety of equipment and personnel:

(1) Secure the cylinders so they cannot be upset, and remove the protective caps from the cylinders.

(2) Open each cylinder shutoff valve for an instant to blow out any foreign matter that may be lodged in the outlet. Close the valves and wipe off the connections with a clean cloth.

(3) Connect the acetylene pressure regulator to the acetylene cylinder and the oxygen regulator to the oxygen cylinder. Use a regulator wrench and tighten the connecting nuts enough to prevent leakage.

(4) Connect the red (or maroon) hose to the acetylene pressure regulator and the green (or black) hose to the oxygen regulator. Tighten the connecting nuts enough to prevent leakage. Do not force these connections, since these threads are made of brass and are easily damaged.

(5) Release both pressure regulator adjusting screws by turning the adjusting screw handle on each regulator counterclockwise until it turns freely. This is to avoid damage to the regulators and pressure gages when the cylinder valves are opened.

(6) Open the cylinder valves slowly and read each of the cylinder pressure gages to check the contents in each cylinder. The oxygen cylinder shutoff valve should be opened fully and the acetylene cylinder shutoff valve is opened approximately one and one-half turns.

(7) Blow out each hose by turning the pressure adjusting screw handle inward (clockwise) and then turning it out again. The acetylene hose should be blown out only in a well-ventilated space which is free from sparks, flame, or other sources of ignition.

(8) Connect both hoses to the torch and check the connections for leaks by turning the pressure regulator screws in, with the torch needle valves closed. When 20 p.s.i. shows on the oxygen working pressure

gage and 5 p.s.i. on the acetylene gage, close the valves by turning the pressure regulator screws out. A drop in pressure on the working gage indicates a leak between the regulator and torch tip. A general tightening of all connections should remedy the situation. If it becomes necessary to locate a leak, use the soap suds method. Do this by painting all fittings and connections with a thick solution of the soapy water. **Never hunt for an acetylene leak with a flame,** since a serious explosion can occur in the hose or in the cylinder.

(9) Adjust the working pressure on both the oxygen and acetylene regulators by turning the pressure-adjusting screw on the regulator clockwise until the desired settings are obtained.

Oxyacetylene Flame Adjustment

To light the torch, open the torch acetylene valve a quarter to a half turn. Hold the torch to direct the flame away from the body and ignite the acetylene gas, using the flint lighter. The pure acetylene flame is long and bushy and has a yellowish color. Continue opening the acetylene valve until the flame leaves the tip approximately one-sixteenth of an inch. Open the torch oxygen valve. When the oxygen valve is opened, the acetylene flame is shortened, and the mixed gases burn in contact with the tip face. The flame changes to a bluish-white color and forms a bright inner cone surrounded by an outer flame envelope.

Oxyacetylene Welding Process

The oxyacetylene process of welding is a method in which acetylene and oxygen gases are used to produce the welding flame. The temperature of this flame is approximately 6,300° F., which is sufficiently high to melt any of the commercial metals to effect a weld. When the oxyacetylene flame is applied to the ends or edges of metal parts, they are quickly raised to a melting state and flow together to form one solid piece when solidified. Usually some additional metal is added to the weld, in the form of a wire or rod, to build up the weld seam to

a greater thickness than the base metal.

There are three types of flames commonly used for welding. These are neutral, reducing or carburizing, and oxidizing. The characteristics of the different kinds of flames are shown in figure 6–4.

The neutral flame (figure 6–4A) is produced by burning acetylene with oxygen in such proportions as to oxidize all particles of carbon and hydrogen in the acetylene. This flame is distinguished by the well-rounded, smooth, clearly defined white central cone at the end of the tip. The envelope or outer flame is blue with a purple tinge at the point and edges. A neutral flame is generally used for welding and gives a thoroughly fused weld, free from burned metal or hard spots.

To obtain a neutral flame, gradually open the oxygen valve. This shortens the acetylene flame and causes a "feather" to appear in the flame envelope. Gradually increase the amount of oxygen until the "feather" disappears inside a clearly defined inner luminous cone.

The reducing or carburizing flame is shown in figure 6–4B. Since the oxygen furnished through the torch is not sufficient to complete the combustion of the acetylene, carbon escapes unburned. This flame can be recognized by the greenish-white

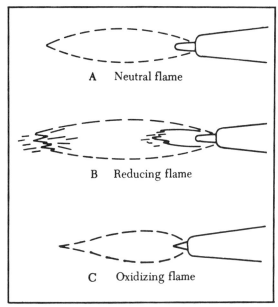

A   Neutral flame

B   Reducing flame

C   Oxidizing flame

FIGURE 6–4. Characteristics of oxyacetylene flames.

brushlike second cone at the tip of the first cone. The outer flame is slightly luminous and has about the same appearance as an acetylene flame burning freely in air alone. This type of flame introduces carbon into the steel.

To obtain a reducing flame, first adjust the flame to neutral; then open the acetylene valve slightly to produce a white streamer or "feather" of acetylene at the end of the inner cone.

An oxidizing flame (figure 6–4C) contains an excess of oxygen, which is the result of too much oxygen passing through the torch. The oxygen not consumed in the flame escapes to combine with the metal. This flame can be recognized by the short, pointed, bluish-white central cone. The envelope or outer flame is also shorter and of a lighter blue color than the neutral flame. It is accompanied by a harsh sound similar to high-pressure air escaping through a small nozzle. This flame oxidizes or burns most metals and results in a porous weld. It is used only when welding brass or bronze.

To obtain the oxidizing flame, first adjust the flame to neutral; then increase the flow of oxygen until the inner cone is shortened by about one-tenth of its length. The oxidizing flame has a pointed inner cone.

With each size of tip, a neutral, oxidizing or carburizing flame can be obtained. It is also possible to obtain a "harsh" or "soft" flame by increasing or decreasing the pressure of both gases.

For most regulator settings the gases are expelled from the torch tip at a relatively high velocity, and the flame is called "harsh." For some work it is desirable to have a "soft" or low-velocity flame without a reduction in thermal output. This may be achieved by using a larger tip and closing the gas needle valves until the neutral flame is quiet and steady. It is especially desirable to use a soft flame when welding aluminum, to avoid blowing holes in the metal when the puddle is formed.

Improper adjustment or handling of the torch may cause the flame to backfire or, in very rare cases, to flashback. A backfire is a momentary backward flow of the gases at the torch tip, which causes the flame to go out. A backfire may be caused by touching the tip against the work, by overheating the tip, by operating the torch at other than recommended pressures, by a loose tip or head, or by dirt or slag in the end of the tip. A backfire is rarely dangerous, but the molten metal may be splattered when the flame pops.

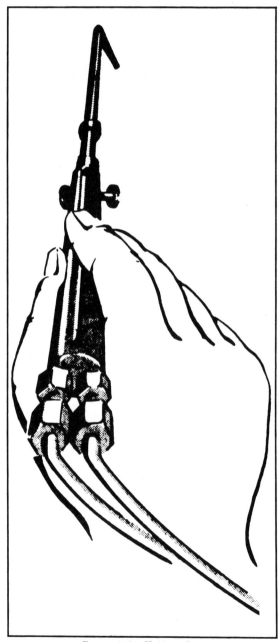

FIGURE 6–5. Holding the acetylene torch to weld light-gage metals.

198

A flashback is the burning of the gases within the torch and is dangerous. It is usually caused by loose connections, improper pressures, or overheating of the torch. A shrill hissing or squealing noise accompanies a flashback; and unless the gases are turned off immediately, the flame may burn back through the hose and regulators and cause great damage. The cause of a flashback should always be determined and the trouble remedied before re-lighting the torch.

Fundamental Oxyacetylene Welding Techniques

The proper method of holding the acetylene weld-

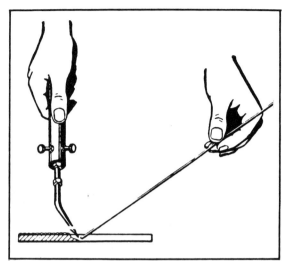

FIGURE 6–7. Forehand welding.

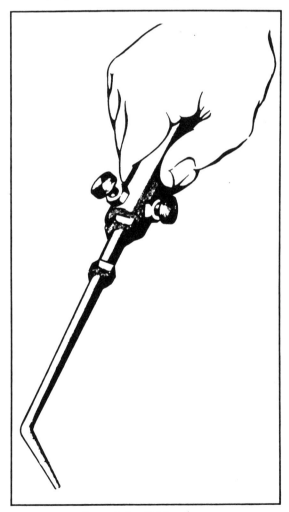

FIGURE 6–6. Holding the acetylene torch to weld heavy materials.

ing torch depends on the thickness of the metal being welded. When welding light-gage metal, the torch is usually held as illustrated in figure 6–5, with the hose draped over the wrist.

Figure 6–6 shows the method of holding the torch during the welding of heavy materials.

The torch should be held so that the tip is in line with the joint to be welded, and inclined between 30° and 60° from the perpendicular. The best angle depends on the type of weld to be made, the amount of preheating necessary, and the thickness and type of metal. The thicker the metal, the more nearly vertical the torch must be for proper heat penetration. The white cone of the flame should be held about 1/8 in. from the surface of the base metal.

If the torch is held in the correct position, a small puddle of molten metal will form. The puddle should be composed of equal parts of the pieces being welded. After the puddle appears, movement of the tip in a semicircular or circular motion should be started. This movement ensures an even distribution of heat on both pieces of metal. The speed and motion of the torch movement are learned only by practice and experience.

Forehand welding is the technique of pointing the torch flame forward in the direction in which the weld is progressing, as illustrated in figure 6–7. The filler rod is added to the puddle as the edges of the joint melt before the flame. The forehand method is used in welding most of the lighter tubings and sheet metals.

Backhand welding is the technique of pointing the torch flame toward the finished weld and moving away in the direction of the unwelded area, melting the edges of the joint as it is moved (figure 6–8). The welding rod is added to the puddle between the flame and the finished weld.

Backhand welding is seldom used on sheet metal because the increased heat generated in this method is likely to cause overheating and burning. It is preferred for metals having a thick cross section. The large puddle of molten metal required for such welds is more easily controlled in backhand welding, and it is possible to examine the progress of the weld and determine if penetration is complete.

WELDING POSITIONS

There are four general positions in which welds are made. These positions are shown in figure 6–9 and are designated as flat, overhead, horizontal, and vertical.

Welding is done in the flat position whenever possible, since the puddle is much easier to control in this position. Quite often, though, it is necessary to weld in the overhead, vertical, or horizontal position in aircraft repair.

The flat position is used when the material can be laid flat, or inclined at an angle of less than 45° and welded on the topside. The welding torch is

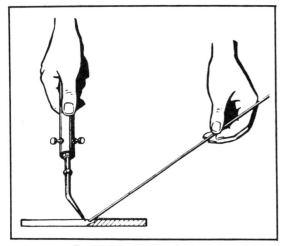

FIGURE 6–8. Backhand welding.

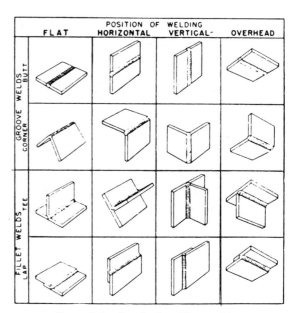

FIGURE 6–9. Four basic welding positions.

pointed downward toward the work. This weld may be made by either the forehand or backhand technique, depending upon the thickness of the metal being welded.

The horizontal position is used when the line of the weld runs horizontally across a piece of work, and the torch is directed at the material in a horizontal or nearly horizontal position. The weld is made from right to left across the plate (for the right-handed welder). The flame is inclined upward at an angle of from 45° to 60°. The weld can be made using the forehand or backhand technique. Adding the filler rod to the top of the puddle will help prevent the molten metal from sagging to the lower edge of the bead.

The overhead position is used when the material is to be welded on the underside with the seam running horizontally or in a plane that requires the flame to point upward from below the work. In welding overhead, a large pool of molten metal should be avoided, as the metal will drip or run out of the joint. The rod is used to control the size of the molten puddle. The volume of flame used should not exceed that required to obtain good fusion of the base metal with the filler rod. The amount of heat needed to make the weld is best controlled by selecting the right tip size for the thickness of metal to be welded.

When the parts to be joined are inclined at an angle of more than 45°, with the seam running vertically, it is designated as a vertical weld. In a vertical weld, the pressure exerted by the torch flame must be relied upon to a great extent to support the puddle. It is highly important to keep the puddle from becoming too hot, to prevent the hot metal from running out of the puddle onto the finished weld. Vertical welds are begun at the bottom, and the puddle is carried upward using the forehand technique. The tip should be inclined from 45° to 60°, the exact angle depending upon the desired balance between correct penetration and control of the puddle. The rod is added from the top and in front of the flame.

WELDED JOINTS

The five fundamental types of welded joints (figure 6–10) are the butt joint, tee joint, lap joint, corner joint, and edge joint.

Butt Joints

A butt joint is made by placing two pieces of material edge to edge, so that there is no overlapping, and then welded. Some of the various types of

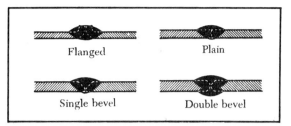

FIGURE 6–11. Types of butt joints.

butt joints are shown in figure 6–11. The flanged butt joint can be used in welding thin sheets, $\frac{1}{16}$ in. or less. The edges are prepared for welding by turning up a flange equal to the thickness of the metal. This type of joint is usually made without the use of filler rod.

A plain butt joint is used for metals from $\frac{1}{16}$ in. to $\frac{1}{8}$ in. in thickness. A filler rod is used when making this joint to obtain a strong weld.

If the metal is thicker than $\frac{1}{8}$ in., it is necessary to bevel the edges so that the heat from the torch can penetrate completely through the metal. These bevels may be either single- or double-bevel type or single- or double-V type. A filler rod is used to add strength and reinforcement to the weld.

Tee Joints

A tee joint is formed when the edge or end of one piece is welded to the surface of another, as shown in figure 6–12. These joints are quite common in aircraft work, particularly in tubular structures. The plain tee joint is suitable for most aircraft metal thicknesses, but heavier thicknesses require the vertical member to be either single or double beveled to permit the heat to penetrate deeply enough. The dark areas in figure 6–12 show the depth of heat penetration and fusion required.

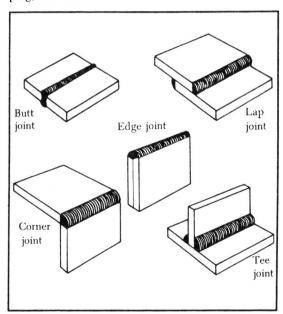

FIGURE 6–10. Basic welding joints.

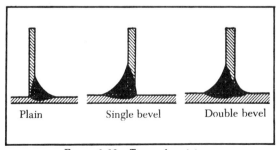

FIGURE 6–12. Types of tee joints.

Edge Joints

An edge joint may be used when two pieces of sheet metal must be fastened together and load stresses are not important. Edge joints are usually made by bending the edges of one or both parts upward, placing the two bent ends parallel to each other or placing one bent end parallel to the upright unbent end, and welding along the outside of the seam formed by the two joined edges. Figure 6–13 shows two types of edge joints. The type shown in fig. 6–13A requires no filler rod, since the edges can be melted down to fill the seam. The type shown in fig 6–13B, being thicker material, must be beveled for heat penetration; filler rod is added for reinforcement.

Corner Joints

A corner joint is made when two pieces of metal are brought together so that their edges form a corner of a box or enclosure as shown in figure 6–14. The corner joint shown in fig. 6–14A requires little or no filler rod, since the edges fuse to make the weld. It is used where load stress is unimportant. The joint shown in fig 6–14B is used on heavier metals, and filler rod is added for roundness and strength. If much stress is to be placed on the corner, the inside is reinforced as shown in fig. 6–14C.

Lap Joints

The lap joint is seldom used in aircraft structures when welding with oxyacetylene, but is commonly used when spot welding. The single lap joint (figure 6–15) has very little resistance to bending,

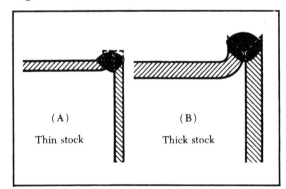

FIGURE 6–13. Edge joints.

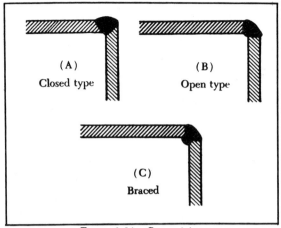

FIGURE 6–14. Corner joints.

and will not withstand the shearing stress to which the weld may be subjected under tension or compression loads. The double lap joint (figure 6–15) offers more strength, but requires twice the amount of welding required on the simpler, more efficient butt weld.

EXPANSION AND CONTRACTION OF METALS

Heat causes metals to expand; cooling causes them to contract. Uneven heating, therefore, will cause uneven expansion, or uneven cooling will cause uneven contraction. Under such conditions, stresses are set up within the metal. These forces must be relieved, and unless precautions are taken, warping or buckling of the metal will take place. Likewise, on cooling, if nothing is done to take up the stress set up by the contraction forces, further warping may result; or if the metal is too heavy to permit this change in shape, the stresses remain within the metal itself.

The coefficient of linear expansion of a metal is the amount in inches that a 1 in. piece of metal will expand when its temperature is raised 1° F. The amount that a piece of metal will expand when heat

FIGURE 6–15. Single and double lap joints.

is applied is found by multiplying the coefficient of linear expansion by the temperature rise, and that product by the length of the metal in inches. For example, if a 10 ft. aluminum rod is to be raised to a temperature of 1,200° F. from a room temperature of 60° F., the rod will expand 1.75 in.—0.00001280 (aluminum's coefficient of linear expansion) X 120 (length in inches) X 1140 (temperature rise).

Expansion and contraction have a tendency to buckle and warp thin sheet metal ⅛ in. or thinner. This is the result of having a large surface area that spreads heat rapidly and dissipates it soon after the source of heat is removed. The most effective method of alleviating this situation is to remove the heat from the metal near the weld, and thus prevent it from spreading across the whole surface area. This can be done by placing heavy pieces of metal, known as "chill bars," on either side of the weld; they absorb the heat and prevent it from spreading. Copper is most ofen used for chill bars because of its ability to absorb heat readily. Welding jigs sometimes use this same principle to remove heat from the base metal.

Expansion can also be controlled by tack welding at intervals along the joint.

The effect of welding a long seam (over 10 or 12 in.) is to draw the seam together as the weld progresses. If the edges of the seam are placed in contact with each other throughout their length before welding starts, the far ends of the seam will actually overlap before the weld is completed. This tendency can be overcome by setting the pieces to be welded with the seam spaced correctly at one end and increasing the space at the opposite end as shown in figure 6–16. The amount of space depends on the type of material, the thickness of the material, the welding process being used, and the shape and size of the pieces to be welded.

The weld is started at the correctly spaced end and proceeds toward the end that has the increased gap. As the seam is welded, the space will close and should provide the correct gap at the point of welding. Sheet metal under $\frac{1}{16}$ in. can be handled by flanging the edges, tack welding at intervals, and then by welding between the tacks.

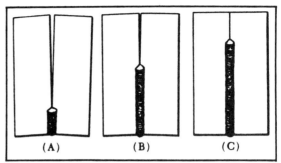

FIGURE 6–16. Allowance for a straight butt weld when welding steel sheets.

There is less tendency for plate stock over ⅛ in. to warp and buckle when welded because the greater thickness limits the heat to a narrow area and dissipates it before it travels far on the plate.

Preheating the metal before welding is another method of controlling expansion and contraction. Preheating is especially important when welding tubular structures and castings. Great stress can be set up in tubular welds by contraction. When two members of a tee joint are welded, one tube tends to draw up because of the uneven contraction. If the metal is preheated before the welding operation begins, contraction still takes place in the weld, but the accompanying contraction in the rest of the structure is at almost the same rate, and internal stress is lessened.

CORRECT FORMING OF A WELD

The form of the weld metal has considerable bearing upon the strength and fatigue resistance of a joint. The strength of an improperly made weld is usually less than the strength for which the joint was designed. Low-strength welds are generally the result of insufficient penetration; undercutting of the base metal at the toe of the weld; poor fusion of the weld metal with the base metal; trapped oxides, slag, or gas pockets in the weld; overlap of the weld metal on the base metal; too much or too little reinforcement; and overheating of the weld.

Characteristics of a Good Weld

A completed weld should have the following characteristics:

(1) The seam should be smooth, the bead ripples evenly spaced, and of a uniform thickness.

(2) The weld should be built up, thus providing extra thickness at the joint.

(3) The weld should taper off smoothly into the base metal.

(4) No oxide should be formed on the base metal close to the weld.

(5) The weld should show no signs of blowholes, porosity, or projecting globules.

(6) The base metal should show no signs of burns, pits, cracks, or distortion.

Although a clean, smooth weld is desirable, this characteristic does not necessarily mean that the weld is a good one; it may be dangerously weak inside. However, when a weld is rough, uneven, and pitted, it is almost always unsatisfactory inside. Welds should never be filed to give them a better appearance, since filing deprives the weld of part of its strength. Welds should never be filled with solder, brazing material, or filler of any sort. Additional information about weld characteristics is contained in Chapter 10, of the Airframe and Powerplant Mechanics General Handbook, AC 65-9.

When it is necessary to re-weld a joint, all old weld material must be removed before the operation is begun. It must be remembered, though, that reheating the area may cause the base metal to lose some of its strength and become brittle.

OXYACETYLENE WELDING OF FERROUS METALS
Steel

Low-carbon steel, low-alloy steel, cast steel, and wrought iron are easily welded with the oxyacetylene flame. Plain, low-carbon steel is the ferrous material that will be gas welded most frequently. As the carbon content of steel increases, it may be repaired by welding only under certain conditions. Factors involved are carbon content and hardenability. For corrosion- and heat-resistant nickel chromium steels, the allowed weldability depends upon their stability, carbon content, or re-heat treatment.

In order to make a good weld, the carbon content of the steel must not be altered, nor can other chemical constitutents be added to or subtracted from the base metal without seriously altering the properties of the metal. Molten steel has a great affinity for carbon, and oxygen and nitrogen combine with the molten puddle to form oxides and nitrates, both of which lower the strength of steel. When welding with an oxyacetylene flame, the inclusion of impurities can be minimized by observing the following precautions:

(1) Maintain an exact neutral flame for most steels, and a slight excess of acetylene when welding alloys with a high nickel or chromium content, such as stainless steel.

(2) Maintain a soft flame and control the puddle.

(3) Maintain a flame sufficient to penetrate the metal and manipulate it so that the molten metal is protected from the air by the outer envelope of flame.

(4) Keep the hot end of the welding rod in the weld pool or within the flame envelope.

Proper preparation for welding is an important factor in every welding operation. The edges of the parts must be prepared in accordance with the joint design chosen. The method chosen (bevel, groove, etc.) should allow for complete penetration of the base metal by the flame. The edges must be clean. Arrangements must be made for preheating, if this is required.

When preparing an aircraft part for welding, remove all dirt, grease or oil, and any protective coating such as cadmium plating, enamel, paint, or varnish. Such coatings not only hamper welding, but also mingle with the weld and prevent good fusion.

Cadmium plating can be chemically removed by dipping the edges to be welded in a mixture of 1 lb. of ammonium nitrate and 1 gal. of water.

Enamel, paint, or varnish may be removed from steel parts by a number of methods, such as a steel wire brush or emery cloth, by gritblasting, by using paint or varnish remover, or by treating the pieces with a hot, 10% caustic soda solution followed by a thorough washing with hot water to remove the solvent and residue. Gritblasting is the most effective method for removing rust or scale from steel parts. Grease or oil may be removed with a suitable grease solvent.

Enamel, paint, varnish, or heavy films of oxide on aluminum alloys can be removed using a hot

10% solution of either caustic soda or tri-sodium phosphate. After treatment, the parts should be immersed in a 10% nitric acid solution, followed with a hot water rinse to remove all traces of the chemicals. Paint and varnish can also be removed using paint and varnish remover.

The tip of the filler rod should be dipped below the surface of the weld puddle with a motion exactly opposite the motion of the torch. If the filler rod is held above the surface of the puddle, it will melt and fall into the puddle a drop at a time, ruining the weld.

Filler metal should be added until the surface of the joint is built up slightly above the edges of the parts being joined. The puddle of molten metal should be gradually advanced along the seam until the end of the material is reached.

As the end of the seam is approached, the torch should be raised slightly, chilling the molten steel to prevent it from spilling over the edge or melting through the work.

Chrome Molybdenum

The welding technique for chrome molybdenum is practically the same as that for carbon steels, except that the surrounding area must be preheated to a temperature between 300° and 400° F. before beginning to weld. If this is not done, the sudden application of heat causes cracks to form in the heated area.

A soft neutral flame should be used for welding; an oxidizing flame may cause the weld to crack when it cools, and a carburizing flame will make the metal brittle. The volume of the flame must be sufficient to melt the base metal, but not so hot as to weaken the grain structure of the surrounding area and set up strains in the metal. The filler rod should be the same as the base metal. If the weld requires high strength, a special chrome molybdenum rod is used and the piece is heat treated after welding.

Chrome molybdenum thicker than 0.093 in. is usually electric-arc welded, since for this thickness of metal, electric arc provides a narrow heat zone, fewer strains are developed, and a better weld is obtained, particularly when the part cannot be heat treated after welding.

Stainless Steel

The procedure for welding stainless steel is basically the same as that for carbon steels. There are, however, some special precautions that must be taken to obtain the best results.

Only stainless steel used for nonstructural members of aircraft can be welded satisfactorily; the stainless steel used for structural components is cold worked or cold rolled and, if heated, loses some of its strength. Nonstructural stainless steel is obtained in sheet and tubing form and is often used for exhaust collectors, stacks or manifolds. Oxygen combines very readily with this metal in the molten state, and extreme care must be taken to prevent this from occurring.

A slightly carburizing flame is recommended for welding stainless steel. The flame should be adjusted so that a feather of excess acetylene, about $\frac{1}{16}$ in. long, forms around the inner cone. Too much acetylene, however, will add carbon to the metal and cause it to lose its resistance to corrosion. The torch tip size should be one or two sizes smaller than that prescribed for a similar gage of low carbon steel. The smaller tip lessens the chances of overheating and subsequent loss of the corrosion-resistant qualities of the metal.

To prevent the formation of chromium oxide, a flux should be spread on the underside of the joint and on the filler rod. Since oxidation is to be avoided as much as possible, sufficient flux should be used. Another method used to keep oxygen from reaching the metal is to surround the weld with a blanket of hydrogen gas. This method is discussed later. The filler rod used should be of the same composition as the base metal.

Since the coefficient of expansion of stainless steel is high, thin sheets which are to be butt-welded should be tacked at intervals of 1-¼ to 1-½ inches, as shown in figure 6–17. This is one means of lessening warping and distortion during the welding process.

When welding, hold the filler rod within the envelope of the torch flame so that the rod is melted in place or melted at the same time as the base metal. Add the filler rod by allowing it to flow into the molten pool. If the weld pool is stirred, air will

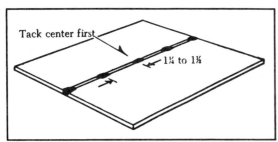

FIGURE 6–17. Tacking method for stainless steel welding.

enter the weld and increase oxidation. Avoid re-welding any portion or welding on the reverse side of the weld. Such practices result in warping and overheating of the metal.

WELDING NONFERROUS METALS USING OXY-ACETYLENE

Nonferrous metals are those that contain no iron. Examples of nonferrous metals are lead, copper, silver, magnesium, and most important in aircraft construction, aluminum. Some of these metals are lighter than the ferrous metals, but in most cases they are not as strong. Aluminum manufacturers have compensated for the lack of strength of pure aluminum by alloying it with other metals or by cold working it. For still greater strength, some aluminum alloys are also heat treated.

Aluminum Welding

The weldable aluminum alloys used in aircraft construction are 1100, 3003, 4043, and 5052. Alloy numbers 6053, 6061, and 6151 can also be welded, but since these alloys are in the heat-treated condition, welding should not be done unless the parts can be re-heat treated.

The equipment and technique used for aluminum welding differ only slightly from those of methods discussed earlier. As in all welding, the first step is to clean the surface to be welded—steel wool or a wire brush may be used, or a solvent in the case of paint or grease. The welder should be careful not to scratch the surface of the metal beyond the area to be welded; these scratches provide entry points for corrosion. The piece should then be preheated to lessen the strains caused by the large coefficient of expansion of aluminum.

Never preheat aluminum alloys to a temperature higher than 800° F. because the heat may melt some of the alloys and burn the metal. For thin sheet aluminum, merely passing the flame back and forth across the sheet three or four times should be sufficient.

Either of two types of filler rod can be used in welding aluminum alloys. Choosing the proper filler rod is important.

Aluminum and its alloys combine with air and form oxides very rapidly; oxides form doubly fast if the metal is hot. For this reason it is important to use a flux that will minimize or prevent oxides from forming.

Using the proper flux in welding aluminum is extremely important. Aluminum welding flux is designed to remove the aluminum oxide by chemically combining with it. Aluminum fluxes dissolve below the surface of the puddle and float the oxides to the top of the weld where they can be skimmed off. The flux can be painted directly on the top and bottom of the joint if no filler rod is required; if filler rod is used, it can be coated, and if the pieces to be welded are thick, both the metal and the rod should be coated with flux.

After welding is finished, it is important that all traces of flux be removed by using a brush and hot water. If aluminum flux is left on the weld, it will corrode the metal. A diluted solution of 10% sulfuric acid may be used if hot water is not available. The acid solution should be washed off with cold water.

Thickness of the aluminum alloy material determines the method of edge preparation. On material up to 0.062 in., the edges are usually formed to a 90° flange about the same height as the thickness of the material (figure 6–18A). The flanges should be straight and square. No filler rod is necessary when the edges are flanged in this manner.

Unbeveled butt welds are usually made on aluminum alloy from 0.062 to 0.188 in. thick. It may also be necessary to notch the edges with a saw or cold chisel in a manner similar to that shown in figure 6–18B. Edge notching is recommended in aluminum welding because it aids in getting full penetration and also prevents local distortion. All butt welds in

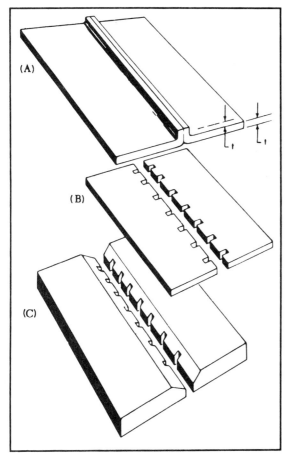

FIGURE 6–18. Edge preparation for welding aluminum.

material over 0.125 in. thick are generally notched in some manner.

In welding aluminum over 0.188 in. thick, the edges are usually beveled and notched as shown in figure 6–18C. The included angle of bevel may be from 90° to 120°.

A neutral flame should generally be used to weld aluminum alloys. In some cases a slightly carburizing flame can be used. However, the excess of acetylene should not be too great, as it will be absorbed into the molten metal, resulting in a weakened joint. The torch must be adjusted to give the mildest flame that can be obtained without popping. The use of a strong, harsh flame makes it difficult to control the melting metal, and holes are often burned through the metal.

When starting to weld, the two joint edges should begin to melt before the filler rod is added. The work must be watched carefully for signs of melting. The melting point of aluminum is low and heat is conducted rapidly through the material. There is very little physical or color change to indicate that the metal is reaching the melting point. When the melting point is reached, the metal suddenly collapses and runs, leaving a hole in the aluminum.

A filler rod can be used to test the metal's condition. Aluminum begins to feel soft and plastic just before it reaches the melting point. Any tendency of the metal to collapse can be rectified by rapidly lifting the flame clear of the metal. With practice it is possible to develop enough skill to melt the metal surface without forming a hole.

The flame should be neutral and slanted at an approximate 45° angle to the metal. The inner cone should be about ⅛ in. from the metal. A constant and uniform movement of the torch is necessary to prevent burning a hole through the metal.

The correct integration of torch and rod action is important when welding aluminum. After heating the metal and when melting has begun, the filler rod is dipped into the pool and allowed to melt. The filler rod is lifted and the torch movement continues as the weld progresses. The rod is never lifted out of the outer envelope of flame, but is held there until almost melted and then added to the pool.

Magnesium Welding

Many aircraft parts are constructed of magnesium because of its light weight, strength, and excellent machinability. This metal is only two-thirds as heavy as aluminum and, like aluminum, is very soft in its pure state. For this reason, it is generally alloyed with zinc, manganese, tin, aluminum, or combinations of these metals. Repair of magnesium by welding is limited by two factors:

(1) If the magnesium is used as a structural member, it is usually heat treated and, like heat-treated aluminum, the welded section can never have the strength of the original metal. (As a rule, failures do not occur in the welded area, but in the areas adjacent to the weld, because the heat applied to

the metal weakens the grain structure in those areas.)

(2) It is necessary to use flux in making all magnesium welds, and to remove all the flux from the metal after welding or severe corrosion will take place.

The type of joint is limited to those that provide no possibility of trapping the flux—therefore, only butt welds can be made. Magnesium cannot be welded to other metals, and magnesium alloy castings are not considered suitable for stressed welds. If varying thicknesses of magnesium are to be welded, the thicker part must be preheated. The filler rod should be of the same composition as the base metal and one prepared by the manufacturer to fuse with his alloy. The filler rod comes with a protective plating that must be cleaned off before using.

The method of preparing the butt joint depends on the thickness of the metal. Sheet magnesium alloy up to 0.040 in. thick should be flanged by about $\frac{3}{32}$ in. to the angle as indicated in figure 6–19. Butt joints on metal from 0.040 to 0.125 in. thick are neither flanged nor beveled, but a $\frac{1}{16}$-in. space should be allowed between the edges of the joint. For butt joints in metal thicker than 0.125 in., each edge should be beveled down 45° to make a 90° included angle for the "V." A $\frac{1}{16}$-in. space should be allowed between the edges of the joint for metal 0.125 to 0.250 in. thick and a $\frac{1}{8}$-in. space for metal 0.250 in. and up (figure 6–19).

Remove oil or grease with a suitable solvent, and then use a wire brush or abrasive cloth to clean and brighten the metal for a distance of $\frac{3}{4}$ in. back from the weld area. Select a filler rod of the same material as the base metal. The filler rod and both sides of the seam should be covered with flux. Use a neutral or slightly carburizing flame, and hold it at a flat angle to the work to avoid burning through.

Two rod techniques are recommended for the welding of magnesium. One method requires that the filler rod be kept in the puddle at all times; the other method is the same as that used in welding aluminum.

It is preferable to make the weld on one uninterrupted pass, but if oxidation occurs, the weld should be stopped and scraped out before continu-

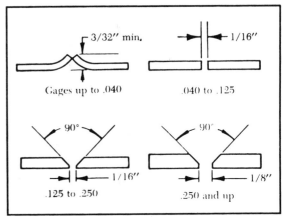

FIGURE 6–19. Preparation of edges for welding magnesium sheet.

ing. The joint edges should be tack-welded at the ends at intervals of $\frac{1}{2}$ to 3 in., depending upon the shape and thickness of the metal.

Welding should be accomplished as quickly and with as little heat as possible. Buckling and warping can be straightened while the metal is still hot by hammering with a soft-faced mallet. The metal should be allowed to cool slowly. When the weld is cool enough to handle, the accessible portions should be scrubbed lightly, using a bristle brush and hot water, to remove excess flux. The part should then be soaked in hot water (160° to 200° F.) to float off the flux adhering to any portions not reached by the scrub brush. When soaking is completed, the part should be immersed in a 1% solution of citric acid for approximately 10 min.

After the citric acid bath the part should be drained thoroughly and then rinsed clean in fresh water. The part must be dried quickly and completely to prevent oxidation.

CUTTING METAL USING OXYACETYLENE

Cutting metals by the oxyacetylene process is fundamentally the rapid burning or oxidizing of the metal in a localized area. The metal is heated to a bright red (1,400° to 1,600° F.), which is the kindling or ignition temperature, and a jet of high-pressure oxygen is directed against it. This oxygen blast combines with the hot metal and forms an intensely hot oxide. The molten oxide is blown down the sides of the cut, heating the metal in its path to a kindling temperature. The metal thus heated also burns to an oxide which is blown away on the underside of the piece. The action is precisely that which the torch accomplishes when the mixing head is replaced with a cutting attachment or when a special cutting torch is used.

Figure 6–20 shows an example of a cutting torch. It has the conventional oxygen and acetylene needle valves, which control the flow of the two gases. Many cutting torches have two oxygen needle valves so that a finer adjustment of the neutral flame can be obtained.

BRAZING METHODS

Brazing refers to a group of metal-joining processes in which the bonding material is a nonferrous metal or alloy with a melting point higher than 800° F., but is lower than that of the metals being joined. Brazing includes silver soldering, also called hard soldering, copper brazing, and aluminum brazing.

Brazing requires less heat than welding and can be used to join metals that are damaged by high heat. However, because the strength of brazed joints is not so great as welded joints, brazing is not used for structural repairs on aircraft. In deciding whether brazing of a joint is justified, it should be remembered that a metal which will be subjected

to a sustained high temperature in use should not be brazed.

As the definition of brazing implies, the base metal parts are not melted. The brazing metal adheres to the base metal by molecular attraction and intergranular penetration; it does not fuse and amalgamate with them.

In brazing, the edges of the pieces to be joined are usually beveled as in welding steel. The surrounding surfaces must be cleaned of dirt and rust. Parts to be brazed must be securely fastened together to prevent any relative movement. The strongest brazed joint is one in which the molten filler metal is drawn in by capillary action, thus a close fit must be obtained.

A brazing flux is necessary to obtain a good union between the base metal and the filler metal. A good flux for brazing steel is a mixture containing two parts borax and one part boric acid. Application of the flux may be made in the powder form or dissolved in hot water to a highly saturated solution. A neutral torch flame should be used, moved with a slight semicircular motion.

The base metal should be preheated slowly with a mild flame. When it reaches a dull red heat (in the case of steel), the rod should be heated to a dark or purple color and dipped into the flux. Since enough

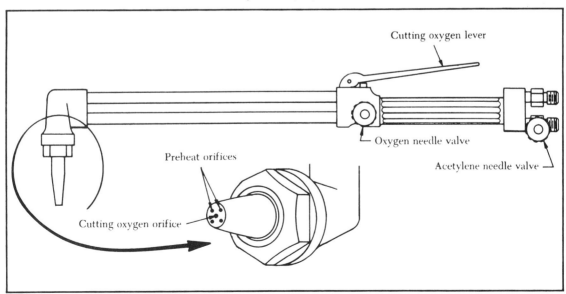

FIGURE 6–20. Cutting torch.

flux adheres to the rod, it is not necessary to spread it over the surface of the metal.

A neutral flame is used for most brazing applications. However, a slightly oxidizing flame should be used when copper/zinc, copper/zinc/silicon, or copper/zinc/nickel/silicon filler alloys are used. When brazing aluminum and its alloys a neutral flame is preferred, but if difficulties are encountered, a slightly reducing flame is preferred to an oxidizing flame.

The filler rod can now be brought near the tip of the torch, causing the molten bronze to flow over a small area of the seam. The base metal must be at the flowing temperature of the filler metal before it will flow into the joint. The brazing metal melts when applied to the steel and runs into the joint by capillary attraction. The rod should continue to be added as the brazing progresses, with a rhythmic dipping action so that the bead will be built to a uniform width and height. The job should be completed rapidly and with as few passes as possible of the rod and torch.

When the job is finished, the weld should be allowed to cool slowly. After cooling, remove the flux from the parts by immersing them for 30 minutes in a lye solution.

Silver Solder

The principal use of silver solder in aircraft work is in the fabrication of high-pressure oxygen lines and other parts which must withstand vibration and high temperatures. Silver solder is used extensively to join copper and its alloys, nickel and silver, as well as various combinations of these metals, and thin steel parts. Silver soldering produces joints of higher strength than those produced by other brazing processes.

It is necessary to use flux in all silver soldering operations because of the necessity for having the base metal chemically clean without the slightest film of oxide to prevent the silver solder from coming into intimate contact with the base metal.

The joint must be physically clean, which means it must be free of all dirt, grease, oil, and/or paint, and also chemically clean. After removing the dirt, grease, and/or paint, any oxide should be removed by grinding or filing the piece until bright metal can be seen. During the soldering operation, the flux continues the process of keeping oxide away from the metal, and aids the flow of the solder.

In figure 6–21, three types of joints for silver soldering are shown. Flanged, lap, and edge joints, in which the metal may be formed to furnish a seam wider than the base metal thickness, furnish the type of joint which will bear up under all kinds of loads. If a lap joint is used, the amount of lap should be determined according to the strength needed in the joint. For strength equal to that of the base metal in the heated zone, the amount of lap should be four to six times the metal thickness for sheet metal and small-diameter tubing.

The oxyacetylene flame for silver soldering should be neutral, but may have a slight excess of acetylene. It must be soft, not harsh. During both preheating and application of the solder, the tip of the inner cone of the flame should be held about ½ in. from the work. The flame should be kept moving so that the metal will not become overheated.

When both parts of the base metal are at the right temperature (indicated by the flow of flux), solder can be applied to the surface of the under or inner part at the edge of the seam. It is necessary to simultaneously direct the flame over the seam and keep moving it so that the base metal remains at an even temperature.

EXTINGUISHING THE TORCH

The torch can be shutoff simply by closing both needle valves, but it is better practice to turn the acetylene off first and allow the gas remaining in the torch tip to burn out. The oxygen needle valve can then be turned off. If the torch is not to be used again for a long period, the pressure should be turned off at the cylinder. The hose lines should then be relieved of pressure by opening the torch needle valves and the working pressure regulator,

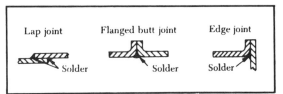

FIGURE 6–21. Silver soldering joints.

one at a time, allowing the gas to escape. Again, it is a good practice to relieve the acetylene pressure and then the oxygen pressure. The hose should then be coiled or hung carefully to prevent damage or kinking.

SOFT SOLDERING

Soft soldering is used chiefly for copper, brass, and coated iron in combination with mechanical seams; that is, seams that are rivited, bolted, or folded. It is also used where a leakproof joint is desired, and sometimes for fitting joints to promote rigidity and prevent corrosion. Soft soldering is generally performed only in very minor repair jobs. This process is also used to join electrical connections. It forms a strong union with low electrical resistance.

Soft solder yields gradually under a steadily applied load and should not be used unless the transmitted loads are very low. It should never be used as a means of joining structural members.

A soldering copper (called a soldering iron if it is electrically heated) is the tool used in soldering. Its purpose is to act as a source of heat for the soldering operation. The bit, or working face, is made from copper, since this metal will readily take on heat and transmit it to the work. Figure 6–22 shows a correctly shaped bit.

To tin the copper, it is first heated to a bright red, then the point is cleaned by filing until it is smooth and bright. No dirt or pits should remain on its surface. After the copper has been mechanically cleaned, it should be re-heated sufficiently to melt solder, and chemically cleaned by rubbing it lightly on a block of sal ammoniac. (If sal ammoniac is not available, powdered resin may be used.)

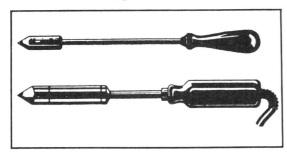

FIGURE 6–22. Soldering copper and soldering iron.

Then solder is applied to the point and wiped with a clean cloth.

The last two operations may be combined by melting a few drops of solder on a block of sal ammoniac (cleaning compound) and then rubbing the soldering copper over the block until the tip is well coated with solder. A properly tinned copper has a thin unbroken film of solder over the entire surface of its point.

Soft solders are chiefly alloys of tin and lead. The percentages of tin and lead vary considerably in various solders, with a corresponding change in their melting points, ranging from 293° to 592° F. "half-and-half" (50–50) solder is a general purpose solder and is most frequently used. It contains equal proportions of tin and lead and melts at approximately 360° F.

The application of the melted solder requires somewhat more care than is apparent. The parts should be locked together or held mechanically or manually while tacking. To tack the seam, the hot copper is touched to a bar of solder, then the drops of solder adhering to the copper are used to tack the seam at a number of points. The film of solder between the surfaces of a joint must be kept thin to make the strongest joint.

A hot, well-tinned soldering copper should be held so that its point lies flat on the metal at the seam, while the back of the copper extends over the seam proper at a 45° angle, and a bar of solder is touched to the point. As the solder melts, the copper is drawn slowly along the seam. As much solder as necessary is added without raising the soldering copper from the job. The melted solder should run between the surfaces of the two sheets and cover the full width of the seam. Work should progress along the seam only as fast as the solder will flow into the joint.

ELECTRIC ARC WELDING

Electric arc welding is a fusion process based on the principle of generating heat with an electric arc jumping an airgap to complete an electrical circuit. This process develops considerably more heat than an oxyacetylene flame. In some applications, it reaches a temperature of approximately 10,000° F. Variations of the process are metallic arc welding, inert-gas (helium) welding, and multi-arc welding. The metallic arc and helium processes have the widest application in aircraft maintenance.

The welding circuit (figure 6–23) consists of a welding machine, two leads, an electrode holder, an electrode, and the work to be welded. The electrode, which is held in electrode holder, is connected to one lead, and the work to be welded is connected to the other lead. When the electrode is touched to the metal to be welded, the electrical circuit is completed and the current flows. When the electrode is withdrawn from the metal, an airgap is formed between the metal and the electrode. If this gap is of the proper length, the electric current will bridge this gap to form a sustained electric spark, called the electric arc.

METALLIC ARC WELDING

Metallic arc welding is used mainly for welding low-carbon and low-alloy steels. However, many nonferrous materials, such as aluminum and nickel alloys, can be welded using this method.

To form an arc between the electrode and the work, the electrode is applied to the work and immediately withdrawn. This initiates an arc of intense heat. To maintain the arc between the electrode and the work, the metal electrode must be fed at a uniform rate or maintained at a constant distance from the work as it melts.

Metallic arc welding is a nonpressure fusion welding process which develops welding heat through an arc produced between a metal electrode and the work to be welded. Under the intense heat developed by the arc, a small part of the base metal

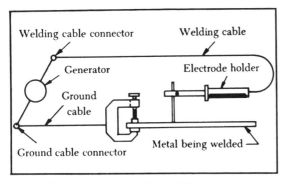

FIGURE 6–23. Typical arc-welding circuit.

or work to be welded is brought to the melting point instantaneously. At the same time, the end of the metal electrode is also melted, and tiny globules or drops of molten metal pass through the arc to the base metal. The force of the arc carries the molten metal globules directly into the puddle formed on the base metal, and thus filler metal is added to the part being welded. By moving the metal electrode along the joint and down to the work, a controlled amount of filler metal can be deposited on the base metal to form a weld bead.

The instant the arc is formed, the temperature of the work at the point of welding and the welding electrode increases to approximately 6,500° F. This tremendous heat is concentrated at the point of welding and in the end of the electrode, and simultaneously melts the end of the electrode and a small part of the work to form a small pool of molten metal, commonly called the crater.

The heat developed is concentrated and causes less buckling and warping of work than gas welding. This localization of the heat is advantageous when welding cracks in heat-treated parts and when welding in close places.

ATOMIC HYDROGEN ARC WELDING

This system employs two tungsten electrodes. An arc is maintained between the ends, and a stream of hydrogen gas is passed into the arc and around the electrodes. The heat of the arc breaks up the molecules of hydrogen into atoms, which re-combine outside the arc to form molecular hydrogen again. The intense heat liberated by the hydrogen as it re-combines is used to fuse the metal.

Atomic hydrogen welding is frequently used in welding aluminum and its alloys, and corrosion- and heat-resistant steels.

INERT-GAS WELDING

In the inert-gas welding process a tungsten or carbon electrode surrounded by helium or argon gas is used. The helium or argon gas are inert and exclude the oxygen and hydrogen present in air from the area being welded. This process is particularly adaptable to the welding of magnesium. It can also be used for welding aluminum, and if argon is used as the shielding gas, no flux is required.

WELDING PROCEDURES AND TECHNIQUES

The first step in preparing to arc weld is to make certain that the necessary equipment is available and that the welding machine is properly connected and in good working order. Particular attention should be given to the ground connection, since a poor connection will result in a fluctuating arc, which is difficult to control.

The electrode should be clamped to its holder at right angles to the jaws. Shielded electrodes have one end of the electrode free of coating to provide good electrical contact. The electrode holder should be handled with care to prevent accidental contact with the bench or work, since such contact may weld it fast.

Before starting to weld, the following typical list of items should be checked:

    (1) Is the machine in good working order?
    (2) Have all connections been properly made? Will the ground connection make good contact?
    (3) Has the proper type and size electrode been selected for the job?
    (4) Is the electrode properly secured in the holder?
    (5) Has sufficient protective clothing been provided, and is it in good condition?
    (6) Is the work metal clean?
    (7) Does the polarity of the machine coincide with that of the electrode?
    (8) Is the machine adjusted to provide the necessary current for striking the arc?

The welding arc is established by touching the plate with the electrode and immediately withdrawing it a short distance. At the instant the electrode touches the plate, a rush of current flows through the point of contact. As the electrode is withdrawn, an electric arc is formed, melting a spot on the base metal and the end of the electrode.

The main difficulty confronting a beginner in striking the arc is freezing; that is, sticking or welding the electrode to the work. If the electrode is not withdrawn promptly upon contact with the plate, the high amperage will flow through the electrode and practically short circuit the welding machine. The heavy current melts the electrode which sticks to the plate before it can be withdrawn.

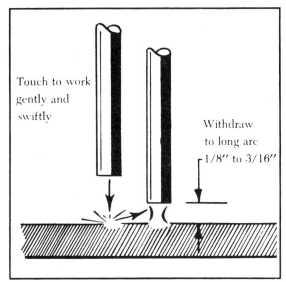

FIGURE 6–24. Touch method of starting the arc.

There are two essentially similar methods of striking the arc. The first is a touch method, illustrated in figure 6–24, and the second is a scratch method, shown in figure 6–25.

When using the touch method, the electrode should be held in a vertical position, and lowered until it is an inch or so above the point where the arc is to be struck. Then the electrode is touched

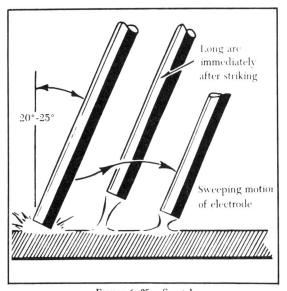

FIGURE 6–25. Scratch method of starting the arc.

very gently and swiftly to the work, using a downward motion of the wrist, followed immediately by withdrawing the electrode to form a long arc (approximately $\frac{1}{8}$ to $\frac{3}{16}$ in. long).

To strike the arc by the scratch method, the electrode is moved downward until it is just above the plate and at an angle of 20° to 25°, as illustrated in figure 6–25. The arc should be struck gently, with a swiftly sweeping motion, scratching the electrode on the work with a wrist motion. The electrode is then immediately withdrawn to form a long arc. The purpose of holding an excessively long arc immediately after striking is to prevent the large drops of metal, passing across the arc at this time, from shorting out the arc and thus causing freezing.

To form a uniform bead, the electrode must be moved along the plate at a constant speed in addition to the downward feed of the electrode. The rate of advance, if too slow, will form a wide bead resulting in overlapping, with no fusion at the edges. If the rate of advance is too fast, the bead will be too narrow and have little or no fusion at the plate. When proper advance is made, no overlapping occurs, and good fusion is assured.

In advancing the electrode, it should be held at an angle of about 20° to 25° in the direction of travel, as illustrated in figure 6–26.

If the arc is broken during the welding of a bead, a crater will be formed at the point where the arc ends. The arc may be broken by feeding the electrode too slowly or too fast, or when the electrode should be replaced. The arc should not be re-started in the crater of the interrupted bead, but just ahead of the crater on the work metal. Then, the electrode should be returned to the back edge of the crater. From this point, the weld may be continued by welding right through the crater and down the line of weld, as originally planned. Figure 6–27 illustrates the procedure for re-starting the arc.

Every particle of slag must be removed from the vicinity of the crater before re-starting the arc. This prevents the slag from becoming trapped in the weld.

Multiple-Pass Welding

Groove and fillet welds in heavy metals often

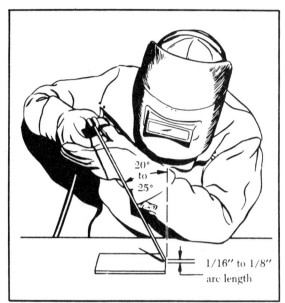

FIGURE 6–26. Angle of electrode.

require the deposit of a number of beads to complete a weld. It is important that the beads be deposited in a predetermined sequence to produce the soundest welds with the best proportions. The number of beads is, of course, determined by the thickness of the metal being welded.

The sequence of the bead deposits is determined by the kind of joint and the position of the metal. All slag must be removed from each bead before another bead is deposited. Typical multiple-pass groove welding of butt joints is shown in figure 6–28.

Techniques of Position Welding

Each time the position of a welding joint or the type of joint is changed, it may be necessary to change any one or a combination of the following:

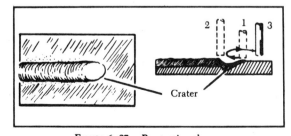

FIGURE 6–27. Re-starting the arc.

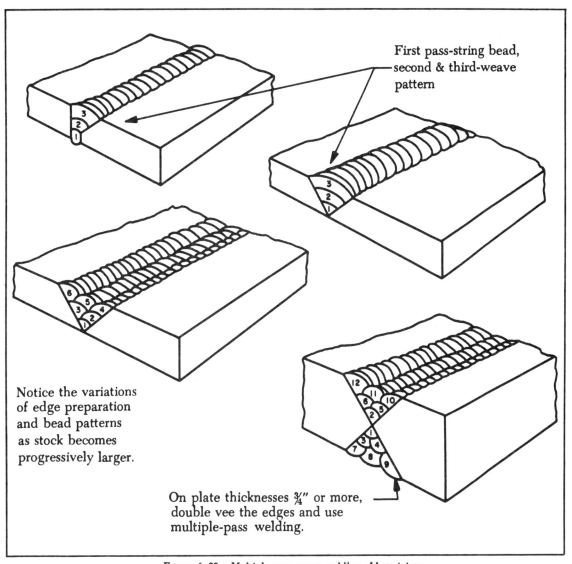

First pass-string bead, second & third-weave pattern

Notice the variations of edge preparation and bead patterns as stock becomes progressively larger.

On plate thicknesses ¾" or more, double vee the edges and use multiple-pass welding.

FIGURE 6–28. Multiple-pass groove welding of butt joints.

(1) Current value, (2) electrode, (3) polarity, (4) arc length, or (5) welding technique.

Current values are determined by the electrode size as well as the welding position. Electrode size is governed by the thickness of the metal and the joint preparation, and the electrode type by the welding position. Manufacturers specify the polarity to be used with each electrode. Arc length is controlled by a combination of the electrode size, welding position, and welding current.

Since it is impractical to cite every possible variation occasioned by different welding conditions, only the information necessary for the commonly used positions and welds is discussed here.

Flat Position Welding

There are four types of welds commonly used in flat position welding. They are the bead, groove, fillet, and lap joint welds. Each type is discussed separately in the following paragraphs.

215

Bead Welds

Welding a square butt joint by means of stringer beads involves the same techniques as depositing stringer beads on a flat metal surface. Square butt joints may be welded in one, two, or three passes. If the joint is welded with the deposition of one stringer bead, complete fusion is obtained by welding from one side. If the thickness of metal is such that complete fusion cannot be obtained by welding from one side, the joint must be welded from both sides.

When the metals to be welded are butted squarely together, two passes are necessary. If the metals must be spaced, three passes are required to complete the weld. In the latter case, the third pass is made directly over the first and completely envelops it.

It must be constantly kept in mind that beads, either the stringer or weave type, are used to weld all types of joints. Even though the bead may not be deposited on the same type of surface, its action in the different welding positions and joints is basically the same as its action on the surface of flat metal. The same fundamental rules apply regarding electrode size and manipulation, current values, polarity, and arc lengths.

Bead welds can be made by holding a short arc and welding in a straight line at a constant speed, with the electrode inclined 5° to 15° in the direction of welding. The proper arc can best be judged by recognizing a sharp cracking sound heard all during the time the electrode is being moved to and above the surface of the plate. Some of the characteristics of good bead welds are as follows:

(1) They should leave very little spatter on the surface of the plate.
(2) The arc crater, or depression, in the bead when the arc has been broken should be approximately 1/16 in. deep.
(3) The depth of the crater at the end of the bead can be used as a measure of penetration into the base metal.
(4) The bead weld should be built up slightly, without any weld metal overlap at the top surface, which would indicate poor fusion.

Figure 6–29 illustrates a properly made bead weld.

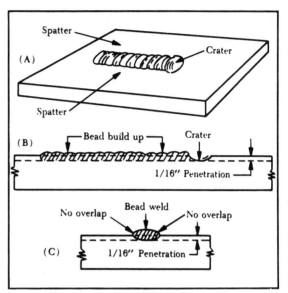

FIGURE 6–29. Properly made bead weld.

Groove Welds (Butt Joint)

Groove welding may be executed in either a butt joint or an outside corner joint. A outside corner joint corresponds to a single vee butt joint, and the same welding technique is used for both. For this reason, these two types of joints are classified under the heading of grooved welding. There are certain fundamentals which are applicable to groove welds, regardless of the position of the joint.

Groove welds are made on butt joints where the metal to be welded is 1/4 in. or more in thickness. Butt joints with a metal thickness of less than 1/4 in. require no special edge preparation and can be joined with a bead weld on one or both sides.

Groove welds can be classified as either single groove or double groove. This is true whether the shape of the groove is a V, U, J, or any other form. Regardless of the position in which a single-groove weld is made, it can be welded with or without a backing strip. If a backing strip is used, the joint may be welded from only one side. When a single-groove weld is made without a backing strip, the weld may be made from one side, if necessary, although welding from both sides assures better fusion.

The first pass of the weld deposit may be from either side of the groove. The first bead should be deposited to set the space between the two plates and to weld the root of the joint. This bead, or layer off weld metal, should be thoroughly cleaned to remove all slag before the second layer of metal is deposited. After the first layer is cleaned, each additional layer should be applied with a weaving motion, and each layer should be cleaned before the next one is applied.

The number of passes required to complete a weld is determined by the thickness of the metal being welded and the electrode size being used. As in bead welding, the tip of the electrode should be inclined between 5° and 15° in the direction of welding.

Double-groove welds are welded from both sides. This type of weld is used primarily on heavy metals to minimize distortion. This is best accomplished by alternately welding from each side; *i.e.*, depositing a bead from one side and then from the other. However, this necessitates turning the plates over several times (six times for ¾-in. plate.)

Distortion may be effectively controlled if the plates are turned over twice, as follows: (1) Weld half the passes on the first side; (2) turn the plate over and weld all the passes on the second side; and (3) turn the plates over and complete the passes on the first side.

The root of a double-groove weld should be made with a narrow bead, making sure that the bead is uniformly fused into each root face. When a few passes have been made on one side, the root on the opposite side should be chipped to sound metal to make the groove and then welded with a single-bead weld.

Any groove weld made in more than one pass must have the slag, spatter, and oxide carefully removed from all previous weld deposits before welding over them. Figure 6–30 shows some of the common types of groove welds performed on butt joints in the flat position.

Fillet Welds

Fillet welds are used to make tee and lap joints. In welding tee joints in the flat position, the two

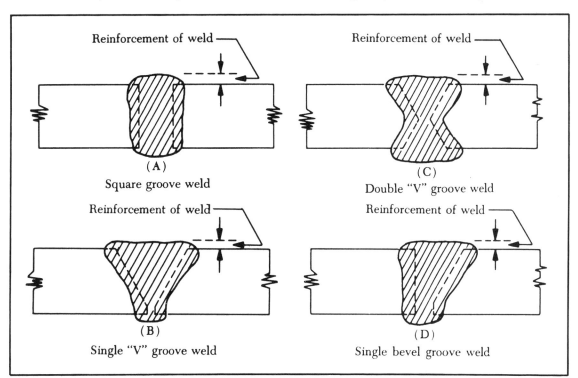

(A)
Square groove weld

(B)
Single "V" groove weld

(C)
Double "V" groove weld

(D)
Single bevel groove weld

FIGURE 6–30.   Groove welds on butt joints in the flat position.

plates are placed to form an angle of 90° between their surfaces, as shown in figure 6–31. The electrode should be held at an angle of 45° to the plate surface. The top of the electrode should be tilted at an angle of about 15° in the direction of welding. Light plates should be welded with little or no weaving motion of the electrode, and the weld is made in one pass. Fillet welding of heavier plates may require two or more passes. In that case, the second pass or layer is made with a semicircular weaving motion. In making the weave bead, there should be a slight pause at the end of each weaving motion to obtain good fusion to the edges of the two plates without undercutting them.

The procedure for making the lap joint fillet weld is similar to that used for making the fillet weld in a tee joint. The electrode should be held at an angle of 30° to the vertical. The top of the electrode should be tilted to an angle of 15° in the direction of welding. Figure 6–32 illustrates a typical lap joint. The weaving motion is the same as that used for tee joints, except that the hesitation at the edge of the top plate is prolonged to obtain good fusion with no undercut. When welding plates of different thickness, the electrode is held at an angle of 20° to the vertical. Care must be taken not to overheat and undercut the thinner plate edge. The arc must be

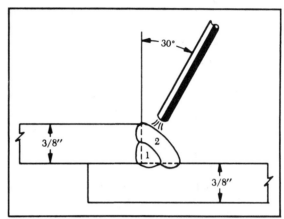

FIGURE 6–32. Typical lap joint fillet weld.

controlled to wash up the molten metal to the edge of this plate.

Overhead Position Welding

The overhead position is one of the most difficult in welding, since a very short arc must be maintained constantly to retain complete control of the molten metal.

The force of gravity tends to cause the molten metal to drop down or sag on the plate. If a long arc is held, the difficulty in transferring metal from the electrode to the base metal is increased, and large globules of molten metal will drop from the electrode and the base metal. The transfer of metal is aided by first shortening and then lengthening the arc. However, care should be taken not to carry too large a pool of molten metal in the weld. The procedures for making bead, groove, and fillet welds in the overhead position are discussed in the following paragraphs.

Bead Welds

For bead welds, the electrode should be held at an angle of 90° to the base metal. In some cases, however, where it is desirable to observe the arc and the crater of the weld, the electrode may be held at an angle of 15° in the direction of welding. Weave beads can be made by using the weaving motion. A rather rapid motion is necessary at the end of each semicircular weave to control the molten metal deposit. Care should be taken to avoid excessive weaving. This will cause overheating of

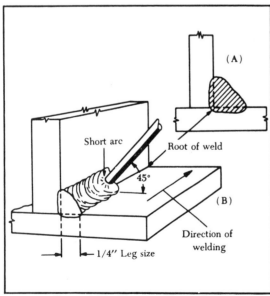

FIGURE 6–31. Tee joint fillet weld.

the weld deposit and form a large pool of metal, which is hard to control.

Groove Welds (Butt Joints)

Improved overhead groove welds can be made by using a backup strip. The plates should be prepared in a manner similar to preparing plates for welding butt joints in the flat position. If no backup strip is used and the plates are beveled with a featheredge, the weld will burn through repeatedly, unless the operator is extremely careful.

Fillet Welds

When making fillet welds on overhead tee or lap joints, a short arc should be held, and there should be no weaving of the electrode, The electrode should be held at an angle of about 30° to the vertical plate, and moved uniformly in the direction of welding.

The arc motion should be controlled to secure good penetration to the root of the weld and good fusion with the sidewalls of the vertical and horizontal plates. If the molten metal becomes too fluid and tends to sag, the electrode should be whipped away quickly from the crater ahead of the weld to lengthen the arc and allow the metal to solidify. The electrode should then be returned immediately to the crater of the weld and the welding continued.

Welding on heavy plates requires several passes to make the joint. The first pass is a string bead with no weaving motion of the electrode. The second, third, and fourth passes are made with a slight circular motion of the end of the electrode, while the top of the electrode is held tilted at an angle of about 15°.

Vertical Position Welding

The vertical position, like the overhead position just discussed, is also more difficult than welding in the flat position. Because of the force of gravity, the molten metal will always have a tendency to run down. To control the flow of molten metal, a short arc is necessary, as well as careful arc voltage and welding current adjustments.

In metallic arc welding, current settings for welds made in the vertical position should be less than those used for the same electrode size and type on welds made in the flat position. The currents used for welding upward on vertical plate are slightly lower than those used for welding downward on vertical plate. The procedure for making bead, groove, and fillet welds in the vertical position are discussed in the following paragraphs.

Bead Welds

When making vertical bead welds, it is necessary to maintain the proper angle between the electrode and the base metal to deposit a good bead. In welding upward, the electrode should be held at an angle of 90° to the vertical. When weaving is necessary, the electrode should be oscillated with a "whipping up" motion. In welding downward, bead welds should be made by holding the top end of the electrode at an angle of about 15° below the horizontal to the plate with the arc pointed upward toward the oncoming molten metal. When a weave bead is necessary, in welding downward, a slight semicircular movement of the electrode is necessary.

In depositing a bead weld in the horizontal plane on a vertical plate, the electrode should be held at right angles to the vertical. The top of the electrode should be tilted at an angle at about 15° toward the direction of welding to obtain a better view of the arc and crater. The welding currents used should be slightly less than those required for the same type and size of electrode in flat position welding.

Groove Welds (Butt Joints)

Butt joints in the vertical position are "groove welded" in a manner similar to the welding of butt joints in the flat position. To obtain good fusion with no undercutting, a short arc should be held, and the motion of the electrode should be carefully controlled.

Butt joints on beveled plates ¼ in. in thickness can be groove welded by using a triangular weaving motion. In groove welding butt joints in the horizontal position on identical plates, a short arc is necessary at all times. The first pass is made from left to right or right to left, with the electrode held at an angle of 90° to the vertical plate. The second, third, and, if required, any additional passes are made in alternate steps, with the electrode held approximately parallel to the beveled edge opposite to the one being welded.

Fillet Welds

When making fillet welds in either tee or lap joints in the vertical position the electrode should be held at an angle of 90° to the plates or at an angle of up to 15° below the horizontal, for better control of the molten puddle. The arc should also be held short to obtain good penetration, fusion, and molten metal control.

In welding tee joints in the vertical position, the electrode should be moved in a triangular weaving motion. The joint should be started at the bottom and welded upwards. A slight hesitation in the weave, as shown in figure 6–33, will improve sidewall penetration and allow good fusion at the root of the joint. If the weld metal overheats, the electrode should be lifted away quickly at short rapid intervals without breaking the arc. This will allow the molten metal to solidify without running down. The electrode should be returned immediately to the crater of the weld to maintain the desired size of the weld.

When more than one layer of metal is needed to make a vertical tee weld, different weaving motions may be used. A slight hesitation at the end of the weave will result in good fusion without undercut-

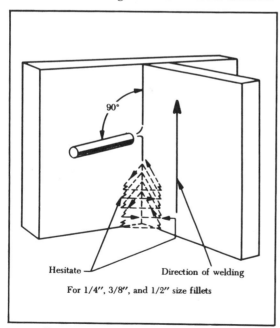

Figure 6–33. Vertical tee joint fillet weld.

ting the plate at the edges of the weld. When welding lap welds in the vertical position, the same procedure is followed as that outlined for welding vertical tee joints, except that the electrode is directed more toward the one vertical plate. Care should be taken not to undercut either plate, or to allow the molten metal to overlap the edges of the weave. On heavy plate, lap joints require more than one layer of metal.

WELDING OF AIRCRAFT STEEL STRUCTURES

Oxyacetylene or electric arc welding may be utilized for repair of some aircraft structures, since most aircraft structures are fabricated from one of the weldable alloys; however, careful consideration should be given to the alloy being welded since all alloys are not readily weldable. Also, certain structural parts may be heat treated and therefore could require special handling. In general, the more responsive an alloy steel is to heat treatment, the less suitable it is for welding because of its tendency to become brittle and lose its ductility in the welded area. The following steels are readily weldable: (1) Plain carbon of the 1000 series, (2) nickel steel of the SAE 2300 series, (3) chrome/nickel alloys of the SAE 3100 series, (4) chrome/molybdenum steels of the SAE 4100 series, and (5) low-chrome/molybdenum steel of the SAE 8600 series.

Aircraft Steel Parts Not To Be Welded

Welding repairs should not be performed on aircraft parts whose proper function depends on strength properties developed by cold working, such as streamlined wires and cables.

Brazed or soldered parts should never be repaired by welding, since the brazing mixture or solder can penetrate the hot steel and weaken it.

Aircraft parts such as turnbuckle ends and aircraft bolts which have been heat treated to improve their mechanical properties should not be welded.

Repair of Tubular Members

Welded steel tubing can usually be spliced or repaired at any joint along the length of the tube, but particular attention should be given to the proper fit and alignment to avoid distortion. Some of the many acceptable practices are outlined in the following paragraphs.

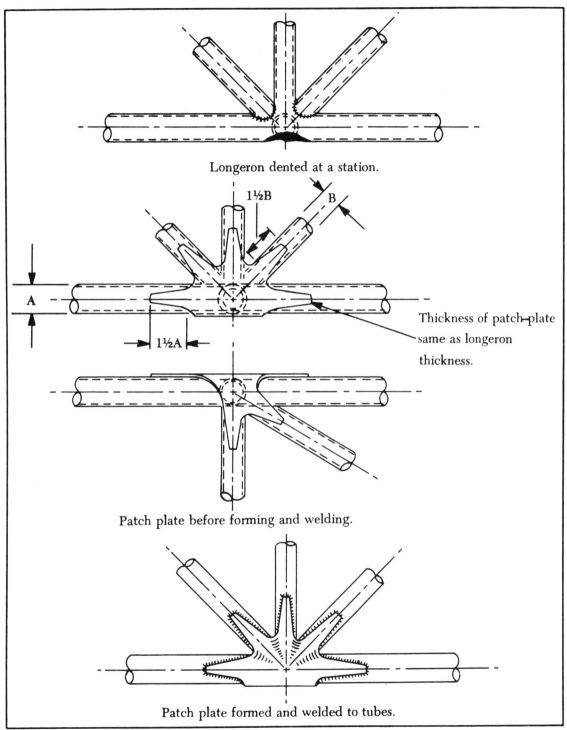

Longeron dented at a station.

1½B

B

A

1½A

Thickness of patch plate same as longeron thickness.

Patch plate before forming and welding.

Patch plate formed and welded to tubes.

FIGURE 6–34. Repair of members dented at a cluster.

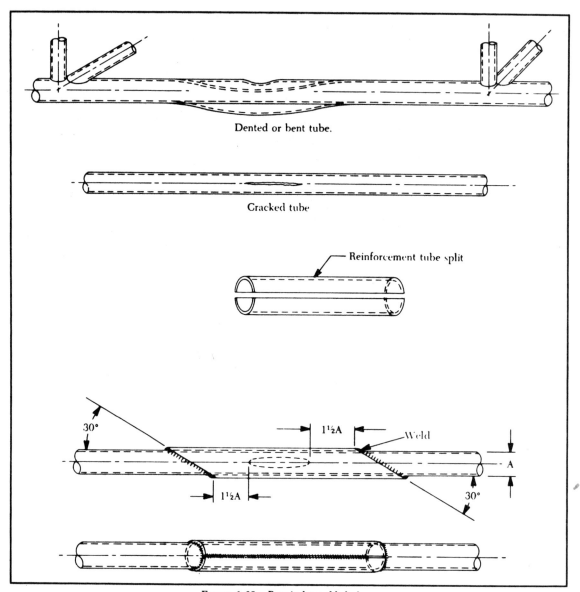

Dented or bent tube.

Cracked tube

— Reinforcement tube split

30°

1½A

Weld

A

1½A

30°

FIGURE 6–35. Repair by welded sleeve.

Dents at a steel tube cluster-joint can be repaired by welding a specially formed steel patch plate over the dented area and surrounding tubes, as shown in figure 6–34.

To prepare the patch plate, a section of steel sheet is cut from the same material and thickness as the heaviest tube damaged. The reinforcement plate is trimmed so that the fingers extend over the tubes a minimum of one and one-half times the respective tube diameters (figure 6–34). The reinforcement plate may be formed before any welding is attempted, or it may be cut and tack welded to one or more of the tubes in the cluster-joint, then heated and formed around the joint to produce a smooth contour. Sufficient heat should be applied to the plate during the forming process so that no gap exists. If a gap exists it should not exceed $\frac{1}{16}$ in. from the contour of the joint to the plate. After the plate is formed and tack welded to the cluster-joint, all the reinforcement plate edges are welded to the cluster-joint.

Repair by Welded Sleeve

This type of repair of a dented or bent tube is illustrated in figure 6–35. The repair material selected should be a length of steel tube sleeving having an inside diameter approximately equal to the outside diameter of the damaged tube and of the same material and wall thickness. This sleeve reinforcement should be cut at a 30° angle on both ends so that the minimum distance of the sleeve from the edge of the crack or dent is not less than one and one-half times the diameter of the damaged tube.

After the angle cuts have been made to the ends, the entire length of the reinforcement sleeve should be cut, separating the sleeve into half-sections (figure 6–35). The two sleeve sections are then clamped to the proper positions on the affected areas of the original tube. The sleeve is welded along the length of the two sides, and both ends are welded to the damaged tube, as shown in figure 6–35.

Repair by Bolted Sleeve

Bolted sleeve repairs on welded steel tubular structure are not recommended unless specifically authorized by the manufacturer or the Federal Aviation Administration. The material removed by drilling the boltholes in this type of repair may prove to weaken the tubular structure critically.

Welded-Patch Repair

Dents or holes in tubing can be safely repaired by a welded patch of the same material but one gage thicker, as illustrated in figure 6–36, with the following exceptions:

(1) Do not use a welded patch to repair dents deeper than one-tenth of the tube diameter, dents that involve more than one-fourth of the tube circumference, or those longer than the tube diameter.

(2) Use welded-patch repairs only if dents are free from cracks, abrasions, and sharp corners.

(3) Use welded-patch repairs only when the dented tubing can be substantially reformed without cracking before application of the patch.

(4) In the case of punctured tubing, use welded-patch repairs if the holes are not longer than the tube diameter and involve not more than one-fourth of the tube circumference.

Splicing Tubing by Inner Sleeve Method

If the damage to a structural tube is such that a partial replacement of the tube is necessary, the inner sleeve splice shown in figure 6–37 is recommended, especially where a smooth tube surface is desired. A diagonal cut is made to remove the damaged portion of the tube, and the burrs are removed from the edges of the cut by filing or similar means. A replacement steel tube of the same material and diameter, and at least the same wall thickness is then cut to match the length of the removed portion of the damaged tube. At each end of the replacement tube a $\frac{1}{8}$-in. gap should be allowed from the diagonal cuts to the stubs of the original tube.

A length of steel tubing should next be selected of at least the same wall thickness and of an outside diameter equal to the inside diameter of the damaged tube. This inner tube material should be fitted snugly within the original tube. Cut two sections of tubing from this inner-sleeve tube material, each of such a length that the ends of the inner sleeve will be a minimum distance of one and one-half tube diameters from the nearest end of the diagonal cut.

If the inner sleeve fits very tightly in the replacement tube, the sleeve can be chilled with dry ice or in cold water. If this procedure is inadequate, the diameter of the sleeve can be polished down with emery cloth. The inner sleeve can be welded to the tube stubs through the $\frac{1}{8}$-in. gap, forming a weld bead over the gap.

Engine Mount Repairs

All welding on an engine mount should be of the highest quality, since vibration tends to accentuate

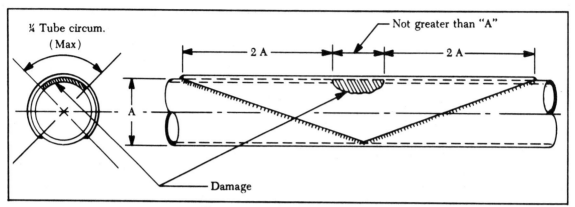

FIGURE 6-36. Welded-patch repair.

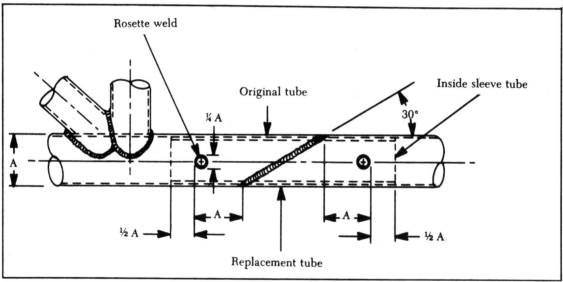

FIGURE 6-37. Splicing by inner-sleeve method.

any minor defect. Engine-mount members should preferably be repaired by using a larger diameter replacement tube telescoped over the stub of the original member, using fishmouth and rosette welds. However, 30° scarf welds in place of the fishmouth welds are usually considered acceptable for engine mount repair work.

Repaired engine mounts must be checked for accurate alignment. When tubes are used to replace bent or damaged ones, the original alignment of the structure must be maintained. This can be done by measuring the distance between points of corre-

sponding members that have not been distorted, and by reference to the manufacturer's drawings.

If all members are out of alignment, the engine mount should be replaced by one supplied by the manufacturer or one built to conform to the manufacturer's drawings. The method of checking the alignment of the fuselage or nacelle points can be requested from the manufacturer.

Minor damage, such as a crack adjacent to an engine attachment lug, can be repaired by re-welding the ring and extending a gusset or a mounting lug past the damaged area. Engine mount rings which are extensively damaged must not be repaired, unless the method of repair is specifically approved by an authorized representative of the Federal Aviation Administration, or is accomplished using instructions furnished by the aircraft manufacturer.

Repair at Built-In Fuselage Fittings

An example of a recommended repair at built-in fuselage fittings is illustrated in figure 6-38. There are several acceptable methods for effecting this type of repair. The method illustrated in figure 6-38 utilizes a tube (sleeve) of larger diameter than the original. This necessitates reaming the fitting holes in the longeron to a larger diameter. The forward splice is a 30° scarf splice. The rear longeron is cut approximately 4 in. from the center line of the joint, and a spacer 1 in. long is fitted over the longeron. The spacer and longeron are edgewelded. A tapered "V" cut approximately 2 in. long is made in the aft end of the outer sleeve, and the end of the outer sleeve is swaged to fit the longeron and then welded.

Landing Gear Repair

Landing gear made of round tubing is generally repaired using repairs and splices illustrated in figures 6-35 and 6-38. One method of repairing landing gear made of streamlined tubing is shown in figure 6-39.

Representative types of repairable and nonrepairable landing gear axle assemblies are shown in figure 6-40. The types shown in A, B, and C of this figure are formed from steel tubing and may be repaired by any of the methods described in this section. However, it will always be necessary to ascertain whether or not the members are heat treated. Assemblies originally heat treated must be re-heat treated after welding.

The axle assembly shown in D of figure 6-40 is, in general, of a nonrepairable type for the following reasons:

(1) The axle stub is usually made from a highly heat treated nickel alloy steel and carefully machined to close tolerances. These stubs are usually replaced when damaged.

(2) The oleo portion of the structure is generally heat treated after welding and is perfectly machined to assure proper functioning of the shock absorber. These parts

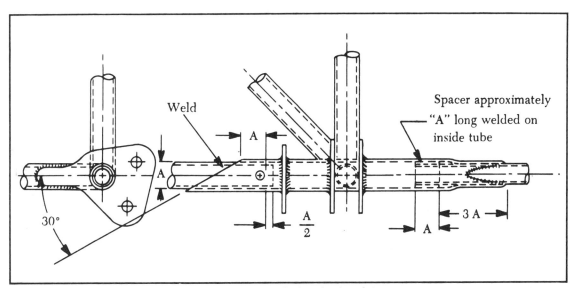

FIGURE 6-38. Repair at built-in fuselage fitting.

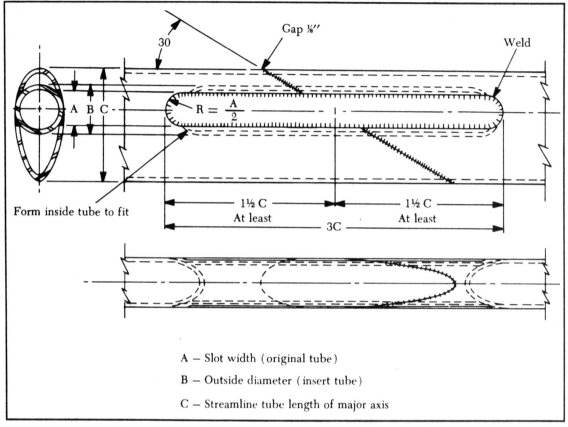

A — Slot width (original tube)

B — Outside diameter (insert tube)

C — Streamline tube length of major axis

FIGURE 6–39. Streamlined tube splice on landing gear using round tube.

would be distorted by welding after the machining process.

A spring-steel leaf, shown in E of figure 6–40, supports each main landing gear wheel assembly on many light aircraft. These springs are, in general, nonrepairable and should be replaced when they become excessively sprung or are otherwise damaged.

Built-Up Tubular Wing or Tail Surface Spar Repair

Built-up tubular wing or tail surface spars can be repaired by using any of the splices and methods outlined in the discussion on welding of aircraft steel structures, provided the spars are not heat treated. In the case of heat treated spars, the entire spar assembly must be re-heat treated to the manufacturer's specifications after completion of the repair.

Wing and Tail Brace Struts

In general, it is advantageous to replace damaged wing-brace struts made either from rounded or streamlined tubing with new members purchased from the aircraft manufacturer. However, there is usually no objection from an airworthiness point of view to repairing such members properly. Members made of round tubes using a standard splice can be repaired as shown in figures 6–35 or 6–37.

Steel brace struts may be spliced at any point along the length of the strut, provided the splice **does not overlap part of an end fitting. The jury strut attachment is not considered an end fitting; therefore, a splice may be made at this point.** The

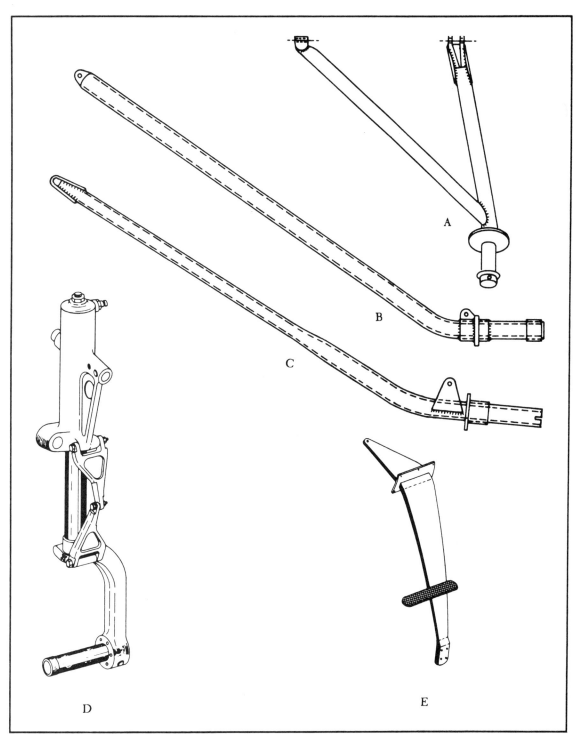

A

B

C

D

E

FIGURE 6–40. Representative types of repairable and nonrepairable assemblies.

227

repair procedure and workmanship should be such as to minimize distortion due to welding and the necessity for subsequent straightening operations. The repaired strut should be observed carefully during initial flights to ascertain that the vibration characteristics of the strut and attaching components are not adversely affected by the repair. A wide range of speed and engine power combinations must be covered during this check.

Index

Index

Edited by Steven Mesner